W9-ATH-763

MASS. 01984

DISCARDED
JENKS LRC
GORDON COLLEGE

CALIFORNIA CONDOR

THE CALIFORNIA CONDOR

by Carl B. Koford

Museum of Vertebrate Zoology
of the University of California

Dover Publications, Inc., New York

Copyright © 1953 by the National Audubon Society.

All rights reserved under Pan American and International Copyright Conventions.

Published in Canada by General Publishing Company, Ltd., 30 Lesmill Road, Don Mills, Toronto, Ontario.

Published in the United Kingdom by Constable and Company, Ltd., 10 Orange Street, London W.C. 2.

This Dover edition, first published in 1966, is an unabridged and corrected republication of the work originally published in 1953 as Research Report Number 4 of the National Audubon Society.

In the 1953 edition the frontispiece was reproduced in color, but is here reproduced as a black-and-white halftone.

This edition is published by special arrangement with the National Audubon Society.

QL
696
. A2
K64
1966

Library of Congress Catalog Card Number: 66-19044

Manufactured in the United States of America
Dover Publications, Inc.
180 Varick Street
New York, N.Y. 10014

FOREWORD

The National Audubon Society considers facts obtainable through scientific research the essential basis for wise policies governing the conservation of wildlife resources.

The third rarest living species of North American bird is the California Condor. Never, in recent times, widely distributed or existing in large numbers, it has been progressively eliminated from considerable portions of its normal range and reduced to a mere remnant of its former population. Apparently man, both directly and as a consequence of his uses of land, has been the principal cause of the Condor's reaching the verge of extinction. This furnishes reason for believing that man, through helpful action, may contribute to its survival and restoration.

In an endeavor to learn the causes of the Condor's decline and the means by which it may be restored, the Society entered into a cooperative undertaking with the University of California at Berkeley. Guidance was sought of the late Dr. Joseph Grinnell and of Dr. Alden H. Miller, both of the Museum of Vertebrate Zoology at the University; it was generously granted. It is they who planned and supervised the research and advised as to the content of the Report. Carl Koford, the author of the Report, was selected and instructed by them. The cooperation of the University has been outstanding. In manpower, time and energy it has contributed abundantly.

The Society contributed money over a three-year period and an Audubon Research Fellowship was granted to Mr. Koford. This did not suffice to cover all costs, and the University financed the balance.

We wish to thank Don Bleitz for his generous contribution of the color frontispiece of the Condor.

We are grateful to those friends who, through cash gifts, have aided in the financing. If the California Condor be saved, they, as well as the University of California at Berkeley, will have been its benefactors.

JOHN H. BAKER,
President,
National Audubon Society.

New York, N. Y.
November 10, 1952

PREFACE

THE CALIFORNIA condor is a majestic bird seen in its natural rugged environment as it sweeps in superbly controlled flight over crests of ridges and great slopes of tangled chaparral. The air passing through its wing tips sets up a steady whine as it is pressed into service to keep the great glider aloft. The condor passes overhead, the sound recedes, and the bird now circles and scans with keen eyes the ground below and the activities of its fellow condors. Here is a picture long to be remembered, a heritage from the past displaying the acme of a specialization for flight which we are still privileged to view as part of our natural esthetic resource.

Pessimism has long prevailed about the ability of the California condor to survive as man takes more thorough control of the country within its range. The condor can not live with man, some people have said; though harmless, it can not survive the changes brought about by him; it is a passing remnant of the Pleistocene. But through several decades of such an attitude of defeatism the condor has hung on as though to prove it could, yet threatened at every turn with extinction and indeed doomed should a few unfortunate accidents take place and a further invasion of its stronghold be allowed. Man will certainly fail to save the California condor unless he tries to save it, and the trying is eminently worth while as anyone with even the most rudimentary appreciation of nature will agree who has actually watched wild condors living in their native mountains.

To understand the condor and its abilities to respond to aid proffered, we must have exhaustive knowledge of its life. Its reactions to intrusion are often subtle—its alarm is not overtly expressed. To understand condors one needs to live with them, think about them daily, gather facts in abundance, analyze and reflect. Such knowledge and understanding has been the objective of the study of the California condor here presented. With this factual basis we can hope as in the conclusion of this report to suggest a wise procedure for conservation. And if the procedure should prove in practice to need modification, the facts are available for recasting the plan of action. And finally, as might happen in any dangerous situation, if we lose and the California condor is gone, we have at least preserved in this report a very full record of this remarkable organism. Such insurance, like all life insurance, is a cold and wholly inadequate payment for a life. Unlike the life of an individual, the life of a species can go on indefinitely if the conditions are right. And so there is much hope for the condor and to provide the essential conditions should be our firm determination.

Carl Koford, the author of this work, early appealed to the late Joseph Grinnell and me as a person equipped with the perseverance, ruggedness, and natural instincts for observation which the field study of the California condor absolutely required. Trained both as zoologist and forester, he knew the country, the animals, the people in it, and the biological and human economies underlying his problem. Koford now tells the full story of the California condor without prejudice, reviewing all factors in the light of his experience. The scientific reporter has been urged to give the whole story, not selected aspects of it, for who knows when we will need or want a particular segment of information.

Condor watching as practiced by Carl Koford meant days on end of patient vigil at nests, some of the time living in a cave not unlike that occupied by the condors a half mile away. It meant traversing cliffs and brush fields, climbing and back-packing, and in other periods penetrating all parts of the recent range of the species. Human residents were extensively interviewed and incidental to gathering information from them, their interest in watching and conserving condors was constantly encouraged. Two and a half years were spent before the war and a half year subsequently in the investigation, a large part of it in the field where condors were often in view. The Audubon Fellowship given by the National Audubon Society for these three years fully sustained the essential field work. Those who through the Audubon Society supported this undertaking may justly feel proud of their contribution to this effort in science and conservation. Koford's year spent in analysis of his voluminous data and in writing was supported by the James M. Goewey Fellowship of the University of California, an aid very essential to the completion of the undertaking. These aids and the continual help of the United States Forest Service have been excellent but it should be realized that the task of conservation of the California condor is only begun by offering this foundation study. We trust there will be enthusiastic participation in the contributing of funds, energy, and ideas for carrying out the program of protection and education which is required.

Berkeley, California
June 3, 1952

Alden H. Miller
Professor of Zoology and
Director of the Museum of
Vertebrate Zoology, Uni-
versity of California

Table of Contents

List of Illustrations

---

[1] Photographs are by the author unless otherwise indicated.

PLATES   FACING PAGE

FIGURES

                                                                                    PAGE

FIGURES

INTRODUCTION

THE PURPOSE of this research has been to seek and record all obtainable data concerning the natural history of the California condor (*Gymnogyps californianus*), to analyze critically these facts with a view to explaining some aspects of the distribution, reproduction, flight, and food habits of condors, and to devise practical methods of working toward the preservation of the species.

My method was primarily that of watching condors for long periods under conditions which were as natural as possible. Because condors are easily disturbed by men, observations were usually made from a considerable distance with binoculars or with a 20-power spotting telescope, and the concealment of a cave or blind was often used. Many entire days were spent in observing from a small lookout house, which the United States Forest Service constructed for my use, and from regular fire lookout stations. During periods unfavorable for observation, I visited areas where condors had occurred in the past or had been reported in recent years, and I interviewed personnel of government forest and agricultural agencies, ranchers, hunters, old-timers, and others. Further information was gained at museums and zoological parks and from the literature.

As a subject for the study of animal behavior the California condor has advantages and disadvantages. These condors are so large that they can be seen from a distance of several miles. If present, they can scarcely escape detection at some time of the day by an observer who is suitably located and watching for them. Many of their actions are performed so slowly that details imperceptible in smaller birds may be easily seen. Condors are so few in number that an observer may see a large proportion, perhaps even half, of the total population at once and individual differences in behavior become apparent. On the other hand, the sexes look alike and the age of immature individuals cannot be determined easily. Because of the danger of injury, it is inadvisable to trap and mark condors. In comparison with smaller birds, condors perform certain essential activities, such as feeding the young, so infrequently that an observer may see an adult condor for only a few minutes in the course of an entire day of watching. One may watch an area where many condors have been the day before and yet not see a single individual. Long distances and rugged terrain make travel difficult for the observer.

In pursuing the field research, I observed living condors between March, 1939, and June, 1941, on approximately 400 days. After a period of service with the United States Navy, I watched condors on 80 days between February and July, 1946, and on 15 days subsequently. The record of my personal observations consists of about 3500 pages of field notes and 350 still photographs of condors and their habitat. Letters mentioned are chiefly from the correspondence files of the Museum of Vertebrate Zoology and of the author.

ACKNOWLEDGMENTS

This study was initiated by the National Audubon Society in 1939 when an Audubon Fellowship was established at the University of California for the purpose of supporting research on the natural history of the California condor. I sincerely appreciate the opportunity provided by the directors of this society. Drs. Joseph Grinnell and Alden H. Miller were named to supervise the work and they selected the writer as the Audubon Fellow. On the death of Grinnell, Dr. Miller continued in charge of the study. For the advice and aid of these men I am deeply grateful. The writing of the final report was accomplished through benefit of the James M. Goewey Fellowship of the University of California.

The field work was greatly facilitated by the active cooperation of the United States Forest Service, particularly that of Cyril S. Robinson, Gordon B. Vance, E. M. Lyda, and Fred P. Cronemiller, and of the field and office personnel of the Santa Barbara Division of the Los Padres National Forest. Among the many ranchers who provided me with information and hospitality, those to whom I am especially indebted are Eugene F. Percy, Perry S. Sprague, Ian I. McMillan, and Eben McMillan. John R. Pemberton, Ed N. Harrison, James A. Reynolds, James S. Fassero, and Richard Howke aided materially in the performance of certain phases of the field work. The chief contributors of extensive and valuable unpublished notes and information were John R. Pemberton, Sidney B. Peyton, W. Lee Chambers, Cyril S. Robinson, Ed N. Harrison, Caroll D. Scott, Joseph P. Herring, Buford

L. Fox, and Harold M. Hill. A great many other contributors are cited in the text in connection with specific information provided by them.

NAMES AND RELATIONSHIPS

The California condor was described technically from the specimen of an adult which was taken by Archibald Menzies at Monterey about December 5, 1792 (Grinnell, 1932:265,266). It was given the name *Vultur Californianus* by George Shaw in Shaw and Nodder's "Naturalist's Miscellany" (1797, vol. 9, plate 301 and text). Subsequently, the species was included in various genera by other authors. Ridgway (in Baird, *et al.*, 1874:338) recognized the California condor as belonging to a distinct genus and named it *Pseudogryphus* but Richmond (1901:49) discovered that Lesson had established the genus *Gymnogyps* for it in 1842. This prior name had escaped notice because it had been published in an obscure Parisian journal. Thus, the condor came to be named *Gymnogyps californianus* (Shaw).

The family of Recent New World Vultures, the Cathartidae, is composed of six species: California condor (*Gymnogyps californianus*), South American condor (*Vultur gryphus*), king vulture (*Sarcoramphus papa*), black vulture (*Coragyps atratus*), turkey vulture (*Cathartes aura*), and the yellow-headed vulture (*Cathartes urubu*). The California condor now occurs only in California, the Andean condor and the yellow-headed vulture only in South America, the king vulture in Central and South America, and the turkey vulture and black vulture in both North and South America. *Gymnogyps* and *Vultur* are very large in size, *Cathartes* and *Coragyps* are relatively small and *Sarcoramphus* is intermediate in size.

The relationships of the five genera to one another, and the relationship of the family Cathartidae to other families of the order Falconiformes, is uncertain. At various times, the exclusion of the family Cathartidae from the order Falconiformes has been urged. Most recently, Hudson (1948:127), on the basis of a comparative study of the musculature of the pelvic limbs of various falconiforms, suggested that the "American Vultures, secretary bird, and the hawk and falcon tribe represent three entirely different lines of avian evolution and are no more closely related to each other than to the owls. . . ." He proposed that these groups be made separate orders: "Cathartidiformes," Sagittariiformes, and Falconiformes.

Fisher (1946:710) found that the skulls, muscles, and pterylosis of the cathartids indicate a closer relationship between the small vultures (turkey and black vultures) and among the large vultures (the two condors and the king vulture) than is present between the two groups. Certain characters tend to show that the small vultures are of a more primitive stock. The fossil record indicates that during the Pleistocene in North America *Gymnogyps* was more abundant than either of the small vultures. Perhaps, then, *Gymnogyps* was the first of the Recent vultures in North America. If the cathartids are of South American origin, possibly *Gymnogyps* and other large vultures moved into North America in the Pleistocene when there were many large mammals, and the small vultures, because of their inability to compete with the large birds, may not have moved north until the decline of the large vultures. If this is the case, *Gymnogyps* is not necessarily the most primitive member of the Recent cathartids.

Fossil bones of *Gymnogyps* are abundant in the Pleistocene deposits at Rancho La Brea in the Los Angeles metropolitan area. These specimens were considered to represent *G. californianus* until Fisher (1944) found that there were fundamental differences between the fossil skulls and the skulls of Recent specimens. *G. amplus,* named from Pleistocene deposits in northern California, was found to be conspecific with the La Brea specimens. Thus, the name *californianus* is restricted to living *Gymnogyps,* and *amplus* is applied to Pleistocene specimens from western North America (Fisher, 1947:227). Possibly *G. californianus* moved into California since the Pleistocene. More probably, the two stocks of condors represent chronological subspecies. *G. amplus* may be the progenitor of *californianus* (Fisher, 1944:292).

Specimens of the two species of *Gymnogyps* can only be segregated on the basis of skull characters although *amplus* tends to be larger than *californianus*. Fisher (1947) found that in nearly all skeletal elements where there was a difference in average size, *amplus* was larger, but the ranges of comparable measurements overlapped.

Possible relationships of the cathartiform genera, Recent and fossil, are shown in figure 1. The fossil species occurred in California unless otherwise noted.

Plate 1. A California Condor near its nest in Eaton Canyon, Pasadena, California, in 1906. Photograph by H. T. Bohlman and W. L. Finley.

Plate 2. An adult Condor nibbling at the neck of its mate. Photograph by H. T. Bohlman and W. L. Finley.

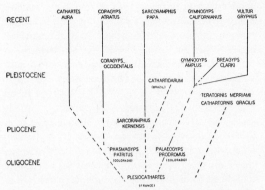

Figure 1. A phylogenetic tree showing the possible relationships of the genera of New World vultures (after Fisher, 1944:294).

In the original description (Shaw, 1797), the vernacular name "California Vulture" was used. Thereafter most authors called the bird the "California vulture." Lewis, Clark, and Douglas wrote of condors as large "buzzards" or "vultures." Bonaparte applied the name "condor" in 1833, but this name was little used until after the publication, from 1855 to 1859, of a series of articles by Alexander Taylor (Harris, 1941: 38). The check-list of the American Ornithologists' Union did not use the name "condor" until the fourth edition (1931). Today, most old-timers and even many young ranchers know the bird as the "California vulture" or simply as "the vulture." These men use the term "condor" only for the South American condor and they call turkey vultures "buzzards."

In 1949, I found that vaqueros in Baja California knew condors as "buitres." Grinnell (1905:12) noted that vaqueros at old Fort Tejon called condors "wietros," apparently the same name. Swann (1924:2) lists "buitre" and "huitre" as names for the South American condor.

As a name for the California condor, Coues (1903: 702) gives "queleli." This is the Mexican name for the caracara. Could Coues' (1866:42) report of condors in Arizona in 1865 have been based on observations of caracaras?

The Yaulamne Indians of the southern San Joaquin Valley know the condor as "wee-itch," according to F. F. Latta of Bakersfield.

SIZE, ANATOMY, MOLT, AND COLOR

Size.—The wingspread of the California condor has often been given in the literature as 11 feet or even 14 feet. To my knowledge, the largest substantiated measurement is 9 feet 7 inches (M.V.Z. 23334). At least three collectors have recorded a wingspread of 9 feet 6 inches or greater on the specimen label. Measurements of a representative group of adult specimens, as recorded on labels or elsewhere, are shown in table 1. E. Z. Rett found the wingspread of one freshly killed adult to be only 8 feet 2½ inches. Of five adults measured by Frank Stephens (letter February 24, 1907), four measured 9 feet 4 inches or a fraction of an inch larger.

The maximum difference in expanse between large and small adults is 17 inches or less, and, allowing for differences in measuring techniques, probably less than 12 inches.

Some birds formerly in the collection of E. B. Towne, Jr., have weights of 27, 29, and 31 pounds recorded on the specimen label. Towne may have learned these weights at second hand from the persons who collected birds for him. The heaviest weight given by Stephens is 21½ pounds. Henshaw (1920:8) tells of collecting one weighing 23 pounds. In round numbers, then, an average adult condor weighs 20 pounds and has a wingspread of 9 feet.

Hill (1944:234) found that the sexes are about the same size in the Cathartidae. Grinnell (MS) noted no difference in size between members of a mated pair seen by him at close range. At one nest which I observed closely, the parent which I believed to be the male seemed the larger. The data in table 1 indicate a tendency for males to be larger than females although the measurements overlap to a large degree.

Immatures with dark gray heads are, in general, smaller than adults (table 1). Subadults are probably as large as adults.

Fisher (1946:553) found the average length of the bony wing of *Vultur* was more than two inches longer than that of *Gymnogyps*. The wingspread of an alcoholic specimen of *Vultur* was found to be 9 feet 10½ inches by Fisher, while a comparable specimen of *Gymnogyps* measured only 9 feet 1 inch. Another specimen (skin) of *Vultur* (M.V.Z. 42838) has a wingspread of 9 feet 10 inches, according to the label (collected by J. R. Pemberton). Murphy (1925:190) tells of the killing of a *Vultur* which was over ten feet in expanse. Evidently *Vultur* is appreciably larger than *Gymnogyps*.

Both condors are much smaller than *Teratornis merriami,* a cathartid-like Pleistocene associate of *Gymnogyps* and perhaps the largest bird which ever flew. Fisher (1945:727) found the average lengths of the bony wing of *Gymnogyps* and *Teratornis* to be 803 millimeters and 1024 millimeters, respectively. Judged by the body skeleton, *Teratornis* may have weighed 50 pounds in life.

Gymnogyps is not as heavy as a big turkey and its wings are not as long as those of the wandering albatross. Its only claim to uniqueness in size is that it has the largest wingspread of any North American land bird.

Anatomy.—The osteology of the Cathartidae has been described and illustrated by Shufeldt (1883). The visceral anatomy has not been studied. Fisher (1946) made an extensive study of the bones and muscles of the locomotor apparatus of the Cathartidae with a view to discovering adaptive modifications. In this work, Fisher found that the phyletic differences between the vultures were so great as to obscure adaptive differences. No single structure showed a simple correlation with flapping or soaring flight for all five genera. The skulls of the cathartid vultures have been described and compared by Fisher (1944). Miller and Fisher (1938) have described the pterylosis of an adult California condor.

Molt.—By observing deficiencies in the flight feathers (primaries and secondaries) of free-living condors, I was not able to ascertain the pattern of molt or even a definite season of molt. In every month of the year I saw condors with missing feathers. Condors in perfect plumage were most frequently noted in December. In mid-March and in summer I found many freshly molted feathers beneath frequented roosts. Symmetrical loss of flight feathers is not the rule. The members of one nesting pair each had one missing primary (number 8) about July 1 and the same primary was several inches short one month later.

Loye Miller (1937:160) tore down a mounted specimen and found the youngest primaries to be numbers 5, 8, and 7. About one-third of the secondaries were developing, the order of their emergence being 1, 14, 18, 3 and 9, 19, and 12.

The lack of obvious regularity in the molt may be due to several factors. Condors lose many feathers through accident. Occasionally I saw a very ragged condor with as many as three or four flight feathers missing from one wing. Probably the molt is not the same in immature and adult birds. In the Cathartidae, as in eagles and large hawks, the replacement of secondaries is comparatively irregular and often individuals do not molt all of the secondaries in a single year (A. Miller, 1941:113). Jollie (1947:559) found that not all of the primaries were molted in a single season by a captive golden eagle although the molt proceeded outward in the series in a fairly uniform manner. For this eagle, Jollie (*op. cit.*:565) suggests that more than one season is required for a complete molt because the bird is dependent upon perfection of flight and much time is required for the growth of a new feather. For the same reasons, condors may require more than one season for a complete molt. The probable existence of three molt centers in the secondaries, as in some other falconiforms, adds to the difficulty of determining the course of the molt in free-living condors.

Color.—Most of the skin of the head of the adult is orange in color. The shade of orange is more reddish, more yellowish, or more grayish in some individuals than in others. The color is most reddish in the rostral region and is generally pale in the occipital region. The anterior interramal region is especially yellowish. Most of the neck is uniform light gray in color. This gray color grades into the orange of the head in the interramal, occipital, and posterior malar regions. On the ventral side of the neck, extending anteriorly to the ruff of elongated neck feathers, there is a well defined patch of purplish-red skin. The naked skin of the base of the throat posterior to the ruff (ventral cervical apterium) is a brighter shade of red. This red area grades into light gray at the borders.

Frequently the skin of the neck, from the area below the ear to the sides of the occiput and hind neck, is of a pinkish or purplish hue. If the skin of the occiput and hind neck is wrinkled and is then drawn tight, the lines of the wrinkles remain for a time as purplish or reddish streaks. Doubtless part of the color of the head is caused by the supply of capillary blood. The colors of the heads of nesting individuals which were watched a great deal were brighter on some days than on others, but the difference was not great, and the head of the supposed female was redder and its plumage was blacker than that of the supposed male. In a captive adult which I saw at Washington, D. C., in May, 1939, the coloring of the head and of the ventral cervical apterium was dull and pale. The iris of the adult is red in both sexes.

Plumage changes with age.—In the juvenal condor, nearly all the head and neck is covered with a short, dark gray woolly down. Possibly this down does not reach its fullest development until the bird is over one year old. The skin of the head, neck, and ventral cervical apterium of the juvenile is dark gray in color and the eye is brown. There is down for about an inch above the heels and usually there is some down on the breast of juveniles in spring. The white patches under the wings are irregularly mottled with dark brown but there is more white than brown in these patches and the darkest spot is at the axilla. This pattern of a central dark spot in a nearly white patch is conspicuous at a distance. In addition, several of the proximal upper greater secondary coverts have light gray tips. The tip of the tail of a soaring juvenile is pointed in comparison with the smoothly rounded tail of the adult. The feathers of the dorsal surface of the wings appear black rather than grayish as in the adult.

Some immatures, presumably those about two years of age, have less white than the juveniles. There is much less white than brown in the area of the under wing coverts and the tips of the upper greater secondary coverts are not gray. The eye appears red, at least in certain light, before any color shows on the head or neck.

As the immature grows older, the skin of the neck becomes pink, commencing at the base, so that the bird has a more or less well defined ring around the base of its neck. Frequently the ruff hides this ring but the ring may show even when the bird is soaring. The pink area increases anteriorly until the entire neck is pink. The ventral cervical apterium turns pink at about the same time. By the time most of the neck is pink the malar area is orange, although most of the head remains sooty. At this stage there is generally no white bar on the upper surface of the wing and there is little white on the lower surface of the wings.

In the adult there is a white bar an inch or more in breadth formed by the white tips of the upper greater secondary coverts and the patches under the wings are pure white.

In the subadult plumage, the head is of the adult color but small feathers on the crown, occiput, and other parts of the head cause an irregular sooty appearance. The neck is pink when the head color is nearly adult. Some subadults appear to be adults at a short distance except that there is a dark triangular area near the axilla in the white patches under the wings. In many gatherings of condors at least four immature plumages can be recognized: juvenal, "black," "ring neck," and subadult.

Age of attaining adult plumage.—Assuming the four immature plumages represent age classes, condors do not achieve the adult plumage until they are at least five years old. Condors in captivity require about six years to attain adult plumage. A condor which Finley (1910:11) had taken as a chick from the nest, was examined when it was 2 years and 8 months old. The bird showed "no signs of bright color about his head, as it was covered with short gray down." A chick taken from the nest on October 23, 1923, died at Selig Zoo, Los Angeles, on May 14, 1928. The condor (L.A.M. 15885) was 5 years old at death. There are many small feathers in the coronal, occipital, submalar, and anterior cervical regions of this specimen although the adult feather pattern predominates. A specimen (U.S.N.M. 192532) of a condor which died at the National Zoological Park in April, 1905, at the age of 4 years, is subadult. A specimen (U.S.N.M. 201427) which died at the same zoo in June, 1907, at the age of 7 years, is adult. Karl Koch, who kept a young condor at Selig Zoo and another at the San Diego Zoo, told me that the head color changed from dark gray to orange between 4 and 6 years of age. A South American condor which was hatched at San Diego in June, 1942, was nearly adult in the spring of 1948, when almost 6 years old (W. M. Mann, letter May 18, 1948).

Distribution and Numbers

Fossil records.—The records of occurrence of fossil species of New World vultures (family Cathartidae) were recently reviewed by Fisher (1944:294, 295). The oldest record is from the Upper Eocene or Lower Oligocene of France. Two genera have been described from the Oligocene of Colorado. One species has been named from the Pliocene of Bolivia and one from the Pliocene of Kern County, California. In Pleistocene deposits, one species has been reported from Brazil and several from North America (California to Florida, and Mexico). According to Loye Miller (1931*b*:71), "Tropical America is apparently the center of the familial area of the Cathartidae, and from this center various species range more or less widely."

Pleistocene records of *Gymnogyps* are as follows:

California. Rancho La Brea (L. Miller, 1910).

California. Carpinteria (L. Miller, 1927).

California. Samwel Cave, Shasta County (L. Miller, 1911).

Mexico. San Josecito Cavern, Nuevo León (L. Miller, 1943).

Florida. Sarasota and Seminole Field (Wetmore, 1931*b*).

In recent years, condors have been seen within 20 miles of the first two of these localities. These birds may have occurred in Shasta County as late as 1855. The last three localities are outside of the present range of the condor. In view of the wandering habits of condors, there is no reason to suppose that they inhabited all these localities at any one time during the million years of the Pleistocene.

Howard (1930*a*) made a census of the number of individual birds represented in one collection of fossils from the Rancho La Brea asphalt pits. She found that of all birds *Gymnogyps* was fourth in abundance, and that of the six cathartiform birds represented, *Gymnogyps* was the most abundant. Because of the nature of the asphalt trap, predators far outnumber prey species in the La Brea pits and probably *Gymnogyps* was trapped more readily than some other carnivorous birds which fed on mammals caught in the tar, for condors usually land at some distance from a carcass, then walk to it, and they must run for several yards on flat ground before becoming airborne. However, there is little doubt that *Gymnogyps* reached its peak of abundance and attained its widest distribution during the Pleistocene.

In the several thousand years since the Pleistocene, *Cathartes aura* and *Coragyps atratus* have become abundant, some cathartids have become extinct, and *Gymnogyps* has become nearly extinct.

Loye Miller (1942:212) considers *Gymnogyps* to be a "senile species that is far past its prime." The concept of "species senescence" is highly questionable (Allee, *et al.*, 1949:639). It implies evolution independent of changes in the environment. A paleontologist, detecting specialization unsuited to later changes in the environment, may consider a species to be senile. Yet, the selective pressures acting on the organism cannot be influenced by future changes in the environment so that certain genetic characters which might later prove of survival value may be lost. The decrease in the range and numbers of condors may be due to inability to compete with better adapted species rather than to becoming unsuited to the physical environment.

Prehistoric Recent records.—Records of occurrence of *Gymnogyps californianus* in Recent but prehistoric time are as follows:

California. Emeryville Shellmound, Alameda County (Howard, 1929).

Oregon. Shellmound near Brookings, Coos County (A. Miller, 1942).

Nevada. Gypsum Cave, near Las Vegas (L. Miller, 1931*a*).

Texas. Brewster County (Wetmore and Friedmann, 1933).

New Mexico. Rocky Arroyo, about 50 miles west Carlsbad (Wetmore, 1931*a*).

New Mexico. Conkling Cavern, Dona Ana County (Howard, 1930*b*).

New Mexico. Shelter Cave, Dona Ana County (Howard and Miller, 1933).

The age of the bones discovered at the foregoing localities has been variously estimated at from 500 to 3000 years. At some localities condor bones were found associated with the bones of now extinct mammals and with human cultural materials. The latter fact substantiates the idea that the practice of keeping condors for ceremonial purposes may once have been widespread. All these localities are outside of the present range of the condor although in the early 1800's these birds probably ranged to the California and Oregon sites. It is evident that condors once occurred with regularity in south-central New Mexico.

One might expect that such a huge bird as the condor would become a part of the art and legends of the Indians. Kroeber (1925:495) states that the condor has a totemic affiliation among the Yokuts of the southern San Joaquin Valley and is a prominent character in their legends. F. F. Latta has interviewed hundreds of Indians near Bakersfield. He has found legends of the condor as far north as the Tuolumne River. The Yaulamne near Bakersfield had a condor song, dance, and story, and the Wuckchumne, a Tule River tribe, had a condor story. Condors still occur in the areas of these tribes. Evidence of the former occurrence of condors in other regions, such as Oregon, might be obtained through anthropological investigation.

Historical records.—The historical records of the condor before 1900 have been traced by Harry Harris (1941) who was able to consult many original manuscripts and rare editions. He ascribes the first written mention of the condor to Fr. Antonio de la Ascención of the Vizcaino Expedition which arrived at Monterey in December of 1602. Fr. Ascención wrote in his journal of seeing large birds, "the shape of turkeys," which had a wingspread of 17 spans (11 feet 4 inches, considering a span to be 8 inches) (Harris, 1941:4).

Three members of a land force which traveled from San Diego Bay to Monterey Bay in 1769 made notes in their diaries of seeing large "eagles" having a wingspread of 11 to 15 spans. Near the present town of Watsonville, they saw a "royal eagle" which the natives had killed and stuffed. Because of this event, the Pajaro River was so-named (Harris, 1941:8).

A letter written by Don Jose de Longinos Martinez in April, 1792, mentioned a shipment to Spain which included a specimen of *"Vultur Harpyia"* (variety: *Monstruosa)*." There is no further trace of this specimen (Harris, *loc. cit.*).

"On or about December 5, 1792," Archibald Menzies, a member of the Vancouver Expedition, collected an adult condor at Monterey (Grinnell, 1932:251). This specimen became the type in 1797.

The principal mentions of condors in the published journals of Lewis and Clark and of Patrick Gass who accompanied them on their expedition to the lower Columbia River are as follows:

1805, October 30: mouth Wind River, some seen (Lewis and Clark, 1905; 3:174).

1805, November 18: mouth Columbia River, one killed (*ibid.;* 3:232).

1805, November 30: mouth Columbia River, seen (*ibid.;* 3:259).

1806, January 3: Fort Clatsop, near mouth Columbia River; seen (*ibid.;* 3:309).

1806, February 17: near Fort Clatsop, one wounded and captured (*ibid.;* 4:81).

1806, March 15: near Fort Clatsop, two killed (Gass, 1904:203).

1806, March 28: Deer Island, Columbia River; hunters said eagles and vultures devoured four deer (Lewis and Clark, *op. cit.;* 4:211).

A photostat of the original journal of Meriwether Lewis for February 17, 1806, was published by Harris (1941:14-16). These pages include an excellent description of a living condor and an accurate sketch of the head. There is no doubt as to the identity of the bird. Furthermore, a skull and primary feather of a condor were donated to Peale's Museum by Lewis and Clark.

John Scouler (1905:280), a botanist who accompanied Douglas to the Pacific Northwest, obtained a specimen of a condor near Fort Vancouver about September 22, 1825. This specimen, the second to reach Europe, arrived at the Leiden Museum in 1827 (Harris, 1941:19).

David Douglas, the Scotch botanist, killed two condors near Fort Vancouver, not far from the present city of Portland, and he shot at others. One was killed in 1826 before March 20 but was not preserved (Douglas, 1914:62,154). The other was taken in February of 1827 (*ibid.:*241). Of the condors in that region, Douglas (*ibid.:*154) wrote: "Seldom more than one or two are together." As nearly as I can determine, Douglas was in the present location of eastern Linn County, Oregon, when he noted on October 3, 1826 (*ibid.:*216) that "the Large Buzzard, so common on the shores of the Columbia, is also plentiful here: saw nine in one flock." Douglas collected a condor between October 10 and 15, 1826, when in the present location of eastern Lane or Douglas County. His two specimens were deposited in the museum of the London Zoological Society.

The last specimen collected near the Columbia River was an immature taken by J. K. Townsend in the fall of 1834 (Harris, *op. cit.*:21). Townsend (in Audubon, 1839:241) reported that it was rare to see "more than two or three" condors at a time. J. G. Cooper spent much time along the Columbia River in the 1850's and sought condors there but found none [one doubtful sight record] (Cooper and Suckley, 1859:141). Gabrielson and Jewett (1940:181) relate a possibly valid record of condors being seen near Drain, Douglas County, Oregon, in 1903 and 1904.

The localities for all of the definite records of occurrence of condors in the Pacific Northwest are within 120 miles of the coast and mostly in the region of the lower Columbia River. Published reports that condors ranged inland to 500 miles from the mouth of the Columbia River and northward to 49 degrees (Audubon, 1839:240, 242) are apparently based on hearsay. In view of the fact that condors have an extensive yearly range, yet tend to forage over the same area for many days in succession, the presence of two or three dozen condors in northwestern Oregon would be sufficient to account for all the records for that area.

The occurrence and disappearance of condors along the Columbia River cannot be satisfactorily explained on the basis of the available facts. In order to explain this situation, one must know whether the birds were breeding, at what season they were most numerous, and upon what they were feeding. As there is no evidence of the breeding of condors north of San Francisco, the northern birds probably were immatures and non-breeding adults. Today the seasonal distribution of such birds is largely determined by the location of a constant suitable supply of food. Townsend (*op. cit.*:240, 241) wrote of the condor in 1834: "It is seen on the Columbia only in summer, appearing about the first of June, and retiring, probably to the mountains, about the end of August. It is . . . attracted by the dead salmon which strew the shores. . . . Their food while on the Columbia is fish almost exclusively. . . ." However, Townsend (*op. cit.*:240) also wrote that the condors were "most abundant in spring." Douglas (1914:241) stated that condors were seen "in great numbers" on the Columbia River in summer but that they were "less abundant" in winter. Unfortunately, hearsay is not always separated from fact in Douglas' account. Douglas did not

mention that condors fed upon fish. Lewis, Clark, and Gass did not mention that condors fed on salmon although there was one mention of condors feeding on "fish" on the sea coast. The idea that condors fed mainly on salmon along the shores of the river seems to be attributable to Townsend only.

Judging from various mentions of salmon in the accounts of Lewis, Clark, and Douglas, the run of salmon commenced in April and declined during the summer. In mid-October great numbers of dead salmon lined the shores of the Columbia. In winter the Indians starved for lack of fish. The idea that condors were most common on the river in summer correlates well with the time of the salmon run. On this basis, one might suggest that the condors moved northward in summer to feed on the salmon and that they retired southward in winter. A seasonal northward and southward movement of about 100 miles occurs in the condor population today. Turkey vultures also tend to retire southward in winter. The only difficulty with this supposition is that all of the definite records of condors in the region of the Columbia River are included between the months of September and March, the opposite of the season of the salmon run. Possibly the population of condors was so scattered in summer, when there was an abundance of food for 100 miles or more along the river, that the explorers did not notice them.

Douglas (1914:216) mentioned that the country had been extensively burned over by the Indians in the area where he saw nine condors. Perhaps this burning killed many animals and opened up the forests so that the carcasses were available to condors. Presumably burning would occur in late summer or fall at about the time that the condors arrived (judging by the written records of occurrence).

Whatever the source of food near the Columbia River, condors evidently found it attractive. It may be that unfavorable food conditions in California forced the condors northward in search of food, and, finding it, they tended to stay in that area or to return in subsequent years. Then as the production of livestock and the slaughter of these animals for hides increased in California, the condors withdrew to the south and were not again forced northward. The other possibility is that the condors in the Pacific Northwest were the remnant of a formerly widespread population in that area, but there are no fossil or sub-fossil

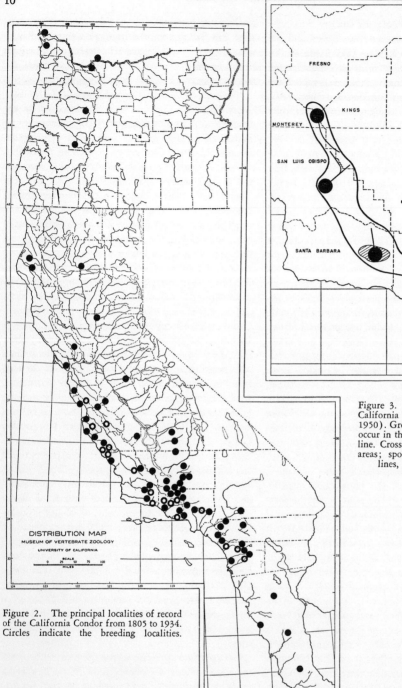

Figure 3. The principal range of the California Condor at present (1935 to 1950). Groups of ten or more Condors occur in the area enclosed by the heavy line. Cross-hatching indicates breeding areas; spots, major roosts; radiating lines, major routes of flight.

DISTRIBUTION MAP
MUSEUM OF VERTEBRATE ZOOLOGY
UNIVERSITY OF CALIFORNIA
SCALE
0 25 50 75 100
MILES

Figure 2. The principal localities of record of the California Condor from 1805 to 1934. Circles indicate the breeding localities.

specimens to support this idea. As condors were apparently present in the Sacramento Valley and in Humboldt County in the middle 1800's, the southward withdrawal of the population seems more probable.

The second known specimen from California was an adult collected by Ferdinand Deppe near San Diego about 1830 (Harris, 1941:23). E. L. Kern, an artist accompanying Fremont, collected an adult in California in 1845 (*ibid.*:35). William Gamble, first American ornithologist to collect in California (1842 to 1845), left no evidence that he had handled a specimen of a condor. Neither did Heermann who spent much time in California between 1849 and 1854 (*ibid.*:35, 36). Harris (*ibid.*:39) lists more than a dozen collectors who sought birds in California before 1860 but did not secure a specimen of a condor.

J. S. Newberry (1857:73), surgeon of a railroad surveys party, traveled northward through the Sacramento Valley to Klamath Lakes in 1855. Condors were seen daily in the Sacramento Valley but "very few" were seen in the Klamath Basin in California and none was seen in Oregon. Newberry's account seems to be free from hearsay and fancy and provides the only evidence that condors once may have been common in the Sacramento Valley. Of the condor in that valley, Belding (1879:437) wrote: "I have seen it on no more than two or three occasions in Yuba County in winter." Subsequently Belding (1890:24) wrote: "It has been very rare in the center of the State north of . . . 38° since the spring of 1856." That was the year Belding arrived in California.

The principal localities of record from 1805 to 1934 are shown in figure 2. The present range (since 1935) of flocks of condors is shown in figure 3.

The records of occurrence of condors which are tabulated in the appendix (pages 139 to 146) have been selected with a view to indicating changes in distribution and numbers since 1835. Following are comments on these distributional records for each important area.

Areas from which condors have disappeared since 1850.

California. Humboldt County.—Two specimens are reported to have been taken about 1890. A mounted specimen seen at the Eureka Public Library by C. H. Merriam (MS) in 1898 and by J. Grinnell (MS) in 1923 was probably the "Kneeland" bird. Apparently condors were present in Humboldt County many years after they had disappeared from the Columbia River. Salmon in the lower Eel and Klamath rivers, or refuse from whaling operations, may have attracted them. At any rate, the condors were gone from there by 1900.

Napa County.—Condors were reported, by two authors, between 1845 and 1860. In physical features, the Napa Valley appears suitable for condors.

Marin County.—There is one report by Grayson for 1847. If condors occurred in Napa and Humboldt counties in the middle 1800's, they probably occurred in Marin County as well.

San Mateo County.—Probably condors were present in the late 1800's. This county is only 40 miles from Sargents (San Benito County) where condors were common in the 1880's and parts of it appear to be physically suitable for condors.

Santa Clara County.—The few condors reported in this county in the late 1800's were probably wanderers from Santa Cruz or San Benito counties. Very rare by 1900.

Santa Cruz County.—Condors were not uncommon until the 1880's and a few remained until shortly after 1900. There is no evidence substantiating this county as the locality for two eggs taken in 1879. If the egg data are correct, this county is the northernmost known breeding place for condors.

Tuolumne County.—There are two records by one man for 1850. Even then condors were rare in the foothills of the Sierra Nevada north of Tulare County.

San Bernardino County.—Condors were present in the San Bernardino Mountains in the 1880's. There are no certain records for this county subsequent to 1900 although it would seem that, until about 1910, condors from the vicinity of Mount Wilson (Los Angeles County) easily could have wandered to Bear Valley.

Riverside County.—Near Mount San Jacinto condors were present from the 1880's until the early 1900's. There is no evidence substantiating the existence of a nest there. In recent years the sighting of a single individual near Mount San Jacinto has been reported a few times but these records lack confirmation.

Orange County.—There are several undoubted records of individuals from 1872 to 1938. There is no evidence of former large numbers in this county. Forest Service men have reported an occasional individual near Santiago Peak as late as 1940. This area is similar to other areas inhabited by condors. Birds roosting near Santiago Peak could easily forage on Santa Margarita Ranch in northwestern San Diego County and account for occasional reports from that vicinity. I do not know of any certain records south of Orange County since 1938.

San Diego County.—Many condors foraged in northwestern and north-central San Diego County in the 1880's and 1890's. The largest group reported was only seven (1898) although at least 18 specimens were taken between 1875 and 1900. In 1940 I questioned many ranchers and old-timers in the Palomar Mountain, Ramona, and Julian regions. Men who had lived there since the 1880's believed that the last birds were seen about 1900 and that before then it was rare to see over two at a time. James B. Dixon (verbal, 1940) saw condors near the upper San Luis Rey River until about 1910.

There are no substantiated records since 1910 although I have heard several reports of from one to four condors being seen near Palomar Mountain or Santa Margarita Ranch in recent years. If the condors seen in Lower California were not resident there, they must have passed back and forth through the mountains of southern San Diego County; yet, there are no records for that area.

The roosts which were used by condors foraging in central San Diego County are unknown. Palomar Mountain seems to be the most likely roosting spot for condors in that region. Three nesting localities are known (see figure 2), the last recorded nesting being in 1900.

Arizona.—There is one report, for 1865, and this is doubtful. Other published reports for Arizona are even more doubtful (see Swarth, 1914:83). Woodhouse (1853) and Cooper (1870) found no condors along the Colorado River. The Yuma area, at present, appears unsuitable for condors.

Mexico. Lower California.—There are records from 1887 to 1937, principally for the Sierra San Pedro Mártir. The southernmost record (east of El Rosario) is less than 200 miles south of the California border. There are no definite records for Lower California between November 5 and May, but there is little travel in the mountains in winter. Swann (1924:21) states that he has an egg taken in Lower California, but no year of collection is given, the locality is indetermi-

nate, and the color of the egg is atypical. Possibly the egg was a fake or the locality was falsified by the collector. There is no other evidence of breeding in Lower California.

The man usually questioned regarding condors in the Sierra San Pedro Mártir is Salve Melling, owner of Rancho San José, who has lived in that area since 1908. The ranch is the main departure point for persons packing in to the higher mountains. Until about 1941 Melling ran cattle in the high meadows (La Grulla, La Encantada) every summer. In 1925, Melling told Grinnell (MS) that he had seen seven or eight condors during some previous summers. Melling told me (1949) that since about 1914 condors have become scarce. He could not recollect having seen a condor since 1932. Condors had been seen only in the high country (above 6000 feet elevation) Melling said, never over the ranch proper (about 2500 feet elevation). In the summer of 1949 I questioned many vaqueros in and near the Sierra San Pedro Mártir and Sierra Juárez, but I found none who had seen a condor in recent years.

Evidently condors ceased to frequent the mountains of Lower California in the 1930's. The birds formerly seen there may have wandered down the Laguna Range from San Diego County in search of food and found cattle carcasses in the high meadows in summer. Probably, in historical times, there has not been more than one or two dozen condors at a time in Lower California.

Areas in which condors are still present.

San Benito County.—Condors were common in western San Benito County in the 1880's but became rare about 1900. In summer, vagrants still wander northward to this county, probably from the vicinity of Castle Mountain, less than 60 miles south of Pinnacles. A. S. Leopold and W. C. Russell identified a condor near Bitterwater on September 2, 1951.

Fresno County.—There are a few records of one or two individuals in the southwestern portion of this county between 1890 and 1900 but no definite records between 1900 and 1945. Apparently many condors roosted on Castle Mountain (at the extreme southern corner of the county) in the summers of 1944 to 1947 but they were not found feeding in Fresno County. As there are many sheep and cattle in the foothills south of Coalinga, condors may sometimes visit that area.

Monterey County.—There are records, almost continuously, from 1855 to the present with the exception of about 20 years between 1920 and 1940. The oldest specimen records for the presence (1792) and breeding (1859) of condors in historical time are for the vicinity of Monterey. Condors were rare at Monterey by 1890. Near Big Sur they were still present in the late 1890's. Near Jolon, condors were common in the 1880's and present in groups after 1900; the last specimen from that area was taken in 1917. Probably the huge cattle ranches (Las Milpitas, San Miguelito, and El Piojo) were once the primary feeding areas for condors in Monterey County.

I have been unable to substantiate several reports of one or two condors being seen in the Santa Lucia Mountains since 1938. These mountains are exceedingly rough in some sections so that a few condors could be present yet undetected. From near Castle Mountain in Monterey County a condor could travel the 40 miles to the Nacimiento River in a few hours.

In 1940 I questioned many persons in and near the Santa Lucia Mountains. The old residents believed that the decrease in numbers of condors had been gradual and that, rather than being killed off, the birds had moved to other areas. The time of greatest decrease was variously placed from 1890 to 1910.

Since 1940, an extension of range into southeastern Monterey County has become evident. The birds feed primarily on Cholame Ranch and roost on Castle Mountain. These occurrences are discussed with the San Luis Obispo County records.

Nesting records (4) before 1870 were apparently for the northern Santa Lucia range. Between 1895 and 1902 at least eight eggs and three young birds were collected in Monterey County, mostly by collectors (Harris brothers and Wallace Mathes) who operated in the southern Santa Lucias. Some specimens were taken at Los Burros Gorge and The Shut In (near Bryson).

San Luis Obispo County.—Before 1900, condors were resident in northwestern San Luis Obispo County. Herbert DeTracey and Walter Harris, long resident in that area and interested in condors, state that many roosted near Rocky Butte and Vulture Rock before 1900. The birds were gone from that area by 1915. In 1940 I was unable to find anyone in that vicinity who had seen a condor in recent years. At least 10 eggs were taken in this county between 1889

and 1905, probably all from the northwestern section (near Rocky Butte, Burnett Peak, Pebblestone Shut In, and possibly Lopez Canyon).

Since the early 1900's McChesney Mountain, overlooking Carrizo Plains, has been known as a nesting locality. According to Fred Truesdale, veteran collector of eggs, some specimens of condors and at least five eggs were taken there between 1905 and 1920. Apparently only one breeding pair was present at a time. In a great many visits to this mountain between 1902 and 1923, Truesdale did not see more than five condors at once. Yet, in 1948, I saw at least six, and in 1947 Alden H. Miller saw 14, at this locality. The increase in birds here corresponded with an increase in extreme northeastern San Luis Obispo County.

At various times I have heard reports of 10 or more condors being seen on Carrizo Plains close to Painted Rock, Soda Lake, or Chimeneas Ranch. Probably birds from McChesney Mountain forage in these areas as well as near Simmler, Temblor Valley, San Juan Ranch, and Bitterwater Valley. I have heard, second hand, reports of one or two condors being seen near Lopez Canyon, a dozen miles southeast of the city of San Luis Obispo. It is possible that a few condors forage westward from the McChesney Mountain roosts. Condors are rarely seen at Black Mountain and Branch Mountain lookout stations which are situated only 10 miles north and south of McChesney Mountain.

Eben and Ian McMillan, lifetime residents and ranchers of northeastern San Luis Obispo County, told me that they first started hearing reports of condors in that region about 1940. Their father had settled near Shandon in 1884 and had done much hunting, but he had not seen a condor. In June from 1944 to 1947, a dozen or more condors were seen on Cholame Ranch by various persons; the maximum count was 22 (1947). In 1946 I found that these birds roosted on the north side of Castle Mountain, just inside Fresno County, and that they foraged as far as Shale Hills at the western edge of the San Joaquin Valley. Usually the condors were gone from the Cholame area by the end of August although in some years (including 1950) large groups have been reported in mid-October.

In Bitterwater Valley, and near Pinole Ranch at the northern end of the Carrizo Plains, Eben McMillan has watched for condors throughout the year. His earliest records are for March (1946-1948) but not more than two or three condors at a time were seen until about June 1. Again after early October not over two or three were seen until 1949 when 19 were noted on October 4; few were seen that summer.

Santa Barbara County.—In the Santa Ynez Mountains and the foothills near Santa Barbara, a few condors were resident between 1880 and 1910. No groups of more than two or three were reported. Some specimens were taken in this area. At least four eggs were collected close to Santa Barbara between 1897 and 1902. Since 1910, condors have been rare in the Santa Ynez Range. No more than two at once have been reported there since 1936. A few wanderers probably reach the western end of the range near Buellton.

The mountains surrounding the upper Sisquoc River have been frequented by condors since the 1890's or earlier. Since 1939 I have seen condors roosting at several locations along the San Rafael Mountains from San Rafael Peak to Strawberry (Madulce) Peak, a distance of about 13 miles. The greatest roosting concentrations have occurred in Falls Canyon. In the 1890's, many condors are reported to have been seen (75 by Willett, 15 by Zahn). Pemberton saw 32 there in 1936; Maples saw 29 in 1937. Since 1938 not more than nine at once have been reported in Falls Canyon although in 1940 I saw 20 condors within five miles of that roost. Since 1936, at least 10 condors at once have been reported in the Big Pine Mountain area in every month of the year except January, February, and April. Because of snow and washed out roads, the area is rarely visited by men in winter. Since 1938 the largest numbers have been seen between July and November. At least four eggs and one young bird were taken from the vicinity of upper Sisquoc Canyon between 1895 and 1902. In two recent years a young bird, not long out of the nest, has been seen there.

There is no evidence of a general decrease in the condor population in the Sisquoc-Cuyama Valley region between 1900 and 1940. J. D. Reyes, resident of Cuyama Valley since 1887 and ranger in that vicinity from 1900 to 1931, recalled (1940) seeing no flocks of more than seven or eight condors in the old days. The same maximum was given by Gene Johnston, cattleman in Cuyama Valley since 1907.

From roosts in the San Rafael Mountains, condors forage over Santa Barbara, Salisbury, and Montgomery potreros, over the southern side of Cuyama Valley, and probably as far as Spanish Ranch at the western end of Cuyama Valley. To a lesser extent they forage in the Santa Ynez drainage, going as far as Figueroa Mountain and the Santa Ynez Range. In the lower Sisquoc drainage (Sisquoc, Webber, and Goodchild ranches) condors are rarely seen. Forest Service lookout men at McPherson Peak have rarely seen more than two or three condors at a time although large flocks have been seen within six miles of that peak (Branch Canyon).

Condors moving from the San Rafael Mountains eastward toward the Sespe River probably pass between the Santa Ynez Mountains and Pine Mountain (Ventura County). Those working northward toward McChesney Mountain probably travel along the Sierra Madre Mountains and the foothills north of them.

Ventura County.—Condors have been present in this county since the 1880's or earlier and are still resident in numbers.

In southern Ventura County (Santa Monica Mountains, Simi Hills, and Conejo Ranch) condors were common between 1880 and 1910 and have become rare since. In recent years a few individuals have been reported from the Santa Monica Mountains on occasions. Probably these birds were wanderers from roosts in the Sespe River region.

The main condor roosts in Ventura County are in Big Sespe Canyon and its tributaries near Sulphur Peak, and in Hopper Canyon. A few condors roost in parts of adjacent Santa Paula and Piru canyons. From these roosts, they forage in all directions. Large feeding aggregations have been seen in Pole and Hopper canyons, on Oak Ridge, on Liebre Mountain, and in Antelope Valley. Until about 1910 condors were sometimes seen feeding on the floor of the Santa Clara Valley in areas now covered by citrus groves.

Nesting has occurred since 1940, just as in the early 1900's in the same canyons in which the condors roost. Between 1900 and 1909 at least five young and one egg where taken from Piru Canyon (or its branch, Agua Blanca Canyon). At least eight eggs and one young were taken from the other three canyons between 1902 and 1923. I know of fifteen nestings which have occurred in this region between 1939 and 1946.

There has been at least one major shift in principal roosting location within the Sespe region. In 1917 groups of 20 or more condors were seen roosting in the head of Coldwater Canyon while not more than nine were reported from Hopper Canyon. Since 1939 I have often seen more than 20 birds in Hopper Canyon but never over three in Coldwater Canyon. It is believed that disturbance of the condors by road building and use in Sespe Canyon caused this change.

There has been no consistent decrease in the condor population in the Sespe region. Tom Arundell, a rancher living in Pole Canyon, recognized no decrease in the 25 years preceding 1907 (letter, September 15, 1907). His son Frank, collector of 10 condor skins and some eggs, believed (1939) that there had been no decrease since 1900. Evidently there has always, within the past 50 years, been a concentration of condors in that region in winter and spring. Dale King, rancher in Reasoner Canyon since 1901, recognized no decrease in numbers of condors (verbal, 1940). J. R. Pemberton (1910:19), who surveyed in the Topatopa and Santa Ynez mountains in 1910, considered three condors seen at once to be worthy of publication. Condors are not infrequent in these areas today.

Condors occur regularly over Pine Mountain and small groups roost there. Near Thorn Point, at the eastern end of this mountain, condors have been seen almost daily from June to November (1937-1949) by lookout men. In some years the maximum number of birds seen at once has been three, in other years as high as six. Condors utilize the south-facing slopes of this mountain as a flight lane from east to west. W. H. Green, who manned a lookout station at Reyes Peak on Pine Mountain from 1925 to 1932, did not see more than two or three condors at a time there. The only nesting record for the Pine Mountain area is an egg taken in 1905 from a branch of Sespe Canyon.

At almost any high peak in Ventura County north of Fillmore and Ojai a patient observer can see condors in every season. Forest Service men occasionally have seen individuals near Whiteledge Peak and Nordhoff Peak (lookout) near Ojai, and over Alamo Mountain and Frazier Mountain (former lookout) in northeastern Ventura County. Other men have seen one or two condors over Mount Pinos. There are cattle in the less rough northwest corner of the county (Lockwood Valley and eastern Cuyama Valley drainage) but records of condors for that region are lacking.

For the vicinity of Hopper Mountain I obtained sufficient data to illustrate the seasonal change in numbers of condors. The numbers detected there at various times of the year in 1939, 1940, 1941, and 1946 are shown in figure 4. The height of the bars indicates the maximum number of condors seen at one time in each five-day period when counts were made. The intensity of observation varied from time to time, and the detectability of the birds varied because of storms and fog. Some counts were of feeding birds, others of flying or roosting birds. All counts were made in the upper five miles of Hopper Canyon.

Commencing in December there were many condors in the Hopper Mountain region. In general, the concentration ended about the first of May. The usual population in summer was three or four pairs of adults

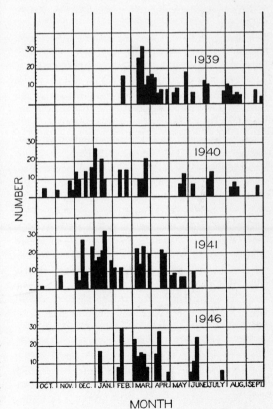

Figure 4. Seasonal and yearly variation in numbers of Condors near Hopper Mountain, Ventura County.

and two or three immature birds. Occasionally, perhaps only when there was food in the vicinity, larger numbers visited the area in summer (for example, June, 1946). The increase in numbers in winter corresponded approximately with the time that young became able to fly well, the commencement of courting, the start of the cold winds and storms of winter, and certain shifts in the distribution of livestock. The time of decrease more or less corresponded with the hatching of young, the cessation of winter storms, the drying up of green feed on the lowlands with consequent movement of livestock and commencement of squirrel poisoning, and the appearance of large groups of condors in the northern parts of their range. My data are insufficient to permit evaluation of the relative importance of these factors in influencing the concentration of condors in the Hopper Mountain area. The winter concentration in this area may be associated with breeding, with the supply of food, or with both.

Los Angeles County.—A few condors were resident in the San Gabriel Mountains between 1890 and 1910. The largest group reported was four. Only one nest was known (Eaton Canyon near Pasadena) although Pasadena was a center for egg collectors. Since 1936 one or two condors have occasionally been reported by Forest Service lookout men at Mount Josephine. Except for rare vagrants, condors are now absent from the San Gabriel Mountains.

In the Santa Monica Mountains of western Los Angeles County, condors were resident about 1900 and foraged both north and south of this range. At least one young (1898) and one egg (1900) were taken from these mountains. Before 1900 condors often perched near a falls in Escondido Canyon. A few times in spring within the past several years, one or two birds have been reported in this region. As condors are not uncommon 20 miles north of these mountains in spring, I believe that the birds seen recently were wanderers from roosts north of Fillmore and Piru in Ventura County.

In northwestern Los Angeles County (Gorman, Liebre Mountain, western Antelope Valley) condors frequently forage, especially from August through January. Probably the incidence of condors in this area has increased since the early 1900's or even since 1930. Condors in this area are from roosts north of Fillmore and Piru, I believe. No roosts used by more

than four condors have been reported in Los Angeles County. There are no records for the desert north of the San Gabriel Range and east of the vicinity of Neenach.

Kern County.—There are records almost continuously from about 1850 to date. Apparently there was an increase in the incidence of condors in the southeastern San Joaquin Valley about 1890, the very time when the birds were decreasing in northern Monterey County, San Benito County, and San Diego County. Before 1890 groups of no more than three were mentioned. A flock of 26 seen by Stephens in 1894 was the largest group reported by a qualified observer before the 1930's.

Since 1935, the number of condors in Kern County, or at least the size of flocks there, has shown further increase. Flocks of more than 20 condors have been seen several times. I saw 30 at once near Arvin in 1940. The flock of 43 reported in 1947 by Perry Sprague was the largest group he had seen in 30 years at Tejon Ranch. Antonio Aroujo, head vaquero of Tejon Ranch for many years, believes that the number of condors has increased there. Lester Arnold, game warden at Bakersfield since 1926, saw few condors before the middle 1930's. Recently he wrote me (February 13, 1949) that he had seen 30 or 40 condors at three different localities in Kern County.

In Kern County the main roosts (perches where condors spend the night) seem to be on Bear Mountain and Breckenridge Mountain, east of Bakersfield. Condors foraging near the county line north of Bakersfield may roost in Tulare County, and those foraging near the line south of Bakersfield may roost in Ventura County. Condors foraging near Temblor Ranch in western Kern County evidently roost at McChesney Mountain, San Luis Obispo County, while those foraging in extreme northwestern Kern County roost on Castle Mountain, Fresno County.

There are many records for Tejon Ranch east of U. S. Highway 99 to Los Angeles but few records for San Emigdio Ranch west of this highway. The numbers of livestock, potential food for condors, are similar on and near these two ranches. It may be that the mountains near San Emigdio Ranch are unsuitable for roosting or that air currents unfavorable for soaring exist there.

There are no definite records of condors breeding in Kern County. However, in 1950, a nest was discovered about 15 miles north of this county. Although occasional nesting in Kern County is probable, I believe that nearly all of the condors frequenting this area are non-breeding.

Tulare County.—There evidently were condors within the present boundaries of Tulare County long before 1900, and perhaps vagrants reached Sequoia National Park. As in northeastern San Luis Obispo County and southeastern Monterey County, condors were apparently rare for approximately 20 years from about 1920 to 1940. The frequency of occurrence of condors in south-central Tulare County has increased since the 1930's. Marion J. Vincent has lived on ranches near White River since 1920 and knows condors. The 35 he reported in 1944 were the largest group he had ever seen. W. L. Richardson has lived near Porterville since about 1916 and has always been interested in birds. His son (W. B. Richardson) collected mammals throughout the county in the 1930's. Each saw one or two condors on single occasions. Yet, in 1946 I saw two condors low over their home and I saw 12 about 10 miles to the south. Occasionally condors have been reported from Blue Ridge Lookout east of Exeter. Oscar L. Hemphill, Agricultural Commissioner of Tulare County, writes (letter, December 7, 1949) that groups of condors have been seen by his rodent control inspectors from late July to early September in the foothills as far north as Yokohl Valley. Although up until 1950 condors seemed to be absent from Tulare County in winter, the recent finding of a nest east of Porterville shows that a few condors are present in winter. Perhaps this nesting indicates an actual extension of breeding range within the past several years.

Groups of condors which I watched feeding near Fountain Springs in 1946 roosted in a canyon near Parker Peak near the south boundary of the Tule River Indian Reservation. From that vicinity they could forage as far as Yokohl Valley and Blue Ridge (about 25 miles) and could easily reach White River, California Hot Springs, and the Greenhorn Mountains. It is likely that there is another roost area in Tulare County east of Exeter.

Present total number.—Only by a simultaneous count by many trained observers at strategic locations could one discover the total number of condors. The highest combined count that I was able to obtain was on March 26, 1941, when I saw 20 condors in the Sespe region and James C. Reynolds, a State trapper previously instructed by me, reported 22 at Tejon Ranch (42 total). On July 6, 1940, I saw 14 condors in the Sespe region and two days later R. E. Williamson recorded 20 at once at West Big Pine Lookout (34 total). Some counts were made many days apart but probably separate groups of condors were involved. On May 25, 1945, Joseph Keyes saw 16 condors east of Famoso, on May 27, Henry Hjersman saw five at McChesney Mountain, on June 1, the McMillan brothers saw 14 near Cholame, and on June 3, Harold Hill saw eight at Hopper Canyon (possibly 43 total).

As many condors have been counted in one flock as have been counted simultaneously at two localities. Some of the high counts which have been made by persons with whose ability in identifying condors I am acquainted:

Place	Date	No.	Observer
Hopper Canyon	Jan. 13, 1936	30	E. Percy
Sisquoc Canyon	June 24, 1936	32	J. R. Pemberton
Cuyama Valley	Oct. 8, 1938	30	J. R. Pemberton
Hopper Canyon	March 16, 1939	32	C. B. Koford
Near Arvin	Sept. 16, 1940	30	C. B. Koford
Hopper Canyon	Jan. 16, 1941	33	E. Percy
Hopper Canyon	Jan. 21, 1945	42	E. Percy
Hopper Canyon	Feb. 11, 1946	30	C. B. Koford
Tejon Ranch	Nov. 1947	43	P. Sprague

By considering the observed and probable number of condors at various localities in any season of any year of this study, I have estimated the total number of condors to be 60. There is no valid reason to suppose that this population is unstable in size. It probably has been fairly constant for 30 years or more, but there has been no increase. Nearly all of the condors seen north of Bakersfield and the Carrizo Plains are probably non-breeding birds. Considering the records of distribution and the low proportion of immatures to adults in the northern parts of the range of condors, there are at least 30 non-nesting adults each fall. Allowing for two adults each at an estimated five nests and for 20 other condors including all the immatures, the total population would be about 60. At the season when Percy and Sprague saw over 40 condors the birds are rare north of the Kern and Cuyama rivers and the young are out of the nests; therefore, breeding adults were probably included in these counts.

Altitudinal range.—In altitude, condors have been

seen from sea level to above the summit of Mount Pinos (8826 feet), the highest point in the present range of the condor. It is improbable that California condors have exceeded 10,000 feet in elevation in recent years. South American condors ascend to much higher elevations above sea level.

Summary.—During the Pleistocene *Gymnogyps* was widespread and, at least in southern California, numerous. At the time of prehistoric Indians in North America condors were more widespread than in historic times. In the 1800's they were seen as far north as the mouth of the Columbia River and as far south as 200 miles below the border in Lower California. Condors have become extinct or very rare in many localities as shown in the following table:

Locality	Year
Columbia River	1840
Sacramento Valley	1860
Tuolumne River	1860
Marin County	1860
Napa County	1870
San Mateo County	1880
Humboldt County	1890
Monterey vicinity	1890
Santa Clara County	1900
Santa Cruz County	1900
Big Sur vicinity	1900
San Bernardino County	1900
Orange County	1900
San Benito County	1900
Fresno County (except southern tip)	1900
Riverside County	1910
Jolon vicinity	1910
San Gabriel Mountains	1910
Southern Santa Lucia Mountains	1910
San Diego County	1910
Santa Ynez Range	1910
Santa Monica Mountains	1910

Vagrants are occasionally reported from some of the localities where condors became rare about 1900 or later.

There is evidence that in some areas the frequency of occurrence of condors has increased since the 1880's. These areas are:

Kern County—increase about 1890 and further increase since 1930.

Liebre Mountain, Antelope Valley—increase since 1930.

Tulare County—increase since 1930.

Cholame-Simmler area—increase since 1940.

The apparent increase in these areas may have been caused by an increase in the size of flocks rather than by an increase in the total number of condors. As few areas have a suitable supply of food, condors aggregate in these localities. The occurrence of large flocks seems to be an indication of the scarcity of suitable feeding areas rather than an indication of increase in population. In the old days when many feeding areas were available, condors may have foraged in small groups and thus may have been relatively inconspicuous.

In the present principal breeding region, which might be considered the population center, the incidence of condors has remained about the same since the 1880's. These areas are:

Central Ventura County

Northern Santa Barbara County

The main roost areas known to be used by 10 or more condors at various times between 1936 and 1950, from west to east (see figure 3) are:

Castle Mountain (Monterey and Fresno counties)

McChesney Mountain (San Luis Obispo County)

Upper Sisquoc Canyon (Santa Barbara County)

Sespe and Hopper canyons (Ventura County)

Bear and Breckenridge mountains (Kern County)

Parker Peak area (Tulare County)

These roosts are spaced at about 45-mile intervals. Since 1939 all confirmed records of a group of three or more condors have been for localities within cruising radius (30 miles) of one of these roosts. Pine Mountain (Ventura County) is an intermediate roost of secondary importance; probably there are others.

In winter the main roosting concentration is in the Sespe region although often groups may roost in central Kern County. Foraging groups have been seen at Oak Ridge, Pole Canyon, Hopper Canyon, Liebre Mountain, western Antelope Valley, Tehachapi Mountains, and Tejon Ranch. Commencing about May groups of condors work northward in the hills of both sides of the San Joaquin Valley at least as far as extreme southeastern Monterey County on the west side and the Tule River on the east side, and they occupy roosts in the mountains in these areas. In summer and early fall flocks of 10 or more condors might be seen in any part of the condor range. In fall, condors leave the northern areas and retire to their winter range.

Within these general limits, the area occupied by condors varies considerably from year to year depending upon the distribution of suitable food.

It is estimated that the total population of condors consists of about 60 individuals and that the size of the population is approximately stable.

Population and Survival

Proportion of immatures to adults.—The following are some of the high counts of numbers of immature condors seen at one time.

Place	Date	Total	Im-matures	Observer
Hopper Mountain	Jan. 17, 1936	15	5	C. D. Scott
Sisquoc Canyon	July 8, 1937	17	6	J. R. Pemberton
Hopper Canyon	March 14, 1939	18	7	C. B. Koford
Hopper Canyon	July 14, 1939	9	7	C. B. Koford
Hopper Canyon	March 22, 1940	21	9	C. B. Koford
Big Pine Mountain	July 15, 1940	20	8	C. B. Koford
Hopper Canyon	March 20, 1941	19	7	C. B. Koford
Mouth Kern Canyon	June 3, 1941	11	5	C. B. Koford
Hopper Canyon	June 6, 1941	10	5	C. B. Koford
Hopper Canyon	April 3, 1945	9	7	H. M. Hill
East of Famoso	May 25, 1945	16	7	J. Keyes
Hopper Canyon	Feb. 13, 1946	24	8	C. B. Koford
Hopper Canyon	March 15, 1946	16	9	C. B. Koford
Hopper Canyon	April 13, 1946	28	12	C. B. Koford
Hopper Canyon	June 11, 1946	16	9	C. B. Koford

As subadults are often mistaken for adults and as the foregoing counts are minima, the actual number of immatures was probably greater than the figures indicate. With but two exceptions, all the counts of five or more immatures were made close to roosting and nesting areas. Most of the large counts were made where the young birds were gathered near a water hole. At feeding areas in the foothills several miles from the nearest roost the maximum number of immatures seen at once was five or seven (one instance) and was usually not more than three. This fact suggests that even immature condors over one year of age are not as mobile as adults. The highest number of immatures seen at once was 12 (April 13, 1946). At that time, at least two young were in nests. Assuming a total population of 60 condors in 1946, at least one-quarter and possibly one-third were immatures.

Survival rate.—Nice (1937:194) suggests a method of determining the theoretical age composition of a population of breeding birds with a constant annual survival rate. Farner (1945:60) states that this method seems to be applicable to any species in which the death rate is the same for all age groups. Assuming that there is a constant annual survival rate of 90 or 95 per cent among the population of post-nestling condors, and that the rate is the same for all age groups, the theoretical age composition of a breeding population would be as shown in the following table.

Age in Years	Per Cent of Total Population	
	Annual Survival 95 per cent	Annual Survival 90 per cent
1 to 5	24	40
6 to 10	18	24
11 to 15	15	13
16 to 20	10	8
21 to 25	9	5
26 plus	24	10
Total	100	100
Avg. longevity in years	20	10

Condors in the 1 to 5 year age group are immature in plumage. Now, if the actual proportion of immatures is greater than the theoretical value for an assumed survival rate, then the survival rate for the entire population is lower than the assumed value or the survival rate of immatures is less than that of adults. In a stable population, an abnormally high proportion of immatures to adults is not a favorable sign, for it indicates a low survival rate. If the population were increasing in size, I would expect the proportion of immatures to adults to be higher than shown by the table.

It is probable that the mortality among immature condors is appreciably higher than among adults, for young condors are incautious and inexperienced and they are relatively unskillful in flight. Presumably collectors would shoot adult rather than immature condors if the opportunities were equal, but of 112 specimens in collections, not counting those which died in captivity, 42 per cent are immature. This fact suggests that the death rate of immatures, at least from shooting, has been higher than the death rate of adults. Probably very old condors die at a higher rate than middle-aged ones, but the weaknesses of age would be offset, to some degree, by the benefit of long experience.

Granting that the survival rate of immature individuals is less than that of adults and assuming a survival rate of 90 per cent, we would expect, in the theoretical population, to find that less than 60 per cent of the population is adult and that the average age is only 10 years. If this were true, the population would decrease steadily for a pair could not replace itself within an average lifetime. If survival is 95 per cent, the theoretical proportion of immatures to adults would be more nearly in accordance with my estimates and counts. Taking all elements into consideration, I believe the survival rate to be between 90 and 95 per cent.

Maximum potential life span.—In 1939 I saw three condors at the National Zoological Park which had been received there, as young of the year, in 1901 (1) and 1903 (2). The last of these died at 45 years of age (W. M. Mann, letter May 18, 1948). The ages at death of 11 other captives which survived at least two years are: 2, 4, 4, 5, 7, 7, 10, 10, 12, 36, and about 40 years. In the wild a life span of more than 40 years may never be achieved.

One characteristic which has helped the species to survive is the great potential longevity. Even if nesting fails completely in one year or for a few years in succession, the number of birds capable of breeding does not change greatly and the loss can be overcome in favorable years.

Sex ratio.—Of 63 specimens for which I have data, 62 per cent are males. In game birds an excess of males is often associated with a known decline in population (Leopold, 1936:111), but it is doubtful that this applies in other species where both sexes share nest duties and where territoriality is not strong. However, 20 condors of which 60 per cent are males can form only eight pairs instead of ten.

Minimum unit of population.—Leopold (1936:86) states that "there appears in some species to be a minimum population unit or minimum density of population below which the species fails to thrive. The simplest explanation of this is the 'clean sweep' which any local misfortune may make of any small detached colony of animals. . . . Where there is no surrounding population to restock by influx, the extermination is permanent." Maintaining condors solely in a small refuge would increase the possibility of a "clean sweep." The high mobility of condors decreases the chance that a single disaster would kill a high proportion of the population. Nevertheless, many condors could be killed in a few hours by an exceptionally severe storm, by a fire at night, or by shooting them at a carcass or at their roosts.

When a population has a small effective breeding number, certain genes tend to become fixed and others to become lost by chance, regardless of selective pressure (Sewall Wright effect). If the environment changes, the species cannot readily adapt itself to the change. The population tends to lose variability and to become homogeneous. Eventually it may wander from its "adaptive peak" and become extinct through non-adaptive or deleterious genetic changes. Through this mechanism, the condor may become extinct regardless of the extent to which its present environment can be maintained. Even in prehistoric times the adaptive adjustments of the condor may have been diminished by this effect. In addition, the long life cycle of the bird probably operates toward stability rather than evolutionary change (Allee, *et al.,* 1949:680).

For some animals there is a minimal population size below which the species does not thrive. For several species of birds the rate of reproduction has been shown to be lower in small than in large colonies (*op. cit.*:402). It is doubtful that sparseness of population affects the rate of reproduction in condors. Possibly, though, a lack of numbers results in a lowered effectiveness of the group in the finding of food. The proportional effect on the population of the activities of a few collectors or photographers is certainly much greater in a small population than in a large one.

Breeding potential.—The breeding potential of the condor is probably as low as that of any other North American bird. Commencing with one pair of band-tailed pigeons which breed at the age of one year and have but one young, the potential population, disregarding longevity, would be about 3600 in 20 years, according to tables of breeding potential given by Leopold (1936:453). Assuming that condors first breed at the age of five years and produce one young every other year, the potential population in 20 years, starting from one adult pair, would be about 50—less than one and one-half per cent of the potential pigeon population.

Population dynamics.—My data are too meager to justify more than a crude analysis of the population dynamics of condors. Even if data similar to those which have been gained from banded passerines were available, calculations would be greatly complicated by the fact that condors do not breed until they are several years old, that the age groups are not uniformly distributed geographically, that the mortality is not equal in all age groups, and that there are many non-breeding adults. The most practicable means of obtaining significant data would be to determine the ages of immatures by inspection at telescope ranges and to make counts at suitable spots in several successive years.

By making several estimates, one can picture what the present situation among the population of condors might be. In a stable population, mortality must equal reproduction. Given a population of 60 condors of which one-third are immature, there would be a maximum of 20 pairs of adults. At most, these pairs nest only every other year so that there would be an average of not over 10 nestings per year. Assuming, pessimistically, that only half of the nestings produce young which survive to one year of age, the average yearly reproduction and mortality would be about five condors. If five condors from a total population of 60 died each year (91.5 per cent survival), the average life span would be about 12 years. As a condor re- quires at least five years to reach sexual maturity, if it lives only 12 years it can breed for only seven years and produce perhaps three young, and some of these young die before becoming mature. Unless each pair produces at least two young which survive and reproduce themselves, the population will decline. If the rate of mortality of the adults is lower than that of immatures, condors which reach maturity must surpass the average longevity and the effect of the long period of immaturity is somewhat offset.

If the actual situation is somewhat as described, the prevention of the death of a single condor or of the failure of a single nest may mean that the population will show an increase rather than a decrease for that year. Persons in a position to influence the welfare of individual condors, and especially of their nests, should keep in mind that the precarious natural balance of the population can be easily upset in the direction leading to extinction of the species.

General Activities

The primary activities of non-breeding condors are roosting and foraging. Condors spend a great deal more time perched than flying. For example, an adult alighted in a tree near my observation post at 12:05 p.m. and did not leave that group of trees until 9:45 a.m. the following morning, 21 hours and 40 minutes later. Assuming that a condor departs from the roosting area unusually early (8 a.m.) and returns unusually late (5 p.m.), it still spends 15 hours a day perched about the roosting area plus additional hours on various perches while foraging.

Preening.—The most common activity of perched condors is preening. Preening is seldom energetic before sunrise or after sunset although I have seen it as early and as late as the birds could be seen by daylight. The birds preen most diligently in the morning shortly after sunshine strikes them. Condors which have become wet preen especially vigorously and long. There is little system to the sequence of areas preened except that adjacent areas tend to be preened successively. The wings often sag out and down from the body during preening and the primaries may rest on the perch. Condors often preen while sunning. Wiping the head, shaking the head and resetting the wings in place usually accompany preening.

The main method of preening is by moving the rapidly nibbling bill over the feathers. Frequently a quiet bird suddenly thrusts its bill among the feathers as if biting at a parasite. The ruff is preened as much as any other group of feathers, perhaps because it becomes dirty in feeding. In preening the ruff, the head is usually held vertically with the chin drawn upward and against the neck; occasionally the head is held on its side. Groups of ruff feathers may be pulled through the bill. A frequent action is the combing of large feathers lengthwise by running them from base to tip through the bill. In this action the tip of the feather may be raised from its normal position so that the feather snaps back into place when released.

The tail and anal region are reached by extending the neck far over the back. The tail may be tilted on edge or drawn forward at right angles to the body. Brushing of the feathers with the naked throat and chin frequently follows nibbling at the region of the oil gland. In brushing, the chin is placed on the back and brought downward over one wing or is moved posteriorly along the back or wing. The tail may be expanded and drawn to one side so that it too is brushed. Usually the brushing stroke is repeated several times, both sides being brushed about equally. Use of the oil gland is most frequent when the bird is damp. The head may be inverted when preening at the belly or the wings, or under the tail, and it may swing from side to side rapidly in a small arc as the bill works at the breast or ruff. Once I saw a condor preen at the base of its neck for several seconds while soaring in a strong wind.

Shaking often accompanies preening, especially after bathing. I saw one condor shake four times in three-quarters of an hour of preening. Shaking may follow a few minutes after landing and it may precede takeoff by only a few seconds. Evidently shaking puts the feathers in order for flight. The action is performed quickly. The head is thrown back and the closed wings are moved up and down alternately about four times. The sound of shaking is audible for more than 100 yards. A few times I saw a condor shake its tail from side to side rapidly somewhat in the manner of a duck.

Scratching, wiping, and shaking the head.—Frequently a condor scratches its head and neck with one foot. The head is held low and vertically with the bill agape and it is scratched with downward strokes of one foot at the rate of about two strokes per second. The head and neck lie in the angle between digits 2 and 3 and the toes remain extended during the act. The scratching surface seems to be the side of the toes and not the claws. The head may be turned during the scratching so that the occiput and crown are scratched. The same individual uses either foot for scratching. The number of successive scratching motions seldom exceeds 10, but one adult which had been wet by rain scratched 19 strokes in succession. Both condors and turkey vultures may scratch their heads while soaring.

Often a condor scratches its head and neck on a branch, the edge of a cliff, or a flat rock surface. The head may be inverted so that the occiput is scratched. Once I saw this action continued for 20 seconds. The bird crouched on its heels and pushed its neck forward on the rock, then scraped its extended neck on the rock with long sidewise strokes and rolled its neck from side to side on the rock. The side of the bill may be wiped on the perch as if to remove food or other particles from the bill. Once I saw an adult rub its neck on the ground while standing alongside a carcass.

Another frequent action is wiping the head on the back. The crooked neck is thrown suddenly to the rear so that its side lies on the back, then the head is moved in the direction of the bill two or three quick strokes. This action is normally repeated on the opposite side a few seconds later. Perhaps it is to brush the feathers of the head as well as to remove particles not dislodged by shaking of the head.

On occasions the head is given a single quick flip sideways, or it is shaken rapidly from side to side as many as six times. The single flip serves mainly to remove flies which alight on the head. Rapid shaking of the head is for the purpose of removing down, water, sand, or other particles from the head or bill. Head shaking frequently follows preening, pecking at the ground, or bathing. Once when a piece of down stuck near the nostril of a nestling, the bird shook its head from one to five shakes five times in succession.

Sunning and drying the wings.—In the sunning pose a condor holds its wings fully extended to the sides with the distal primaries horizontal but curving strongly forward (plate 3). The tail is expanded, the body and neck are held nearly erect, and the ruff lies at the base of the neck. One or both wings may be partly extended for several minutes before or after they are held fully extended. Condors may flap their wings a few times before extending them or before folding them. In the morning they tend to preen facing the sun but the upper surface of the wings is sunned about twice as frequently as the lower surface. Occasionally a condor turns around 180 degrees while its wings are still extended in order to sun the other side. In turning, one wing may be flexed so as to clear a tree trunk or other obstruction. If the trunk of a tree prevents full extension of the wings, the bird often sidesteps out on the branch while the wings are spread.

Usually the wings are held out for a period of 2 to 4 minutes. The longest period that I saw them fully extended was 7¼ minutes. Including periods when the wings were relaxed somewhat but were still at least halfway extended, the maximum period observed was 11 minutes for a dry bird. Sunning is prolonged when the bird is damp. One which had been flying in fog sunned for 12½ minutes continuously. Another, after roosting in the rain, held its wings out for 20 minutes. The spreading of the wings may be repeated several times. I saw one alight in a tree and then sun four separate times for periods as long as 1½ minutes within the next quarter of an hour. The time and amount of sunning varies greatly. One cool morning I watched seven condors which had roosted in a group of trees. At least five were in sunshine for more than half an hour but only one individual sunned before taking off. Of a group of 16 perched in the sunshine at 6 a.m., not more than three sunned at one time. In general, sunning in the morning occurs about as frequently as stretching.

There may be a tendency for birds perched within a few feet of each other to sun at the same time. I saw an immature follow an adult by about one minute in starting and stopping the action, and a few times I saw a pair of adults sun while facing each other on the same branch. Sunning occasionally follows the action of holding the wings out as if to feel for a breeze. Perhaps actions involving spreading the wings suggest the sunning action to the bird. When the wings are being dried, they are held in a different manner than in normal sunning. The stance is not so erect and the wings are arched to the sides with their backs at an acute angle rather than vertical.

Sunning is most common just after sunshine first strikes the birds in the morning. Occasionally one "suns" a few minutes before sunrise. Commencing about one hour before the morning sun struck two adults which had roosted in an open tree in the rain, the birds held their wings halfway out as if sunning or drying them. On overcast days an increase in brightness may be followed by sunning. It may be the sudden increase in brightness which, on occasions, induces birds flushed from the nest to sun. In the forenoon, immediately after shifting from a shady to a sunny perch, condors often sun. However, there is no significant tendency for birds to shift out of the shade for the purpose of sunning. When sunshine strikes the upper members of a perched group those birds sun, and the lower birds wait until the sunshine reaches them before they perform the action.

Condors often sun after returning to the roost area in the afternoon. One which perched in a tree at noon sunned at 4:30 p.m. and again at 5:08 p.m. After

Plate 3. The sunning posture assumed by an adult near its nest.

Plate 4. W. L. Finley's captive California Condor dries himself and displays the juvenal plumage. Photograph by H. T. Bohlman and W. L. Finley.

bathing in the afternoon they sun for long periods. A few times I saw one "sunning" a few minutes after sunset near a bathing pool. On days of strong wind sunning is uncommon. The act could hardly be accomplished in wind. Once I saw two condors apparently sun at midday while perched on flat ground near a carcass.

Stretching.—In a manner similar to many birds, condors stretch one wing down and back, draw the expanded tail up to that side, and stretch the corresponding leg back beneath the tail. The wing may be extended to the side before it is drawn back. The wrist may not be fully extended or it may be extended after the rest of the wing. When the wing is fully extended, its upper surface is in the plane of the back and the anterior edge is about 45 degrees out from the longitudinal axis of the body. Usually the wing is stretched down behind the perch branch or over the edge of a cliff perch. Often the stretched leg is pushed back through the secondaries. During the stretch, the bird leans forward with its head low. After stretching one wing condors tend to stretch the opposite wing, but I have seen individuals stretch the same wing two or three times and the opposite wing not at all between dawn and the start of flight. For a single adult, before it took off in the morning, the greatest number of side stretches that I noted was six during a period of 65 minutes. The side stretch is a common activity before taking off in the morning but it is uncommon at other times of the day.

The action of stretching the folded wings up and simultaneously bowing forward, I have called the "bow stretch." This stretch occurs about half as often as the side stretch and it is performed in a deliberate manner. The wings are opened slightly and held above the level of the back with the elbows almost touching each other. Then the bird bows forward until its throat is near the perch and its rump, tail, and wing tips are high. This position may be held for more than five seconds. Then the bird slowly stands up and folds its wings. The head may remain low for several seconds after the bow. Occasionally, while in the extreme bow, the bird scratches its neck on the perch. Sometimes it takes off from this position. Juveniles, at least, often do not raise the tail but let it hang rather loosely. The bow stretch may be performed immediately after the side stretch and before the wing is folded; occasionally it is performed as a condor sits

or stands up. I saw one bird, in calm air, bow stretch four times in 50 minutes. Adults do not stretch any more frequently than immatures.

Standing, sitting, sleeping.—When a condor stands on a perch of small area, the distal parts of one or more toes usually extend into space and do not grip the perch. The outer toe may not touch the perch at all when the bird perches at the tip of a stub branch. Only a round perch of large diameter seems to fit the natural curvature of the toes. Even on spacious perches the inner toes may overlap. When a condor stands on flat rocks the tips of the toes are raised momentarily from time to time as if the bird were balancing.

To sit, a condor holds its bill low near the perch and then slowly lowers its body, often one side slightly before the other. The feet may be shifted up and down once or twice as the breast approaches the perch. From the bow stretch position the bird merely lowers its heels and rump in order to sit. On rock ledges condors may sit with the rump and tail protruding over the edge. The red-colored naked skin at the base of the throat of a condor sitting on a branch bulges down over the perch. In the sitting position the body is horizontal as if resting on the sternum as well as on the legs. This position is probably steady as well as restful. Condors sometimes preen vigorously or perform the side stretch while sitting. In rising, the rump is raised slightly before the rest of the body and the bill remains near the perch for a few seconds. The wings may be opened to help balance as the bird rises.

At night condors generally sit on the perch with their heads tucked under the feathers of the back. By observation in moonlight, I found that some condors roost all night standing up. On overcast days when the temperature is about 55° F. or lower, condors may keep their heads tucked in much of the time during the day. In such a situation, two adults which roosted in one tree kept their heads covered nearly all of the daylight hours until 12:20 p.m. On another occasion, one, going to roost, had its head tucked in by 3:45 p.m. when the temperature was 51° F. At 4 p.m., on an overcast day, four of 16 perched condors had their heads tucked in. In contrast, on a calm clear evening, none of 18 birds had their heads tucked in by 6 p.m. although the temperature was only 54° F. On cold mornings condors shift perches, stretch, or look about, and then they tuck their heads in again. They may withdraw their heads several times within an hour.

On mild nights condors might not tuck their heads in at all.

In tucking the head in the bird relaxes the upper arm or humeral feathers so that they separate in the middle of the back. The chin is placed in the center of the back and given a quick "Z" motion, from side to side and posteriorly, so that the bill comes to rest on one side of the back. Then the humerals close over the head and neck. The occiput may be incompletely covered.

Especially in the early morning, but also in the evening, standing or sitting condors may hang their heads and necks straight down and remain in this position for several minutes at a time as if dozing. Malcolm Davis of the National Zoological Park writes me (1949) that South American condors in captivity often sleep with their heads and wings hanging down.

Gaping.—Condors "yawn" by holding the bill wide open for a period of from one to five seconds. The neck may be straightened or the head raised upward at the same time. Most frequently a condor yawns just before taking off, and it may turn its head from side to side during the yawn. Yawning commonly follows landing. Sometimes the tongue is retracted, extended, or moved up and down during a yawn.

Perched condors often work the bill open and closed four or five times as if chewing. Motion pictures taken by Pemberton show a group of condors standing with their bills agape after feeding on a hot day, as if this action were associated with panting.

Raising the ruff.—The ruff of long narrow feathers may cover the neck to varying degrees (plate 5). When fully up it covers the occiput and some of the lanceolate feathers stand upright from the posterior part of the crown so that only the face of the condor is naked. When completely down, the ruff feathers lie flat around the base of the neck and show no tendency to bristle. When the ruff is partly raised, it is lower on the hind neck than on the sides and does not conceal the ventral naked skin of the throat. Generally, in shade in calm air, the ruff of adults is up at 60° F. but down at 65° F. However, I have seen the ruff down at 50° in the shade and up at 80° in wind. At temperatures in the 60's, the ruff may be lowered when sunshine strikes the bird and raised when a breeze strikes it. Usually the ruff is down during sunning but up after bathing. While preening, condors may raise and lower the ruff regardless of temperature. When alarmed, condors often raise the ruff to the head.

Vocal sounds.—When perched, both immature and adult condors occasionally make a sound like a suppressed human belch or cough. One adult repeated this sound three times within one hour. The head may be slightly raised and the neck slightly extended when the grunt is given. Pemberton (MS) continually heard grunting sounds from a group of condors that was feeding. I heard a captive South American condor give a short pig-like grunt with each spring as it climbed some rock. Immatures may utter short snarling or growling sounds, or hiss, when fighting with one another. Grinnell (MS) heard an adult hiss when it was disturbed in the nest. The sounds made by nestlings are described in a later section.

Turning the head and blinking.—Undisturbed condors perched in daylight usually turn their heads quickly at intervals of 6 to 10 seconds, the maximum interval being about 20 seconds for birds which are not dozing. When the bird is alarmed, the head turns every 2 to 5 seconds. In general, each turn is not over 30 degrees and tends to be in the same direction as the preceding turn. Cocking the head to look upward is a frequent action.

Condors blink the nictitating membrane about every 2 to 5 seconds. Herrick (1934:55) found that in the bald eagle blinks occurred every 2½ to 3½ seconds. Adults and late nestlings blink with the same frequency. Alarm does not affect the rate of blinking, but blinking may be more rapid (every one-half to 2 seconds) when the bird is in the sun. Condors may close their eyelids partly or wholly for several seconds or for a few minutes while standing in the sun. The lids are sometimes closed during preening as if to protect the eyes.

Dilation of the cheeks and neck.—Often the cheeks and neck of an adult are distended as if by air. The swelling of the cheeks may continue posteriorly to below the ear and the chin may bulge downward. The skin of the neck is smooth and tight. The red patch at the base of the throat, anterior to the ruff, bulges slightly more than the surrounding naked skin. When the bird moves its head quickly, the swollen throat shakes like jelly. The amount of distension is variable. The cheeks and throat may become collapsed and wrinkled only to become distended a few minutes later. An adult at one nest seemed always to be in the distended condition. One adult that I watched at the

National Zoological Park maintained strong inflation for many minutes.

Distension of the region of the crop and ventral cervical apterium seems to be caused mainly by feeding or drinking and does not necessarily accompany inflation of the neck. When the crop of an adult is fully distended, the gray border of the red ventral cervical apterium may be visible. In warm weather, when the ruff feathers lie flat at the base of the neck, a naked strip can be seen connecting this apterium with the throat. The skin of immatures is tighter than that of adults so that the bulging crop of a young bird appears like a button rather than a bulging bag.

Exploratory pecking and nibbling.—Both adults and immatures habitually peck and bite at objects which are not edible. One morning I saw an adult, apparently using the side of its bill, pull pieces of bark up to five inches long from the trunk of a tree in which it was perched. The bird held each piece in its bill a few seconds, then let the bark fall and watched it drop. This act was repeated four times. Again, an adult pecked hard at the branch near its feet, moving its head downward about eight inches with each peck. It pecked three to six times at intervals of half a second and repeated the series about four times. Near a pool, an adult tugged at an old feather, holding it down with its feet, and then walked 10 feet across the pool carrying the feather in its bill. Occasionally sticks, pebbles, grass, or moss are picked up from under two or three inches of water. Nibbling at twigs and pebbles are common actions.

Immatures nuzzle, nibble, and peck at objects much more frequently than do adults. This activity is especially great around water holes. There immatures nibble at green and dry grass, moss, algae, and shrubs. I saw one probe in the sandy soil with its bill, bring up roots, and nibble at them. Grass stalks, sticks, or feathers are picked up and dropped or carried a short distance. On some occasions immatures pull at growing grass, letting it run through the bill or breaking it off and tossing it aside. Some of this material is eaten, for immatures occasionally regurgitate pellets consisting mainly of vegetable matter. Adults rarely pull at green vegetation or dig in the soil.

Defecation and excrement.—To defecate, a condor usually tilts its rump up about 15 degrees, then pauses for a few seconds before discharging a single stream of excrement. The stream is ejected horizontally and on flat rock surfaces it may land two feet from the vent. In some observations, the length of the stream appeared to be one foot and its volume about four ounces. A single adult in a nest was seen to defecate four times in 23 hours at irregular intervals.

There is a tendency for condors to defecate just before taking off. At one nest the point from which the adults flew to the nest bore much more excrement than several other points where they spent longer periods. A few times I saw a condor defecate while soaring. At least immatures defecate while wading in drinking pools. An adult feeding on a carcass defecated three times in 45 minutes.

The top and upper branches of the most frequented trees are almost solidly white with excrement. At one point atop a cliff about four square feet of area were solidly covered with excrement up to one-eighth of an inch thick. Ridges of excrement are formed below much-used points. Most dry excrement is dead white in color. The beginning and end of white streaks may be yellowish brown. A few black crumbly lumps are usually mixed in the white deposits. Old excrement in nests is frequently pinkish in color. Some deposits of excrement are completely washed from exposed perches by the first hard rains of fall.

Fresh excrement is usually cream colored or yellowish and of thin consistency. A juvenile occasionally voided a dark stool about 20 millimeters long. In nests I found excrement which appeared like a black lump of grease surrounded by a wet spot.

Gait.—The normal unhurried rate of walking is about one step per second. On occasions the pace is quickened to twice that rate. I have seen condors take more than 20 consecutive steps at a steady rate without stopping. In walking a long distance a condor usually pauses for many seconds, as if to look about, after each group of steps. Several times I saw a condor walk 100 yards within several minutes on fairly flat even ground.

The walking gait is somewhat slouching, the bird leaning down on the side of the foot on the ground, and there is a tendency to swing the body from side to side and the head forward and backward. The toes are spread and held approximately horizontally as the foot is brought forward. In walking on rough ground or in hopping depressions, condors hold their wings open and occasionally flap. The ascent of steep slopes is usually accompanied by flapping. In one instance when a condor walked under a low overhanging rock, the bird crouched down and took several steps on its tarsi, scarcely slowing down to do so. In running, the strides are long, the body is steady, and the wings are open or flapping. Frequently the gait is a series of hops, one foot striking the ground slightly before the other.

Footprints.—In the damp sand near pools where condors drank and bathed, I found the footprints of walking condors to be 7 inches between the points of the claws of digits 1 and 3, and 5 inches between the points of the claws of digits 2 and 4. The average length of a single step was 15 inches and the lateral offset between successive footprints was about 3 inches. Digit 3 was directed straight ahead and the deepest part of the footprint was made by the distal third of this toe. In dry sand there was often a groove straight forward from the tip of the impression of digit 3 as if that toe were dragged for several inches.

Climbing.—In ascending to a higher branch in a tree a condor first stretches its neck toward the new perch as if to scrutinize it, then crouches with its wings halfway extended, and then springs, flapping, to the new perch. The preparatory crouch may be repeated two or three times before the bird makes the leap. Upon landing, the condor puts its bill to the perch as if to steady itself, and, as soon as it gains balance, it folds its wings. When the bird climbs to several branches in succession, the wings may not be folded between jumps. Descending from branch to branch is a much less common action than climbing up. The bird extends its neck toward the lower branch, then jumps down, raising its wings as it falls. The upward or downward jumps may be from four to eight feet vertically. An adult which I watched at the National Zoological Park had no difficulty in jumping up from the flat floor to a perch five feet high with a few flaps of the wings.

In turning about on a branch a condor holds its head low and its body and tail horizontally, opens its wings slightly, steps around with a few steps, and then folds its wings and assumes a more erect position. It may move out on a branch by stepping sideways.

Some authors have employed the term "parrot-like" to describe the use of the bill of a condor in climbing. This term is inappropriate, for condors do not grasp branches and pull themselves up by means of the bill.

On rare occasions, I saw one bite a branch to hold on.

Actions preceding and following flight.—Apparently in order to test the breeze before attempting flight in calm air, a condor may hold its wings arched at the sides for many seconds or for as long as two or three minutes, and it may flap a few times, slowly. Turning about on the perch, extending the neck upward and gaping, or moving the feet up and down a few times, often accompany this action. Another action apparently used for testing the air is an exaggerated bow stretch. Frequently a takeoff is made directly from the bowed position. Some of the foregoing actions may be repeated three or four times before the bird takes off.

Most indicative of an immediate takeoff is a crouch with the head low and the partly opened wings above the back. Even this action may be repeated when the air is calm. After making a feint at taking off the bird may walk to another perch. A gust of wind frequently induces the performance of these actions. Commonly a condor moves to a higher branch in a tree before taking off. On the other hand, a condor may quickly crouch and spring into the air without performing any preliminary actions.

For a few seconds after alighting condors hold their wings up as if to balance. Upon landing on flat ground they may run or hop a few yards with their momentum, and young birds have been seen to pitch forward on their breasts. After landing at the tip of a branch a condor often walks several steps toward the trunk before folding its wings. Preening is normally the first action performed after a bird gains its balance.

When a condor loses its balance on a perch or lands on a springy branch, it flaps its wings and then holds them outstretched for a few seconds. The tail tilts up and down violently when the perch branch sways. Once I saw an adult alight on the top of a dead tree which was emitting loud cracking sounds. At each crack the bird raised its wings and looked about quickly. As soon as the tree commenced to fall, the condor took off, flapping.

Pre-roosting activity.—Upon returning to the roosting area from foraging a condor may perch and remain at the same point until dark, or it may drink, bathe, squabble and fly with other birds, and occupy a dozen or more perches before settling down for the night. The pre-roosting schedule of an especially inactive adult one mild day in August was as follows:

12:05 p.m., alighted in tree. 1:20, flew 100 yards to another tree. 1:45, climbed to higher branch. 2:50, turned around. 3:59, sat. 4:10, stood. 4:12, sat. 4:30, stood, sunned. 4:39, sat. 5:08, stood, sunned. 5:23, sat. 5:25, tucked head in. 6:00, no change. Alternate periods of standing and sitting, with sitting becoming more frequent toward evening, are typical of pre-roosting behavior.

When many condors are perched in the same tree or in a small area, there is a great deal of shifting between perches. One evening in February when 10 condors were perched on a favorite cliff in Hopper Canyon, I noted that the longest interval between flights of at least one bird from one perch to another was three minutes. When more condors were in that vicinity, the rate of shifting was often one per minute for many minutes. At about the time of sunset the frequency of flying between perches decreased, perhaps because flight became more difficult. At this cliff roost, when 26 birds were present one evening in April, I heard the last flapping flight at 7:10 p.m., 80 minutes after sunset. Usually there were no flights more than one hour after sunset. One windy evening in July I saw flights between perches of at least one-half mile as late as 6:55 p.m. There is comparatively little shifting between perches on high cliffs during strong wind, probably because the air near the cliffs is very turbulent.

Post-roosting activity.—In mild weather most condors are standing before sunrise. I saw preening and shifting between perches as early as 5 a.m. in April. Usually a condor changes its perch at least once before departing from the roosting area. One morning in April none of 12 condors which roosted on one cliff was on its original perch by 7:10 a.m. The shifting between perches often occurred much later. After 19 condors roosted in a group of trees one night in June the first change of perch did not occur until after 7 a.m. An hour or more after sunrise there is generally a period of quiet among the perched condors. Some sit again. Once when a dozen condors were perched at the favorite cliff in Hopper Canyon, there were no flights between perches for as long as 10 minutes during the quiet period.

The common actions performed each morning by individual condors before they take off are: preening, sitting, side stretch, bow stretch, sunning, turning around, shifting perch, and shaking. Nevertheless, I did not see every one of these activities performed by a single bird before it took off. A condor may not stretch or sun at all when the weather conditions seem to be normal.

There is much variation between individuals in the kind and amount of activity performed before flight. One fair morning in July I watched two adults and an immature which had roosted in a small group of pines. There was no disturbance and the birds paid no apparent attention to one another. The times of their principal actions are shown below.

Bird	Sitting	Side stretch	Bow stretch	Shift branch	Sun	Take off
Adult 1	8:00- 05	7:55	9:37	9:00	8:14	
	8:42- 54		9:46			9:46
Adult 2	7:30- 40					
	8:25- 30					8:31
Immature	6:35-7:20	7:57	7:57	8:36		
	7:40- 50	8:17				8:41

Relation between adults.—At the main nesting cliff in Hopper Canyon many condors may roost within a distance of 100 feet. In groups of trees, however, there is little tendency for the birds to roost close together. On two occasions I saw 16 and 19 condors roosting in trees near food. These birds were scattered over a distance of half a mile and not more than two occupied any one tree. In especially well situated trees I have seen as many as four condors roosting. Two adults roosting overnight in a single small pothole or on a single branch are perhaps always a mated pair. On some evenings in winter I have seen groups of more than three condors roosting at three separate locations spread over a distance of about three miles.

Occasionally adults engage in brief fights. One evening in April two adults (X and Y) were perched on the same branch. Occasionally each pecked at the other. X moved to a springy branch about three feet from Y. Several times X reached out with its open bill toward Y but each time it threw itself off balance. Y sometimes snapped at the extended head or wing of X. They exchanged perches and then snapped back and forth as if taking turns. Several times X grasped the foliage of the perch of Y and Y bit at the head of X. Finally they tumbled from the tree together.

Squabbles often occur near pools. Usually one condor dashes at another a few feet away and the second runs away or takes off and lands nearby. The chase may continue into the air and to other perches. On rare occasions a third condor attacks the first bird. One condor may back two or three feet away from another as if frightened. On some occasions when one extends its wing toward another while sunning, the second nips at the wing and the first withdraws it.

Condors perched at places favored for landing are frequently frightened off or knocked off the perch by other condors landing at about the same spot. Some of these movements are probably correlated with dominance. For example, I saw one supersede another in a pothole. The second flew to another hole. A third superseded the first. The first then displaced the second. The second flew to an unoccupied hole.

Perched condors seem to be excited by seeing others soaring and often seem to be stimulated to fly. Frequently they take off for the first time in the morning after scrutinizing others in the air. Such action results in a group leaving the roost at about the same time. Activities performed while perched rarely appear to stimulate the same activity in other birds although such imitativeness is common in many flocking birds.

Relations between immatures.—When perched, adults tolerate each other and immatures more than immatures tolerate one another. Fights between immatures are frequent, especially where condors are gathered atop cliffs near water holes. Whenever they wander close to one another, they usually bite at each other or wrestle with their heads and necks. Occasionally they fight violently. For instance, one evening four immatures stood near a pool. One drank, another approached it, and the two staggered about, wrestling with their heads and necks. They broke apart and one jumped over the other in dodging a charge. They dashed into each other three times, leaping into the air as they struck and knocking each other down.

In fighting the main object seems to be to put the head and neck under the neck or wing of the other bird and to prevent the other from doing likewise. One may drive the other back or upset it with an upward movement of the neck. Biting at various parts, especially the head and neck, accompanies the struggle. Occasionally I saw one reach over the back of its antagonist and peck at its rump. One which was suddenly pecked from the rear jumped into the air, flapped, and turned completely about. Three may join in a fight. On the other hand, immatures often peck the head and ruff of one another in a gently playful manner.

Most fights are between dark-headed immatures. I believe that the frequent fighting between young birds is caused by the fact that they recognize little dominance among themselves and thus fight back rather than trying to avoid encounters. Older immatures usually best younger birds in fighting. Once when two immatures were nibbling at a dry plant near a pool, the older bird pushed back or pecked at the head of the younger several times as if to defend the "toy."

Frequently one immature condor supersedes another on a perch. Once I saw a young condor land between an adult and an immature which were perched in a small pothole and crowd out the immature. On occasions one crouches and opens its wings as another lands nearby. In trees one bird often moves to a branch occupied by another, the two fight, and they fall, or one pursues the other, into the air.

In perched groups there is a tendency for immatures to remain together. One morning I noted a group of seven adults and four immatures in a large group of roost trees. Three immatures were in one tree and the fourth close by. Except for juveniles, immatures seem to have a greater attachment to each other than to adults.

Relations between adults and immatures.—Generally adults and immatures pay little attention to one another. Young birds may alight within three feet of adults without causing any reaction. In friendly fashion, adults may nibble the heads of young which are too old to be their offspring of the previous year. Yet, immatures are inferior to adults in peck-order. When an adult and immature are perched in the same tree the older bird sometimes moves to the same branch as the young one, and the latter takes off as the adult approaches. Near pools immatures frequently retreat a few feet from advancing adults. Once I saw an adult chase an immature from four successive perches by flying after the young bird and alighting beside it.

Immatures are not always submissive to adults. On one occasion an adult and immature were perched about two feet apart on the same branch. In turning about, the young bird raised its wings and the adult snapped at one wing. The immature snapped back toward the adult and they exchanged two or three snaps without touching each other. Again, an adult and immature (about two years old) stood side by side without reaction for 10 minutes, then the young bird flew to a pothole and the adult superseded it there. Next, the adult flew a few yards to a pool and the young bird landed two feet from the adult. The adult nipped toward the immature and the latter pulled at the feathers of the nape of the adult. Then both drank and bathed. Often adults and immatures wrestle with their heads and necks, neither seeming to be the victor.

In a mixed group of perched or flying condors an immature is frequently the lowest in height. On many occasions, however, the scattering of immatures among adults appears to be random. Immatures, except juveniles, do not seem to follow adults in flight as often as adults follow one another.

Plate 5. The adults perch near the nest site in Eaton Canyon, showing how the ruff
can be elevated to cover the neck. Photograph by H. T. Bohlman and W. L. Finley.

Plate 6. Northeast facing slope with dead big-cone spruces on which Condors often perch and roost. Eleven Condors perched in one of these trees when there was food in the "potrero" at the left.

Plate 7. Favorite roosting ledges above the big cave in Hopper Canyon, Ventura County. Whitewashed spots indicate the frequented perches. The crevice in the cliff is the site of an intermittent waterfall; a favorite water hole is at the top of the fall.

Perching and Roosting

Sites and requirements.—Condors alight in order to roost (remain all night), to rest, to approach water, to approach the nest or young, to approach food, or to avoid accident. This listing is in the usual order of perch requirements, from special to general. Condors will perch anywhere in an emergency but they roost only in certain areas on certain types of perches.

With rare exceptions, condors roost in conifers or on cliffs. Whatever large conifers are suitably located in the roosting area are used. In central Ventura County the principal roosting tree is the big-cone spruce (*Pseudotsuga macrocarpa*). At the head of Sisquoc Canyon and in other similar high areas yellow pines (*Pinus ponderosa* and *P. jeffreyi*) are the main roosting trees although sugar pines (*P. lambertiana*) are also used. At McChesney Mountain condors roost in Coulter pines (*P. coulteri*). At Castle Mountain I have seen condors roost only in digger pines (*P. sabiniana*), although Coulter pines are present. Near Parker Mountain big trees (*Sequoia gigantea*) may be used for roosts.

Probably conifers are preferred to hardwoods for roosting because conifers are tall and have relatively few branches to obstruct flight and because the branches are of large diameter. Large branches (3 to 5 inches in diameter) sway little in the wind and they provide a steady base for toes which cannot grasp strongly. Dead conifers are preferred to living trees (plate 6). Dead trees have no foliage to obstruct flight or visibility or to catch the wind and cause the branches to sway. The loss of some branches further decreases the obstruction of flight. Dead branches are stiff so that they bend and sway but little. Parts of the branches of green trees which condors frequent are bare of foliage, polished, and whitened. When the light is subdued, these whitened branches are conspicuous from a long distance.

Other things being equal, trees are preferred to rocks for perching and roosting. Near cliffs the air is turbulent and the perches can usually be approached only from certain directions. Visibility from cliff perches is rarely over 180 degrees. Rock surfaces are more difficult than branches to grasp. In Sespe Canyon, where there are few conifers, I once saw a condor roost on the face of a huge precipice. Instead of perching on a spur of rock, the bird remained on the horizontal trunk of a solitary scrub tree which grew from a crevice.

Near some nests there are no large conifers and the adults consequently roost on cliffs. At nest 4 (plate 18), on three consecutive nights in August, one adult roosted at the tip of a sandstone outcropping near the nest while the other roosted on the same cliff or on a large boulder nearby. At two other nests the parent birds roosted in the nearest group of large conifers, several hundred yards from the nest, rather than on points of the numerous intervening cliffs.

Roosting trees are generally from 40 to 70 feet tall. At the head of Falls Canyon, however, condors roost in pines about 150 feet tall. If the terrain is steep, the perch does not have to be high above the ground. On cliffs and trees condors may roost within 20 feet of the ground below. Roosting immatures often occupy especially low or unsuitable perches.

In trees which are of moderate size and are protected from the wind roosting is normally in the upper third of the tree and frequently on the highest horizontal perch. One night in December I saw seven condors go to roost in a group of big-cone spruces well below the head of a steep canyon. Each bird was on the topmost long branch of a tree or on a higher stub branch. I have seen as many as five condors roost in the top fourth of one favorite tree. At the head of Falls Canyon, where the pines are tall and exposed to the wind, I found condors roosting on the lowest branches, 60 to 80 feet above the ground.

Condors usually roost within two or three feet of the trunk of a tree. Probably this is because the branches are thick, horizontal, and steady there. Stub branches, some no longer than the width of the body of a condor, are often used for roosting. Although condors frequently perch on the tip of a tree, I have not seen one roost there.

Roosting trees are situated above cliffs or on steep slopes where there is a long unobstructed space for taking off downhill, but they are not situated on the very tops of ridges where there is little protection from the wind. At the head of Falls Canyon the uppermost pines are on nearly level ground while those a few hundred yards to the north are on a

30 per cent slope; the lower trees are favored for roosting. In Hopper Canyon, the most frequented group of trees is several hundred feet below the level of the rim of the canyon but immediately above a cliff. In stormy weather trees near the bed of a canyon rather than those high on the side slopes are used. Even in fair weather, condors may roost in the lowest trees of a group. Most trees used for roosting are on north slopes because large conifers grow mainly on north slopes in dry regions, but some roosting canyons face in other directions. Five of the six main roosting areas allow a descending takeoff directly toward the usual feeding grounds.

A favorite roost in the first few months of the year is a cliff near a big cave and an intermittent waterfall in Hopper Canyon (plate 7). The cliff is more than 100 feet high and is approximately vertical. The soft sandstone contains many potholes and ledges suitable for perching and roosting. The main cliff roost faces west-southwest, but just south of it a higher cliff runs westward so that the principal roosting ledges are protected from all winds except those between north and west.

Another cliff where condors roost is in Falls Canyon (plate 8). Here there is a perennial waterfall. This cliff is of coarse gray conglomerate and is more than 300 feet high. It faces northward, but, because of its low position in a branch of Sisquoc Canyon, it is protected from winds. There are many whitewashed points and holes where condors have perched and roosted in past years.

Many persons have seen a few condors roosting on the red sandstone cliffs in lower Sespe Canyon. Some of these cliffs are more than 500 feet high. The rock cleaves into great angular boulders and forms large crevices. The roosting places, made obvious by accumulations of excrement, are primarily in the space immediately below the topmost thick stratum of the cliffs.

For roosting, potholes, and ledges protected by an overhang are preferred to open ledges, especially when there is much wind. In Hopper Canyon, one evening in May, the sky was clear but there was a fair wind. Of seven condors at the main cliff roost, five were on open ledges at sunset, but all five shifted to more protected perches within 45 minutes. Except when the perches on that cliff were crowded, roosting on open ledges was rare. At midnight on a calm

moonlight night in April, 1946, when at least 26 condors roosted near this cliff, I saw at least 10 on open ledges (plate 7, left center).

Condors do not roost on top of high cliffs; they shift to lower perches before dark. For example, one evening in March, 1946, I saw 10 condors perched on top of a roosting cliff at sunset (5:35 p.m.). Ten minutes later only one condor was on top of the cliff, and it shifted to a lower perch within 20 minutes. On some evenings all the condors did not leave the top of that cliff until one hour after sunset. These shifts took place even when the evening was calm and mild.

Most condors which roost in trees move downhill before dark whether there is a breeze or not. One cool evening in December, seven condors were perched in a certain group of trees at 4 p.m. By 4:30, four had shifted to other trees. The sun set at 4:45. All the condors shifted to perches farther down the slope by 5:12 p.m. and they were on these same perches at dawn. One afternoon in June there were 20 condors in a group of trees at 5:45 p.m. Ten of these shifted to trees lower on the slope before dark and the others did not change perches. In the late afternoon there is often a decrease in the number of condors perched in any one tree. Many times I saw from four to eight condors perched in a single roosting tree at sunset but found only one or two birds there at dawn.

At any time of day, near a roosting area, a condor may perch for a few minutes, or for an hour or longer, in order to rest and look about. One day in August a favorite tree was occupied by an adult, not necessarily the same one, from 9:25 a.m. to 10:30 a.m., from 10:30 a.m. to 1:45 p.m., and from 2:18 p.m. to 3:15 p.m. On another day a certain tree was occupied from 9:30 to 9:35 a.m., 10:03 a.m. to 11:09 a.m., and 12:50 p.m. to 1:30 p.m. These observations were made during good soaring weather. From three fire lookout stations which are situated near roosts, condors are often seen to alight on perches in the late morning and in the late afternoon but they rarely remain perched more than one hour. Apparently the condors seen are departing from, or returning to, the roost areas. Most resting perches are within a mile or two of known roosting, watering, or nesting sites. Perching at other locations is usually for the purpose of approaching food.

Before commencing to feed on a carcass condors

usually perch near it for a time. If typical perches are not available, the bird stands on the ground. Near one carcass on flat ground a rock about one foot high was a favorite perch. Several times I saw condors perch on springy limbs of black walnut or oak trees in approaching food. A photograph by Carl Twisselman shows a condor perched on the top of a fence post near a carcass. The favorite water holes are atop cliffs where there are many suitable perches nearby.

The approach to nests requires the use of perches which are generally lower and less suitable than resting perches. In approaching and leaving one nest low in a canyon, the adults often perched on a small bare branch at the very top of a living canyon live oak. After the young bird leaves the nest, the parents frequently must perch on boulders, small branches, or shrubs in order to feed the youngster. The location of the perch with respect to the nest or young, rather than the physical characteristics of the perch itself, determine whether the perch will be used.

In maneuvering to land at a nest, or near a young bird, a condor may perch briefly on a shrub or on the tip of a branch in order to avoid flying into trees or other obstructions. The perch may be occupied but a moment. When the air is poor for soaring, condors may be forced to land before reaching a good perch. Under these circumstances I have seen them perch on boulders low on slopes and scarcely higher than the chaparral. Condors returning to Hopper Canyon late in the day may perch in the first roost trees that they encounter and remain there all night.

Variation in the use of perches and roosts.—The roost cliff near the big cave in Hopper Canyon was the object of much observation in winter and spring. When many condors were roosting near the cave, the number sometimes changed less than a quarter on successive nights, but at other times the number was doubled or halved on successive nights. The period of use of this cliff for roosting was not exactly coincident with the greatest concentration of condors in that area. In the winter of 1939-40 there were more than 10 condors in that area in December, and more than 20 in early January. Yet, by January 17, I detected no more than four roosting near the cave. In mid-February several condors roosted near the cave each night, but in late May, with a dozen birds still in the area, only one or two roosted near the cave. The following winter (1940-1941),

when about 20 condors were in the area, I saw as many as 15 roosting near the cave by January 12. The indication was that the filling of the drinking and bathing pool above the cave attracted condors to that roost. Similar numbers roosted near the cave in March and April. Storms in late April caused the falls to run, and seven or eight condors, all that I could find in the area, roosted near the falls in early May. A week later, when the pool above the falls was nearly dry, the condors watered elsewhere and rarely perched near the cave.

Although I do not know of more than five condors roosting near the big cave when there was no water in the pool, water may not have been the only factor causing them to roost there in winter. On many occasions when there was water in the pool they did not roost near the cave. In winter many potholes contain water and the need of the birds for water is less than in summer. On many days when condors roosted near the cave none approached the water. Nevertheless, it was in the exceptionally dry spring of 1946 that I saw the greatest numbers of condors roosting near the cave and pool.

The typical fluctuation in numbers of perched condors seen near the big cave and water hole in Hopper Canyon on a day in winter is shown in figure 5. The height of the bars indicates the maximum number of perched condors seen at one time in that vicinity in each period of one-half hour. The stippled area indicates the number of immatures identified.

The daily trend shown in figure 5 was typical for all areas consistently used for roosting by large groups of birds. There was much variation in the pattern because various individuals and groups of birds performed different activities. All the condors did not visit water or nests each day. They were hungry to varying degrees. Some young did not forage. At nests I observed that a single individual varied by as much as two hours in its time of commencing flight or shifting to its final perch for the night, even when the weather was uniform.

There is a tendency for individuals away from nests to use the same roosting site for periods of at least several days. For example, in eight days of continuous observation from a single point in August, 1939, I saw one adult, apparently the same individual, roost in an isolated small group of trees on four nights with one break in succession. In the same period, in

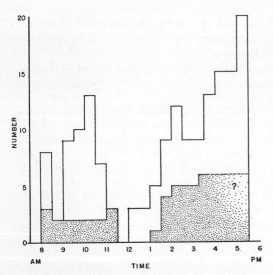

Figure 5. Numbers of Condors seen perched near the big Cave in Hopper Canyon during March 10, 1941.

another isolated group of trees, one or two adults roosted on three non-successive nights. In the latter group of trees I saw from one to three condors roosting on about 25 dates between 1939 and 1941. Usually two adults were there, one or both being on a certain limb, and I saw condors at that spot at some time in every month of the year. Probably a mated pair favored that group of trees.

Often condors do not roost at the same place on successive nights, even when the weather is uniform. In the eight days of observation already mentioned I was able to account for eight roosting condors on three days and for only three on the other days. Even nesting adults roosted at various sites and on some nights they were absent from the vicinity of the nest.

Within a roost area the place of perching and roosting is greatly influenced by the presence of food. On two occasions when the population of Hopper Canyon doubled within a few days (figure 4, April and June, 1946), there was a carcass present in the canyon. Sometimes in winter when there was food in this canyon, half or more of the condors present roosted near the food and the others roosted near the big cave. Once I placed the fresh carcass of a calf near some roosting trees that were rarely used by more than one or two condors at a time. Several condors fed on the calf and 19 roosted within from 200 yards

to one-half mile of the carcass. The following day the birds consumed the carcass and that evening only five roosted in the vicinity. At another site which I watched a great deal, several condors fed one day in December and seven roosted within a half mile of the food remains in a group of trees in which I had never before found more than three condors. Dyer (1935:8) reported that seven condors roosted in trees not far from a carcass from which they had been flushed.

Wind influences the use of a roosting place. Strong east winds are frequent in central Ventura County and during these winds I often saw condors perched on west-facing bluffs where I rarely saw them at other times. The largest number of condors that I saw roosting near the big cave in Hopper Canyon (30), and several monthly maxima, occurred on days of strong cold wind. It appeared that the strong wind made the usual tree roosts untenable. Low temperature (to 30°F.) seemed to have no influence on the choice of roosting place.

Rain has no apparent direct effect upon the type of perch used for roosting. Several times I saw condors remain in the usual dead roost trees in spite of rains occurring before, during, or after the night. I did not discover a significant increase in the use of potholes and protected ledges for perching in rain.

In winter and spring, when many condors are in central Ventura County, fog is common in the mountains there. In the Sespe region condors occupy their usual perches and roosts when fog is forming or flowing into the roost canyons. During fog and rain the air is poor for soaring so that condors which shift perches usually alight farther down the slope. Condors which have remained in a group of trees through a long period of fog and rain are often found in the lowest trees of the group.

Effects of disturbance.—On occasions an adult condor perched alone in a tree will allow a man to approach to a distance of 100 feet or less before it takes off. Yet, groups of condors perched in trees may flush before one approaches within 200 yards of them. In general, condors perched at a higher level than the observer flush less readily than those perched at a lower level. They are especially wary when perched on the ground.

When a perched condor is approached, it usually stands with its body in a horizontal position, holds its head low, raises its ruff, and cocks its head at various angles with quick movements. Frequently it will turn about to face the intruder. It may stretch its neck up or down to look over or under intervening obstacles. The wings are raised when alarm increases and the bird then takes off. If the bird does not flush, it usually stands upright within five minutes and it may preen or sit. In calm air condors seem reluctant to take off, and, if approached to within normal flushing distance, they usually walk in and out on the perch branch, nibble twigs, and show other signs of uneasiness.

Immatures normally flush less readily than adults. When a man approaches a mixed group of adults and immatures, the last bird to depart is nearly always a young one. Dyer (1935:8) tells of a young condor which remained perched on a snag until approached to within six feet by a man climbing the tree. Immatures are more variable than adults in their behavior and, on occasions, may be the first to depart when a mixed group is approached.

Sounds, more than motions, disturb condors. Even the buzz of a motion picture camera 100 yards from a perched adult appears to be noticed. Condors which are not flushed by waving of the arms may be flushed by loud talking. I set up a 7 by 7 foot tent in the open only 50 yards from a drinking pool and departed from the area at 2 p.m. Two hours later 13 condors were perched near the pool and they paid no apparent attention to the flapping tent.

Condors may remember disturbances for hours. Many times photographers have hidden themselves in blinds near habitual perches of the birds but no condors perched nearby. The difficulty seemed to be that the bored photographer stepped out or peered out after a few hours and he was seen by soaring condors. A large blind which I did not have to leave all day was successful. When the condors were disturbed near the main roosting cliff and water hole in Hopper Canyon in the evening, none at all or only a few returned to that area in the morning. One evening 16 condors roosted on that cliff while I was in a blind nearby. At night three men visited me and there was some talking and other commotion. Although everyone was out of sight long before dawn, all the condors departed shortly after sunrise.

The amount of disturbance which a condor will tolerate before flushing decreases rapidly late in the day. For example, I stationed myself below a roost cliff at 4:10 p.m. when 18 condors were there. Six soon departed. The others remained until 5:30 p.m., but by 5:55 p.m. only seven remained and only two condors roosted there. On previous days more than a dozen roosted there. Many other times I had a similar experience. Mild disturbances which will not prevent condors from perching or even from drinking may prevent them from roosting. The disturbance threshold for roosting seems to be lower than that for any other daily activity of condors.

One factor leading to a false idea of the tameness of condors is the lag in the reaction of the birds to disturbance. Commonly when a condor does not leave its perch as a consequence of a man close by, it will leave several minutes later after the man has walked several hundred feet away. The delay is most pronounced when the air is poor for flight.

Some of the largest numbers of condors that I saw near the big cave occurred when there had been disturbance near the main tree roosts. Once when I left the vicinity of the cave in the afternoon before all the condors had arrived, about 10 condors roosted near the cave and 10 at the main tree roost. On two occasions in spring when people disturbed the condors at both of the main roosts in Hopper Canyon on two days in succession, the number of condors detectable in the area dropped from about 20 to a maximum of four or five. A day or two later many condors were back at the usual roosts. One man, by disturbing the birds at critical places late in the day, can prevent roosting over an area of several square miles.

Summary.—For perching, condors require steady places with good footing which are easy to reach or to leave by air and where there is little disturbance by man or enemies. Roosts, in addition, must be high above the ground yet protected from strong winds, utterly free from disturbance, and suitably located with respect to food, water, nests, and perhaps to other condors. Any adequate program for conserving this species must provide for the preservation of a sufficient number of perching and roosting places as well as for the protection of nest sites.

Flight

Soaring.—The outstanding characteristic of the flight of condors is high stability in soaring. Frequently even an experienced observer mistakes a distant transport plane for a condor or a condor for a plane. It is probable that condors can soar for more than one hour at a time without flapping. The general plan of flight is a sequence of periods of circling to gain elevation followed by long straight glides. I have seen condors glide in a straight line, without turning, for as long as 8 minutes. Some glides may be 8 or 10 miles in length. Except in calm air, soaring turkey vultures wobble extremely in comparison with condors.

In the normal soaring position (figure 6), the anterior margin of the wing is nearly straight but it curves slightly forward toward the tip. The dihedral angle is low compared to that of a turkey vulture but about the same as that of a red-tailed hawk. This angle tends to be greater in turbulent air and less in calm air. Perhaps it aids in preserving lateral stability as it does in aircraft. Because of the dihedral angle, when one wing of an airplane is raised that wing is canted more in relation to the airstream than the opposite wing. As a result, the higher wing produces less lift than the lower wing and the airplane regains an even keel. In calm air the wings of turkey vultures are often held out at a low dihedral angle so that these birds appear to soar like condors. Under most air conditions, the inner half of the wing of a turkey vulture makes a sigmoid curve when seen head on while the wing of a condor is straight.

In front or rear view the spread primaries of a soaring condor appear brush-like. From above or below several slots are prominent between primaries 3 and 10 (figure 6). The longest slot is about 30 per cent of the length of the wing from the body. Primaries 8, 9, and 10 curve upward strongly toward the tips, primaries 3 to 6 curve slightly downward, and primary 7 is intermediate in position. The neck is smoothly covered by the ruff and does not appear to be extended. In comparison, soaring turkey vultures appear to be headless and golden eagles appear to have a long neck. The head is turned about freely in flight. The tail is extended widely, especially in calm air. In comparison, the tail of a soaring golden eagle is long and has a narrow base while the tail of a turkey vulture is

Figure 6.   Diagram in ventral view of an adult Condor in normal soaring attitude.

expanded very little. The tail is cambered downward from side to side and its tip, in adults, forms a smooth arc. The feet are held close up under the base of the tail. Many of the contour feathers flutter constantly when the bird is soaring.

The soaring flight of condors produces a steady hissing whistle. Probably the sound is made by the emarginated primary feathers. This whistle is more pronounced and has a more musical quality in adults than in young condors. The primaries of immatures might be more flexible than those of adults and thus produce less sound. Sometimes the whistle is audible at a distance of more than 100 yards while at other times it cannot be heard at a distance of 100 feet.

Wing Slots.—Graham (1930) suggests that the wing slots of soaring birds act like similar safety devices in aircraft. As the angle of incidence of a wing increases, lift and drag increase. Beyond a certain angle the air stream breaks away from the upper surface of the wing (burbling) and lift is lost so that the wing stalls. Slots modify the air flow so that the wing continues to have lift beyond its normal stalling angle. Condors have a conspicuous multiple-slot wing tip. According to Graham, in this type of wing tip the primaries are twisted forward by air pressure because the vane of each emarginated feather is widest on the trailing side. Thus, the leading primaries meet the air at a lower angle of incidence than the rest of the wing and the primaries do not stall when the inner part of the wing does. The leading primaries are pulled somewhat forward of the inner part of the wing because the lifting force, acting approximately perpendicular to the chord of an airfoil (wing or primary feather), has a greater anterior component at a low angle of incidence (primary feather) than at

41

a higher angle (inner wing). Graham (*op. cit.*:37) suggests that each primary from front to rear turns the airstream downward so that the feather behind it does not have to twist so far to gain a similar angle of incidence. The result is that the flow of air is changed through an angle greater than the stalling angle of the wing without burbling. At low speeds the wing tip retains lift and the bird retains control.

Photographs of condors swooping to a landing or giving stop flaps reveal that the alula is separated from the margin of the wing. Graham (*op. cit.*:58, 59) shows that this wrist slot acts like the slot at the leading edge of an aircraft wing. When the bird is about to land, the angle of incidence is increased greatly and consequently the bird is slowed down by the tremendous increase in drag. The opening of the wrist slot may be automatic, as in aircraft, for as the angle of incidence increases the area of upward pressure on the wing moves forward and the alula is sucked upward. As the alula meets the air at a smaller angle of incidence than the main wing, it is pulled forward in the same manner as the leading primaries.

Aspect ratio.—The aspect ratio (ratio of the span of the wing to the width) is about 6 to 1 for a soaring condor. The aspect ratio of an albatross is much higher. A long narrow wing (high aspect ratio) is more efficient, from the standpoint of lift, than a short broad wing because air slides out from beneath the wing at the tip (Graham, *op. cit.*:40). However, in broad-winged soaring birds, each emarginated primary may act like a wing of high aspect ratio and thus reduce this loss.

Loading.—Loading (the ratio of weight to supporting surface) has been frequently used to compare the aerodynamic characteristics of birds. Fisher (1946: 572) gives the total supporting surface of the tail, wings, and body of one specimen as 12,532 square centimeters. Assuming a weight of 20 pounds, this area indicates a loading of 1.48 pounds per square foot. By the same method, Fisher found that the loading of one turkey vulture was only .82 pounds per square foot. The heavy loading of *Gymnogyps* in contrast to *Cathartes* accounts, at least in part, for the stability of the flight of the condor as compared with the flight of the turkey vulture (*loc. cit.*). When turkey vultures and condors are rising together over flat ground, the former, because of their lighter loading, gain altitude much faster than the condors.

Circling.—Hankin (1913:30, 31) points out that the time required to complete a circle is fairly regular for a species and that large birds describe larger circles than small birds. This difference is of value in distinguishing condors from turkey vultures. For each two circles of a turkey vulture, a condor usually turns but one. The average time for each circle of a condor is from 13 to 17 seconds, the extreme times observed being 9 and 20 seconds. It is not uncommon for a condor to turn more than 15 consecutive circles in gaining altitude. Usually the direction of turning is changed before that many circles are completed.

Hankin (*op. cit.*:29) states that the gain in height in a circle is usually on the windward leg and turn. I noted this tendency in condors circling over slopes and being carried downwind. This action suggests that the bird slows down by increasing the angle of incidence on the windward side of the circle and consequently allows itself to be carried to leeward rather than attempting to remain over the same spot of ground. Ascending currents of air slant to leeward and rising condors may drift downwind in order to stay in these currents. Frequently, in order to scrutinize objects, condors circle without attempting to gain altitude.

Steering.—The exact mechanism of steering could not be detected by field observation. Condors normally perform two movements just before turning. First, the tail is tilted downward on the side away from the direction of the turn. By watching for this movement one can predict the direction of turn. Then, but less frequently, the tip of the wing toward the inside of the turn dips momentarily as if lift were lost and the primaries assumed their normal curvature. Perhaps the tail functions as a rudder in starting the turn or like the elevators of an airplane in producing a bank. The dip of the wing tip may be caused by a rotation of the wing, thus slowing down that side of the bird, as suggested by Hankin (1913:191). Throughout a circle the tail may maintain its tilt although often it tilts quickly in the opposite direction as if to control lateral stability. Young immatures tilt their tails from side to side every few seconds as if over-controlling. On occasions they nearly turn themselves over in performing turns. Another clue to the function of the tail in steering is furnished by the observation that in soaring parallel to a crosswind ridge a condor usually keeps the downwind side of

Plate 8.   Sisquoc Falls in Falls Canyon, Santa Barbara County, a Condor roosting area.

Plate 9.　A Condor soars over brush and cliffs on an overcast day.

Plate 10. Outlines of soaring and flex-gliding Condors as seen from below. These are characteristic shapes with which the observer must become familiar in identifying Condors.

Plate 11. An adult Condor soaring slowly with the wings dihedrally up and feet down in preparation for landing.

the tail depressed. Again the action may be either that of a rudder in keeping the bird heading slightly up-wind, or that of elevators in counteracting a canting of the bird caused by a stronger updraft on the windward side.

Double dips.—The "double dip" (Hankin, 1913: 86) is a common action of soaring condors. The wing tips are quickly flexed downward about 90 degrees and backward about 45 degrees at the wrists, then returned to the soaring position. The whole act requires one or two seconds. Condors perform the dip especially rapidly and especially slowly when soaring into strong winds as if strong air currents sometimes counteract and at other times increase the effect of the action. Turkey vultures and golden eagles perform the double dip much more rapidly than condors. This is another characteristic by which these birds can be distinguished from condors at a long distance. Hankin believes that the dip is initiated by a forward and downward rotation of the wing which allows air pressure to force the primaries down, and that the drag of the dipped wings causes a rotation of the bird downward.

In condors the double dip is used to increase speed, to lose elevation, or to prevent a stall. In profile view the bird slows down and rises at the start of the double dip as if about to stall, then it rotates forward and downward into a steep glide which is maintained as long as the wings are depressed. When the wings are again spread, the bird rotates upward, rises somewhat in elevation, and continues on at a normal gliding angle. Frequently the movement is performed at the start of a long glide. Often a condor gives the double dip as it soars out over the edge of a cliff or crosses a ridge, as if to counteract an upcurrent of air or to take advantage of the increased space below by steepening its glide. When one condor pursues another, it may give a double dip with consequent increase in speed and loss of altitude in relation to the pursued bird. At the end of the upward swoop after a dive at or away from another bird a condor usually gives a double dip and drops from an almost stationary stalling position to a normal gliding position. In heading into a strong wind in an ascending air current a condor may dip repeatedly, rising before each dip. Once I saw a condor perform 26 consecutive double dips at intervals of 5 to 15 seconds as it descended into a strong wind.

There are lesser dips of varying degrees, many of which seem to be caused by loss of lift at the tips of the wings. In turbulent air condors constantly dip one wing tip or the other. This action is apparently to control lateral stability, altitude being lost on the side of the dip.

Flex gliding.—In flex-gliding the wings are not only flexed but are arched so that the dihedral angle is diminished or becomes negative. The tips of the leading primaries remain upturned even in a strong flex-glide. The expansion of the tail decreases as the flexion of the wings increases. In a mild flex-glide the wings are approximately horizontal and only the wrist appears to be flexed. In a strong flex-glide the angle at the wrist is about 135 degrees, the tips of the wings are depressed to the level of the breast, and the sides of the tail are almost parallel. The result of increased flexion is an increase in wing loading and a decrease in the aspect ratio and consequently an increase in speed and loss of altitude. In the same air currents turkey vultures flex their wings much more strongly than condors.

Flapping.—For condors flapping is an auxiliary device for supplementing soaring and gliding in special situations. Flapping occurs in taking off, in landing, in gliding or circling where there are no updrafts, in crossing low over ridges and passes, in fleeing from or pursuing other birds, in turning in calm air or where space is restricted, or in regaining stability in rough air. For all these situations the rate of flapping is between two and three beats per second. Possibly as many as four beats per second are given in short bursts of speed. The South American condors at the San Diego Zoo seem to flap faster than free-living California condors. The flaps of condors are slow and heavy, somewhat like those of a brown pelican. Flapping makes a swishing sound which may be audible at a distance of half a mile. The maximum number of consecutive flaps that I witnessed was 40 given as a condor took off from flat ground in calm air. In flap-gliding a dozen flaps is the usual maximum in a series and the number of flaps in successive series varies in an irregular manner. When a condor is ascending in calm air, flapping is more common in the turns than in straight flight. Evidently soaring birds, like airplanes, lose lift when they bank.

Flight in strong wind.—On days of strong winds "heading" (Hankin, 1913:400) is common among condors near their roosts. The bird heads to windward of the direction it is traveling over the ground. Condors may head about 45 degrees from the direction of the wind and travel over the ground 90 degrees from the direction of the wind. Heading is apparently a conscious orientation to the route over the ground, for the same routes between peaks are traveled on days of strong winds as on calm days.

In strong winds groups of condors may hover over the windward side of the crests of certain crosswind ridges for half an hour or longer. They do not remain poised at the same spot in the manner of red-tailed hawks but they always progress into the wind. The rate of movement into the wind may be less than five miles per hour and often it is barely perceptible. Occasionally the birds ascend faster than they move ahead. In heading into some winds condors maintain a strong flex-gliding position, while in other winds the normal soaring position is maintained. The difference is probably caused by differences in the turbulence of the air and the velocity of the winds. Soaring at low altitudes is usually unstable in strong winds. On occasions the wind carries a condor upward or downward quickly, or throws it on its side, and the bird appears as wobbly as a turkey vulture. Flight in very irregular, turbulent air seems to require much energy.

Among condors hovering over a ridge, "wind facing" (Hankin, 1913:404) is common. The birds alternately head to one side or the other of the wind and consequently move from side to side without soaring directly into the wind. On one occasion a condor traveled to and fro six times in 10 minutes. Often they turn so far that they are swept downwind before they again turn into the wind. A similar common action is a modified form of circling. A condor hovering above the windward side of a ridge turns slowly away from the wind and is swept downwind for several hundred feet. The turn continues and becomes steeply banked as the bird checks its speed over the ground and again heads into the wind. Then it slowly soars into the wind back to the starting point. While soaring downwind the condor loses some altitude and occasionally it flaps. The entire action may be repeated again and again over the same ground. Perhaps the rising current of air at the windward side of the crest of the ridge is shallow so that the condors soar into the wind only until they penetrate the front edge of this current, then they drop downwind and turn to head into the rising current again. Hovering over ridges near the roosts seems to be a waiting action.

Over ridges in strong wind condors can rise quickly by facing the wind. This action takes the place of circling to gain altitude. When gliding parallel to the crests of long crosswind ridges, condors merely turn into the wind occasionally, rise quickly, and then continue on their way. In this manner they make flights of several miles without circling. Even in strong winds, however, condors may circle in rising over long windward slopes. In ascending out of a canyon over a certain slope in a strong wind, a condor turned but three circles, whereas 15 circles were required for the same action in a gentle breeze. While heading into a strong wind a condor can descend very steeply, almost vertically, to a perch.

Chasing.—Condor flight is most spectacular when one condor chases another. This occurs at all times of the year near roosting areas and is most frequent on days of strong winds. Chasing is more frequent after the birds return from foraging than before they depart to forage. Usually a single adult chases another. Less frequently an adult chases an immature, one immature chases another, or two adults in succession chase a third condor. The chases are one-sided; condors do not take turns chasing each other. Presumably most of these encounters are manifestations of social dominance.

The usual behavior in a chase is for one condor to overtake another by fast flex-gliding. The pursued bird dives downward in a steep flex-glide, twisting from side to side, and the pursuer follows. Both swoop up out of the dive at about the same time, flapping at the end of the swoop as if to gain every possible inch of altitude. Then the birds soar peaceably or the attack is repeated. Many chases amount to little more than persistent following. In only three or four of more than 100 observations did the pursuer appear to touch the pursued bird. Often the chase continued for eight or nine minutes and extended over a distance of more than one mile. At other times the entire action was completed in five seconds.

The initial glide toward the pursued bird may start from as far as one-half mile away. Occasionally the chase starts when one condor drives another from a perch. In one instance, a sunning adult suddenly took off as another flew toward it. The pursued bird was driven from a perch on a cliff three times in succession, then was chased half a mile from the cliff and back, the pursuer never being more than 25 yards behind it.

The attacking bird sometimes turns on its side at the start of a dive. Often the birds flap in diving. Dives are seldom steeper than 45 degrees. The sound of diving is a distinctive roar like escaping steam and it may be audible at a distance of more than half a mile. A steep twisting dive usually continues about 100 feet, and the dive may be repeated so that the two birds come dangerously close to the ground. The means of avoiding the attacking bird seems to be to keep above it in elevation as long as possible. On one occasion the pursued bird glided a short distance until it rose, then it flapped to prevent stalling and to regain speed, and it repeated this entire action six times in succession. On occassions the pursuing bird craned its neck upward as if to bite at the bird above.

Rarely did I see the attacked bird flee from the vicinity after being chased. Once I saw a third condor attack the pursuer of an immediately preceding chase. Another time I saw one adult pursued by another just after the first had fled from the attack of a peregrine falcon. The submissive action of the condor may have instigated this pursuit. Condors flee from golden eagles and falcons in about the same way as from each other except that they frequently descend and perch when pursued by the other species. Occasionally condors have to flap, twist, or even land in order to avoid collision with others in air.

Taking off.—From high perches, especially in strong wind, condors can take off by merely spreading their wings and hopping into the air. Just after leaving the perch they usually flap two to five times as if to prevent loss of altitude and to gain the speed necessary for soaring. Under less ideal conditions flapping commences at the moment of taking off. At the beginning of the first flap the tail is expanded and raised somewhat, the wings are held nearly straight up, and the legs are straightened, pushing down on the perch. Then the wings and tail are brought down in a strong deep flap which carries the bird away from the perch. Even in strong breezes, takeoffs are usually down the slope rather than into the wind. However, on one day of strong wind, I saw several condors walk a few yards up the leeward side of a steep ridge and take off into the wind from the crest. Perhaps they sought to avoid a strong current of air down the slope. In rolling country condors may walk 50 yards or more up a slope before taking off.

In taking off from flat ground in gentle breezes, condors must run into the wind in order to gain flying speed. The length of the run is usually from 15 to 40 feet. The run may start with several hops, one foot striking the ground slightly before the other, or it may consist entirely of such hops. In average summer weather condors run with great strides with the body horizontal, the neck outstretched, and the wings beating. The feet may be clear of the ground in five to seven flaps when more than 30 flaps are given before the first glide. Once I saw a condor put its feet to the ground and take a few more strides after it had taken off and flown low above the ground for several yards. Usually the initial period of flapping continues until the bird is 10 feet or more above the ground and has made its first turn. Then the bird glides and flaps alternately in flap-circling, the periods of flapping at first being much longer than the periods of soaring but they diminish rapidly as the bird rises.

Alighting.—The feet and tarsi may be extended downward long before a condor alights. Condors returning to the roosts in the afternoon often have their feet down continuously for more than 10 minutes before landing, commencing when they are more than 1000 feet above their perches. At other times the feet are not lowered until the last swoop to the perch. Condors shifting between perches usually hold their feet down throughout the flight. Occasionally the feet are extended downward for a few seconds as if for equilibration. As a bird swoops upward at the end of a dive, the feet may be lowered as if thrown down by centrifugal force. Condors hovering low over ridges in a strong wind may have their feet down part way most of the time, as if in preparation for a quick landing if necessary. In level flight the hanging tarsus slants slightly backward and the toes hang down as if relaxed (plate 11).

When descending rapidly, as toward a disturbed nest or toward food, a condor may hold its wings strongly flexed but high above the level of its back and extend its feet downward. Often condors spiral down steeply in this position. Hankin (1913:397) believes that such a position allows a bird to descend rapidly without the increase in forward speed caused by flex-gliding.

At the end of its descent toward a perch a condor swoops upward and loses speed. In this swoop the wings are fully extended but dihedrally up, the alulae are separated from the margin of the wing, the neck is extended, and the feet are down. Then the bird gives several stop flaps with the plane of the wings and expanded tail vertical and the legs and feet extended toward the perch. The usual number of stop flaps is three to seven. A condor may swoop up to a stall just as it reaches the perch so that stop flaps are not necessary. Landing into a strong wind may also be accomplished without flapping. Usually the bird drops vertically a few feet to the perch while giving stop flaps with the wing tips held high. In landing in brush it may drop several feet in this fashion. On occasions a condor starts to alight but then turns away and makes another approach. At one nest when the wind was toward the nest cliff, an adult passed within a few feet of the edge of the cliff four times, extending its legs downward toward the perch with each approach, before it finally made a landing there. Landings may be audible at a distance of several hundred feet. The sound is sometimes a sharp crack and at other times it is a muffled crash as of feathers striking rock.

Altitude.—In general, condors do not soar as high or as low over the ground as turkey vultures in the same localities. On days of light breezes condors rise higher than on days of strong winds. Strong winds probably flatten the ascending air currents before they rise far above ridges. In addition, condors gain altitude easily on windy days so that there is no necessity for circling up to great heights in order to commence glides. In mountainous areas, on days of strong winds, condors soar especially low over the slopes and at low levels in canyons. In more than 100 observations of adults approaching or leaving one nest the birds flew lowest when there was a strong wind, regardless of whether going upwind or downwind. Probably the air at very low altitudes is poor for soaring during light breezes but is of optimum condition for soaring when the wind is strong. In crossing ridges or passes heading into a strong wind condors fly especially low, frequently not over 10 feet above the ground, and flap. The upward component of the air currents may be proportionately greater close to the ground than farther above it so that the birds make better progress at the low height.

Over high ridges and peaks near roosting areas it is rare to see a condor soaring more than 500 feet above the ground. Over lower hills near feeding areas, where condors circle in rising columns of air in order to gain altitude for long glides, they rise to an estimated 3000 feet. From an airplane, Sumner (1950: 133) saw two condors 2500 feet above the ground in an area where the birds forage. Of course, condors which glide from a high peak out over a low valley may be more than 3000 feet above the floor of the valley. In areas where condors are actively searching for food they usually soar less than 500 feet above the ground except when arriving and departing. Doubtless there is an optimum altitude for searching for food. Great height would not favor the detection of carcasses as small as those of ground squirrels.

Speed.—In the condor country, inexperienced observers generally overestimate the distance of condors in air. Consequently, estimates of the speed of condors are often fantastically high. An observation related by Dawson (1924:1731) indicates a speed of more than 100 miles an hour for a flight of 50 miles. Accurate timing of the speed of condors has not been attempted. By estimating when the birds were over known points and allowing for wind, I have reckoned the speed for normal soaring to be about 30 miles per hour. Condors may soar more slowly when searching for food. They can gain headway directly into winds estimated to be 30 to 40 miles per hour in velocity. At localities where this action occurs the air speed of the birds could be measured with an anemometer.

Time and duration of soaring.—In departing from some of the major roosts to forage, the group of condors merely circles to gain elevation and then soars directly toward the feeding area. At Hopper Canyon the departure is more complicated. Shifts between perches, occasionally involving flights more than one mile in length, may occur as early and as late as there is daylight. Probably some of these shifts serve as trial flights for the purpose of testing air currents. Commonly, one or two condors soar above the rim of the canyon half an hour or longer before the main group rises. At other times, nearly all the condors present rise above the rim within a period of several minutes. Again, some remain perched long after the others have departed.

After arriving above the rim of Hopper Canyon the condors alternately scatter and rejoin in small or large groups, wandering about over the roosting area. On some occasions the entire group disappears within half an hour. At other times the number dwindles gradually over a period of about two hours, and often several condors may be seen near the roosting canyon all day. For a "business-like" bird, about 20 minutes elapse between the time it commences to rise out of the canyon and the time it departs toward a feeding area. At this roost it is rarely apparent in which direction the majority departs. Occasionally groups soar off in opposite directions as far as one can see them.

The result of the interplay of some of the factors influencing the time and duration of soaring is illustrated by figure 7. The height of the bars indicates the largest number of condors seen soaring above the level of the rim of Hopper Canyon in each period of one-half hour during a full day of observation. This figure is comparable to figure 5 except that it is based on soaring rather than on perching. In figure 7 the upper two diagrams show that a group of condors rose out of the canyon in the morning, dispersed gradually, returned in the afternoon, and descended to the roosts. The lower diagram shows that soaring condors were present most of the day.

Relation to sun.—The most extensive observational work concerning the relation of soaring flight to weather was done by Hankin (1913) on several Asiatic soaring birds. He used the term "soarable" for the condition of the air which allowed soaring without loss of speed or elevation. For soaring flight there must be sunshine or wind. "Sun soarability" (*ibid.*: 402) commences a few hours after sunrise and ceases one or two hours before sunset. "Wind soarability" does not require sunshine, but some winds are not soarable. In disturbed weather soarability may be unusually early or absent (*ibid.*:27). For gliders, and presumably for soaring birds, soarability is due to ascending currents of air. Soaring by means of utilizing fluctuations in the velocity of a horizontal wind (dynamic soaring) or micro-turbulence of the air has not been proved to exist.

Hankin found that sun soarability commenced at a definite time of the morning varying with the time of year. This time was earliest in June and latest in December. I found a similar trend for condors although many factors and variations made accurate determinations impossible. As flights between perches, nests, and water within the roosting area are frequently made in unsoarable air, I used the earliest

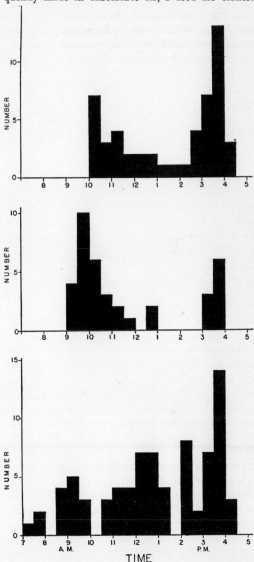

Figure 7. Numbers of Condors soaring above Hopper Canyon during the day. Upper diagram: December 18, 1939; breeze light to moderate; sky clear; maximum temperature 65° F. Middle diagram: July 4, 1940; breeze light to moderate; sky 3/10 cirrus clouds; maximum temperature 85° F. Lower diagram: November 27, 1940; strong northerly wind; sky 1/10 cirro-stratus; maximum temperature 54° F.

time of departure of a group of birds from the roosting area as an index of soarability. At Hopper Canyon,
I took the first time of day when at least five condors
were seen to rise above the rim as the "departure
time." For days of light to moderate breezes (Beau-
fort scale; Knight, 1942:627) when the sky was less
than one-half overcast and the previous day was favorable for foraging, the departure times observed at
Hopper Canyon were as shown in figure 8. In this
figure the area between the heavy curved lines, which
shift with the time of sunrise, would include as well at
least two-thirds of the observed departure times for
groups of less than five condors from the same canyon.
As the time of development of ascending air currents
depends on temperature and other factors in addition
to sunlight, and as the pressure of hunger or other
drives on the bird is an unknown and variable quantity, it is improbable that a close correlation between
departure time and the time of sunrise could be
demonstrated.

From roosts outside of Ventura County condors
departed at about the same time or earlier than from
Hopper Canyon. I saw eight condors leaving Castle
Mountain at 7:50 a.m. on June 30, 1946, six leaving
McChesney Mountain at 8:50 a.m. on July 7, 1946,
and four well on their way from Parker Peak at 8:05

a.m. on July 16, 1946. These observations were made
in clear, warm weather when there was little wind. Of
several hundred observations of condors recorded by
fire lookouts, occurrences before 9:30 a.m. were exceptional. Departures from Hopper Canyon may tend
to be later than from some other roosts because condors must rise several hundred feet in elevation before leaving that canyon. From some roosts, the birds
can depart directly without ascending.

Another criterion for the time of commencing long
foraging flights is the time of arrival at feeding areas
several miles from roosts. At Branch Canyon, Cuyama
Valley, J. R. Pemberton (MS) recorded the time of
arrival of condors on 13 dates in September and
October (1936 to 1938). Three or more condors
arrived before 9:30 a.m. on six dates. None was seen
before 9:00 a.m. Near Arvin on September 16, 1940,
one arrived at 8:30 a.m. and four more by 9:05 a.m.
Near the mouth of Kern Canyon I saw two at 8:10
a.m. and four at 8:30 a.m. on June 3, 1941. Near
Mount Poso, Kern County, on May 4, 1946, I saw
one at 8:04 a.m. and two at 8:30 a.m. At Fountain
Springs, Tulare County, six were present by 8:55 a.m.
on July 14, 1946. Near Cholame I saw three arriving
at 8:30 a.m. on July 17, 1947. Ordinarily condors do
not soar far from the roosts until after 8:00 a.m.

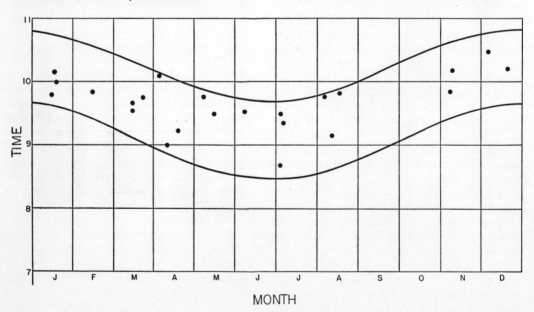

Figure 8. Seasonal variation in the departure time of groups of Condors leaving Hopper Canyon.

Individuals vary in the time of commencing flight, especially when they are away from a roosting group. I watched a pair which roosted near a nest on three successive days of similar weather in August. They departed at 10:30 a.m. on two days and an hour earlier on the intervening day. Of six condors roosting in one group of trees in Sisquoc Canyon on July 21, 1940, one took off at 8:27 a.m., four at 9:00 a.m., one at 10:00 a.m., and one at 10:05 a.m. On this occasion, as on many others, the first and last birds to depart were immatures. Several times I saw an individual remain perched near a nest from dawn until after 11:00 a.m. although soarability was apparently excellent an hour or more earlier. In a moderate breeze three condors took off from an isolated group of trees at 8:15 a.m. while three others remained in a nearby canyon until noon.

Sunshine often seems to determine when condors commence to soar. On some days of stratus overcast I noted that the commencement of soaring corresponded closely with the time that the clouds thinned and the sky brightened. There may be a moderate breeze in the morning for an hour or more before the birds take off, but these early breezes frequently die and spring up in another direction before the condors depart. The soaring schedule might be adjusted to this phenomenon. Departure from the roosts is just as early on days of light breezes as on days of strong breezes.

On occasions, condors which are disturbed at their roosts within about half an hour before their normal departure time circle up and depart from the area in typical fashion. Those disturbed earlier usually perch again. Hankin (1913:26) discovered a similar tendency for other soaring birds. The few condors which depart within an hour before the main group may soar without apparent difficulty. From these observations, it is evident that condors do not fly as early as soaring is possible. Presumably less energy is required for soaring at midday than earlier so that the time of departure is the resultant of the impulse to wait for better soarability, and the urge to feed, avoid disturbance, or perform some other activity. The food of condors does not walk away if the birds are a little late in arriving. In fact, the lighting at midday when shadows are short may be more favorable for discovering food than it is early in the day when shadows may obscure carcasses.

Hankin (1913:26) found that the air did not become soarable for all birds at the same time and that birds of light loading commenced soaring earlier than birds of heavy loading. The difference noted between turkey vultures and condors was not great. Where the two birds roosted in the same area in Sisquoc Canyon and Hopper Canyon, J. R. Pemberton and I, independently, found that in moderate weather turkey vultures undertook extensive flights only about 20 minutes earlier than condors. Yet, I often saw turkey vultures soaring two or three hours later than condors.

The time of returning to the roosting area is much more variable than the time of departing to forage, for the birds do not all feed at the same time and place. One day in September I saw 30 condors near a carcass. The last two did not depart until 4:20 p.m. although I saw 11 soaring over the roosting area, several miles distant, at 2:15 p.m. At Hopper Canyon most of the condors usually returned from foraging by 3:30 p.m. at all times of the year. For example, on a clear day in February when the breeze was light, eight condors had returned by 3:00 p.m., 11 by 3:20 p.m., 14 by 3:26 p.m., and 18 by 3:30 p.m. On eight successive days of observation in August, 1940, when from five to eight condors were present and the weather was fair and uniform, I saw one above the rim of the canyon after 3:30 p.m. on only two days, and one day seven had returned to the canyon by 1:15 p.m. Late returns were more common in winter and spring than in summer, probably because foraging commenced later and the birds were hungrier. Fire lookout men stationed a few miles from roosts rarely saw condors after 4:30 p.m. Disturbance of condors at a carcass in the late afternoon may initiate a return to roost. One day in June, I flushed 11 condors from a carcass near the mouth of Kern Canyon at 4:35 p.m. By 4:50 p.m., the last bird had gone out of sight heading for the roost.

It was rare to see a condor above the level of the rim of Hopper Canyon after 5:00 p.m. unless there was a fresh breeze or a strong wind. Yet, in that area in winter, I once saw six condors leaving a carcass one mile from the nearest roosts at 5:10 p.m. after sunset on the evening preceding a storm. In fair weather I saw three condors approaching a roost in Tulare County at 5:55 p.m. in July. Near Cholame, in June, the last two condors (immatures) did not leave a carcass until 4:56 p.m. Near Big Pine Mountain I saw four condors arriving at the roost trees at 6:25 p.m., but at that locality the sun did not set until 7:05 p.m.

Even when the breeze is moderate, condors are capable of soaring shortly after sunset. Three condors which I flushed from trees on a high ridge a few minutes after sunset soared above the trees for 15 minutes before alighting again. In a broad canyon, three condors which I disturbed shortly after sunset shifted their roosting place two miles, ascending several hundred feet in the process.

Influence of wind.—Thermal updrafts alone seem to be sufficient for the soaring of condors under ideal conditions (high temperature, light colored ground). Near Arvin on a hot sultry day in September when there was only an occasional light breeze, many condors circled up quickly over flat bare ground, half a mile from the nearest hill, and seldom flapped when more than 50 feet above the ground. Usually when condors have been feeding on flat ground, they soar to a point over a slope before rising more than several hundred feet. In mountainous areas, on relatively calm but clear days, I often observed that individuals took off at a time when there was an increase in the breeze, and the settling of a group frequently corresponded with the dying of the breeze.

On calm days condors flap frequently in gliding or circling. They circle for long periods in order to gain altitude and they may have difficulty in ascending high enough to cross ridges. Frequently they cross at the lowest pass of a high ridge, flapping. On calm days in summer some condors departed from Hopper Canyon at about the normal time while others remained perched until about noon. Calm also seemed to favor an early return from foraging. One day in March there was a fair breeze in the morning but the afternoon was calm and sultry. Six condors were back in Hopper Canyon by 12:30 p.m., nine were perched by 2:15 p.m., and 12 by 2:40 p.m. These facts suggest that condors are largely dependent on obstruction currents for soaring.

If obstruction currents are necessary for the prolonged soaring of condors, flat plains would tend to act as barriers to flight. Condors do not venture more than a few miles, about eight at most, out over the flat ground of the San Joaquin Valley from the foothills. Apparently neither condors nor turkey vultures have reached the Channel Islands less than 20 miles

from the coast of Ventura County. The South American condor reaches a few coastal islands (Murphy, 1925), but these islands are close to the mainland.

On days of strong wind (over 25 miles per hour) condors commence flying early. On clear days of strong wind in Hopper Canyon I saw at least five condors above the rim of the canyon before 8 a.m. several times in April and shortly after 8 a.m. in November and December. These times were between one and two hours before the normal departure times for days of moderate breezes. One day in winter I saw four condors above the rim at 7 a.m., only eight minutes after sunrise. Over lower crosswind ridges close to the roosting trees, I saw several condors soaring as early as 6:15 a.m. in winter. On some days when the wind was strong condors which were soaring over high ridges shortly after sunrise descended to perches and did not depart from the roosting area until about the normal time. This fact suggests that soaring in strong wind in the absence of sufficient sunshine requires much energy so that extensive flights are not undertaken. On windy days, especially when the sky was overcast, several condors were visible flying near the roosting area through the middle of the day as if some did not depart (see figure 7). Yet, on one clear, windy day in February I saw six condors soar at least 8 miles from their roost by 10:40 a.m. Eben McMillan saw three condors at least 12 miles from their roost on a day of strong wind in December.

Condors returned to the roosting area at Hopper Canyon no later on days of strong wind than on days of moderate breezes, but after returning many continually soared over the region until about sunset. Commonly, several left perches low in the canyon in order to soar about with the group. One windy evening in March I saw seven condors soaring above the rim of the canyon at 5:30 p.m., 10 minutes before sunset, and on another evening I saw six soaring over a lower ridge, near the roosting trees, at 5:45 p.m., several minutes after sunset.

Influence of clouds, rain, and fog.—When the sky is overcast with thick cirro-stratus, alto-stratus, or stratus clouds, soarability is low when there is not a fresh or strong wind. When soarability is high, the roosts in Hopper Canyon are ordinarily deserted at midday, but when the sky is overcast and the breeze is gentle, several condors may be seen about the roosts all day and few rise above the level of the rim of the canyon. One day in March the sky commenced clouding up at noon. By 2:50 p.m. eleven condors had returned and were perched in the canyon, although the breeze was still fresh.

Feeding on a ranch less than two miles from the roosts was most frequent on overcast days of strong winds as if the birds did not go far to forage. Nevertheless, on an April day of low clouds, I saw a condor soaring near Tejon Ranch headquarters, several miles from a known roost, at 8:35 a.m. Pemberton (MS) found one on the ground near a carcass in Cuyama Valley at 7:30 a.m. on an overcast morning. Not improbably these individuals had failed to return to their regular roosts because of poor soarability on the previous afternoon. Even when the air is poor for soaring, condors may be forced by hunger to search for food. The contrasting effects of wind and overcast may tend to nullify each other so that the departure time is about the same on windy overcast days as in fair weather.

Cirrus clouds, cumulus clouds, and clouds shortly preceding rainfall do not seem to inhibit soaring when there is a breeze. Cirrus clouds are too thin to block sunlight and the other types of clouds are associated with ascending currents of air. Near Arvin, one day in September, five condors arrived near a carcass at 9:05 a.m. although the sky was half overcast with cumulus clouds and the breeze was light. Six condors near another roost did not leave a carcass until 5:10 p.m. on an overcast evening preceding a storm. One day in March I saw several condors soar southward across the Santa Clara Valley from near Hopper Mountain when a rainstorm was imminent. Pemberton (MS) encountered 16 condors on the ground in Cuyama Valley shortly before a rainstorm. Hankin (1913:281) found that wind soarability was best in "stormy winds" under heavy clouds.

Although condors can soar well in winds preceding rainstorms, the commencement of rain is accompanied by conditions unfavorable for soaring. Apparently the air ascends under the clouds at the front edge of the storm but descends in the area of the primary shower of rain. Early one afternoon I saw nine soaring condors descend and perch within 15 minutes after a light shower commenced. On an overcast day in February I saw an adult land on a barren hillside just as a light sprinkle commenced. The bird walked about

100 feet and soon took off. Shortly afterward an immature condor perched in a low walnut tree at another spot. This bird remained for more than one hour, once flying a short distance and alighting, then returning to the tree, before departing. A large group seen in Cuyama Valley by Pemberton was caught by a period of light showers and calm air. These birds flew several hundred yards and landed on the ground. They repeated this process about four times before flapping out of sight going in the direction of their roosts. Near the roosts in strong winds, I have seen condors soaring in light rain and even in light hail for several minutes without apparent difficulty, evidently utilizing ascending obstruction currents.

Condors can fly in fog. Many times I have seen them soaring through the edges of broken fog or circling and rising up out of sight into the base of a cloud. Condors flushed from trees in fog may fly well and even rise in altitude. Yet, when the roosts in Hopper Canyon were buried in fog in the morning, the birds did not depart until the fog had commenced to lift or to break up. Some fogs are accompanied by calm still air so that soarability is low. Other fogs are thick and deep so that they have the same effect as a stratus cloud. Perhaps fog inhibits flight by restricting visibility or by wetting the feathers. In the mountains of the Sespe region, where I watched condors in winter, fog is usually accompanied by wind and visibility is seldom less than 100 yards. It was rare for the roosts to be buried in fog all day, but occasionally periods of fog, low clouds, and drizzle continued for several days and many condors apparently remained about the roosts for days at a time. One such period in January, 1940, lasted for 10 days but the condors were able to find some food near the roosts.

Influence of food and hunger.—The presence of food close to the roosts does not result in especially early or late flight. One day in June several condors fed on a fresh calf carcass which I had put out. The last bird left the carcass at 4:50 p.m. More than a dozen condors roosted near the carcass and some flew over it at 8 a.m. the next morning. Yet, the birds departed from the area at about 9:30 a.m. and did not return to feed until one hour later. One day in December I saw 15 condors circling low over a carcass about one mile from the roosts in the late afternoon, but the next morning none left the roosts until after 10 a.m.

The time of departure from the roosting area was

often earlier than usual on the first day or two following one or several days of poor flying weather, as if
the birds were hungry. One April day, after two days
of fog, drizzle, and overcast, I saw five condors above
the rim of Hopper Canyon at 8:20 a.m. although the
sky was partly overcast and the breeze was light. The
day after a storm in September three condors rose
above the rim at 8:05 a.m. although the breeze was
light and the sky partly overcast. These times were
about three-quarters of an hour before the usual departure times. In the Sespe region days of storm were
frequently followed by days of strong winds and consequently the birds departed especially early. On some
occasions all had departed from the area by 9 a.m.

The length of the soaring day in moderate weather
varies from 5 or 6 hours in winter to 7 or 8 hours in
summer, the maximum being about 9 hours. Only
two or three hours of the soaring day may be used
for foraging. In stormy weather in winter there may
be no foraging at all for a day or more. The winter
season is critical for condors because the time available for finding food is short and the need for food
is great.

Routes and lanes of flight.—Although condors
range widely, they tend to use certain routes in traveling to and from roosts. These lanes are determined by
the location of the roosts and foraging areas, by the
topography, by the wind, and perhaps by custom, and
their limits may be well defined. At certain ranches
and fire lookout stations condors are rarely seen although roosting or feeding groups occur a few miles
away. For example, condors rarely have been reported
from any part of Avenales Ranch west of McChesney
Mountain although they often have been seen at the
top of that mountain. In northeastern San Luis Obispo
County, Eben and Ian McMillan have watched for
condors for many years. Condors occur frequently in
Bitterwater Valley and on the east side of the Red
Hills but rarely in the San Juan River valley just west
of these hills. The McMillan brothers live four miles
apart on opposite sides of the Red Hills where the
topography and the numbers of livestock are similar;
condors have never been seen near Ian's place while
they are seen several times each year near Eben's
place.

The daily cruising radius of condors is frequently
over 12 miles. With 8 x, 30 mm. binoculars, I can
identify soaring condors at distances of at least 8

miles, and I can identify them at greater distances
with a 20 x, 50 mm. telescope. By observing from
near roosts and feeding grounds, and at intermediate
points, I was able to trace routes of flight. Some of
these routes are shown in figure 3.

Following is a list of the distances between various
places where groups of condors have been seen feeding and the roosts from which they came and to which
they returned. Those distances marked with an asterisk
were determined by my own observations. The other
distances are based on the assumed place of roosting.

Castle Mountain to Shale Hills	35 miles*
Castle Mountain to lower Cholame Ranch	12 miles*
McChesney Mountain to Temblor Ranch	26 miles
McChesney Mountain to Choice Valley School	27 miles
Falls Canyon to Branch Canyon	13 miles*
Hopper Canyon to Oak Ridge	13 miles*
Hopper Canyon to Sandbergs	18 miles
Hopper Canyon to Neenach	23 miles
Bear Mountain to Monolith	18 miles
Bear Mountain to mouth Kern Canyon	17 miles*
Bear Mountain to Tejon Ranch headquarters	15 miles
Breckenridge Mountain to Mount Poso	23 miles*
Parker Peak to Fountain Springs	14 miles*
Parker Peak to M. Vincent Ranch	19 miles

I am certain of the record of 35 miles, for several
condors were observed to travel this route three
times in June, 1946. Taking into account all the
circling and deviations from straight flight, a condor
may easily cover a distance of more than 50 miles in
one day of normal activity.

Because the use of each roost varies with the season,
there must be days when condors return to a different
roost than the one which they left in the morning.
After feeding in the vicinity of Mount Poso, Kern
County, some condors departed toward the northeast
as if to go to Parker Peak (28 miles) rather than returning toward Breckenridge Mountain (23 miles).
One morning I watched 10 condors arrive at a ranch
near the mouth of Kern Canyon coming from the
direction of the top of Bear Mountain. Four days
later I flushed 11 condors on the same ranch and they
headed for the Breckenridge Mountain roost.

The location of roosts with respect to feeding areas
might be determined, in part, by the direction of the
prevailing winds. On all (three) occasions when I
saw condors feeding many miles from a roost during
a strong wind, the wind was blowing toward the roost
from the feeding area. Several times Eben McMillan
has seen two or three condors near Pinole Ranch,

many miles northeast of the McChesney Mountain roost, when there was a strong wind from the northeast. In that region the winds are generally northerly or easterly in summer and fall; thus, the wind usually assists the return of condors to McChesney Mountain. On the east side of the San Joaquin Valley where condors forage in summer, the breeze is usually from the southeast in the morning and from the northwest in the afternoon. This shift in the breeze permits a downwind flight both in leaving the roosts in the morning and in returning to them at night. In the Sespe area in spring, when many condors are present, the wind is often strong from the east and northeast. In that region some of the important foraging areas lie to the northeast of the roosts.

Summary.—Condors are specialized for long range soaring flight. Such flight is possible only where air currents are proper. The nature of the air currents is determined by the complicated interaction of sun, wind, and other climatic factors on the mountains, plains, and other surface features of the land. Because of their large size, condors require unobstructed spaces for alighting and taking off. There remain few areas which satisfy the requirements of condors for flight in addition to those for feeding, nesting, and roosting. The maintenance of the remaining favorable areas in their present state is of prime importance for the maintenance of the species.

Feeding Habits

Food items.—My information on the feeding habits of condors is based on personal observations of feeding made on more than 30 dates, about 30 instances related to me by various friends (chiefly Eben Mc-Millan, J. R. Pemberton, and Eugene Percy), and a few published accounts. In approximately half of all the instances the carcasses on which the birds fed were of beef cattle, and they were of calves more often than not. Bones cast up by condors in nests are predominantly those of cattle. The principal food of condors today is Hereford range cattle. There are no records of California condors attacking living mammals although black vultures and South American condors have been reported to make attacks on occasion.

The kinds of animals upon which condors have been reported to feed are listed below. The first five furnish at least 95 per cent of the food of condors.

Item of food	Reference
Cattle	C.B.K. (MS)
Sheep	C.B.K. (MS)
Ground squirrel (*Citellus beecheyi*)	C.B.K. (MS)
Deer (*Odocoileus hemionus*)	C.B.K. (MS)
Horse	C.B.K. (MS)
Coyote (*Canis latrans*)	C.B.K. (MS)
Jack rabbit (*Lepus californicus*)	J. R. Pemberton (MS)
Cottontail (*Sylvilagus audubonii*)	J. Keyes (verbal)
Wildcat (*Lynx rufus*)	H. Shebley (verbal)
Domestic dog	C.B.K. (MS)
Goat	H. Hill (MS), E. Percy (verbal)
Mule	B. Mansfield (verbal)
House cat	E. McMillan (letter)
Pig	Evermann (1886:608). Townsend (in Audubon, 1839:241)
Mountain lion (*Felis concolor*)	C. Tant (*fide* Robinson, 1939:8)
Elk (*Cervus nannodes?*)	Fry (1926:1)
Burro	Fry (*loc. cit.*)
Whale	Taylor (1859c:19), Lewis and Clark (1905, 4:82)
Sea lion; hearsay?	Taylor (*loc. cit.*)
Fish	Lewis and Clark (*loc. cit.*)
Salmon	Townsend (*loc. cit.*)
Skunk (*Mephitis*); actually ate?	F. T. Ross (verbal)
Grizzly bear	Heermann (1859:29)
Mussels (with shell)	Taylor (*op. cit.*:18)

Probably, on occasions, condors feed on the carcasses of gray foxes, badgers, and kit foxes which are caught and thrown aside by trappers or are killed by poison. Grass, leaves, twigs, and other indigestible materials may be eaten and later cast up. California condors are not known to eat the carcasses of birds although South American condors commonly eat birds near the seashore.

A carcass does not have to appear "natural" in order to be eaten. Eugene Percy told me that about 10 condors fed on a black Angora goat near his ranch house. Eben McMillan saw condors feeding on the head and offal of a slaughtered steer. I flushed nine condors from the carcass of a small Australian shepherd dog.

Preferred foods.—Hunger drives condors to eat food which is low in the scale of preference or which lies at an unsuitable site. Disturbance by man, interference by eagles or coyotes, or the unsuitable location of a carcass prevents condors from feeding even when the kind of food is highly preferred. Whether a certain carcass will be taken depends upon the balance among these factors.

Carcasses of deer and young calves are the foods most eagerly eaten by condors and perhaps by competing animals as well. It is doubtful that either a deer or a young calf could lie for many days in a suitable area without being consumed. C. S. Robinson (1939:8) tells of flushing 28 condors from the decayed carcass of a doe in the bottom of Sisquoc Canyon. The location of the carcass and its stage of decomposition were far below optimum for condors. On all occasions when I saw condors alighting in the brush, the food was a deer carcass. In one instance 28 condors ate a fresh deer carcass rather than the nearby carcasses of a sheep and a heifer which had been dead for a few days. Two days later condors ate the sheep.

Even a deer carcass may not be consumed if there is something amiss. Pemberton (MS) put a coyote-killed deer under the favorite roost trees of condors in Sisquoc Canyon; in the next five days no condors came to the carcass. Probably the birds were slightly disturbed. Ed Harrison put out a stuffed doe near another carcass on two occasions. Ravens and turkey vultures fed near the decoy and condors flew over the area, but none of these birds paid any apparent attention to the doe.

Carcasses of horses and mules are comparatively unattractive to condors. At various times Pemberton, Don Bleitz, Ernest Dyer, and I have tried to bait condors with the carcass of a horse, but we have had little success. Dyer (1935) flushed seven condors from the carcass of a horse when a storm was impending but none alighted near the horse on the succeeding three days. Another time, Dyer (letter July 31, 1935) put out a horse at the same locality and the condors fed on a calf several miles farther from their roosts than the horse. I killed a horse at a place where condors passed over it daily. One week later the hide had not been penetrated by any bird or mammal. When this carcass was three weeks old and much decayed, two condors fed on it briefly on the morning following a day of poor flying weather. Nevertheless, the flock of 26 condors seen by Stephens (1895:82) was flushed from the carcass of a young horse. Mules likewise have proven to be poor bait although one killed for bait by S. A. Nash-Boulden eventually attracted a group of 26 condors (B. Mansfield, U.S.F.S. files). It may be that condors prefer not to eat horses, mules, and adult cattle because of the difficulty of penetrating the tough hide.

For one year, Henry Shebley, a State trapper, placed all of his catch on a high ridge where condors foraged. Shebley saw as many as 26 condors over the pile of carcasses but did not see more than six or eight on the ground. He is certain that the condors preferred wildcat to coyote carcasses. Eben McMillan flushed two condors from the carcass of a coyote, and I have heard, from trappers, of five or six condors being seen at one coyote carcass. Apparently coyotes are relished by condors far less than are deer or calves.

Condors alight, take off, and walk in a laborious manner, but they excel at flying long distances. Their specializations fit them for eating carcasses which are large enough to feed them for a day or more at the expense of only one landing and one takeoff. It would be wasteful, from the standpoint of derivable energy, for a condor to descend to the ground in order to feed on a single small carcass. On all (three) occasions when condors have been seen to feed on a rabbit, other food was present. In an area where I watched condors feeding on squirrels for several days in succession the carcasses were so abundant that I could find at least one every 15 minutes by walking over the ground. Often I saw a condor feed on two or three squirrels before taking off. In addition, the birds did not have to ascend high in order to fly from one group of squirrel carcasses to another. Murphy (1925: 89, 190) found that the South American condor may feed on small food when it is abundant. These condors eat the eggs of cormorants and they kill petrels in their breeding grounds.

State of decomposition.—Condors will feed on carcasses which are in any state of decomposition. Pemberton saw condors feed on a sheep which he had killed less than six hours earlier. I saw several condors feed on a calf which I had killed 17 hours earlier, but the carcass was not completely consumed until 30 hours later. Near Cholame, I flushed 11 condors from the slightly swollen fresh carcass of an adult cow. Yet, one day when the air was poor for soaring, I saw 30 condors at the decomposed carcass of a steer when the only remaining meat was on the under side of the legs. In winter, I found 24 condors at the same carcass from which Eugene Percy had flushed 20 condors 10 days previously. Percy told me that once he saw condors tugging at an old horse hide which had been softened by a drizzling rain and that the birds returned to the hide soon after they were flushed. The squirrel carcasses upon which I saw condors feed were in various stages of decomposition. Many were bloated and foul, the hair was slipping, and the eyes were dried up, while others were fresh. Captive condors are fed on fresh meat.

The only apparent advantage to condors of waiting for a carcass to decay is that the hide becomes softened and carnivores may rip it open. Still, no one has improved his success at baiting condors by cutting open a fresh carcass. Waiting is disadvantageous to condors for within a few days coyotes, eagles, insects, and other animals take the choice parts of large carcasses and consume small ones. Perhaps because of the consumption of the choice parts, a carcass which condors have once fed on becomes unattractive to them. Near Cholame I watched 10 condors feed on a large calf and then return to the roost. The carcass was about three days old and was less than half consumed. On the next two mornings the first few condors which arrived perched by the calf and even pecked at it, but these few took off when several others arrived over the area. The entire flock then departed and fed on the carcass of a dog and a sheep, both fresh, many miles away. Often I watched all day at a carcass on which condors had fed the previous day, but seldom did the birds return.

The foregoing facts suggest that old carcasses are of low acceptability but that they act as a reserve supply of food. Condors feed on them if, because of the scarcity of food or because of adverse weather, they can find nothing better. In a period of good soaring weather the presence of a large group of condors at an old carcass seems to indicate that there is a shortage of more suitable food in the area.

Site of food.—Because of the necessity for space in landing and taking off, condors usually feed in open grassland. In some of these feeding areas there is not a tree or shrub within miles and the grass is sparse and low. On four occasions I saw a group of condors descend to a brush covered slope in order to feed. These observations were made in mountainous areas where the slopes were steep and the bushes were several feet apart and not over five feet tall, so that the condors had no difficulty in landing or taking off. On two occasions I saw condors at a carcass which they had dragged beneath a large live oak tree on a grassy slope. Again, I saw 12 feeding on a carcass beneath a leafless walnut tree.

In mountainous areas the higher ridges are preferred to the lower canyons for feeding. In 20 years at Hopper Ranch, Eugene Percy has rarely seen condors feeding below the level of the ranch house (about 3000 feet elevation) but he has frequently seen them feeding at higher levels (up to 4500 feet elevation). On that ranch many carcasses at the lower levels or deep in canyons have not been eaten by condors.

Appearance of food remains.—The remains of carcasses on which condors have fed may be distinguished by various signs. Some feathers or down are usually near the carcass, even if only a single bird has fed. Where a group of condors has fed there may be 20 or 30 separate feathers, including large flight feathers. The tracks of condors are distinctive. When many condors feed on a single carcass, the grass is trampled and the ground is scuffed up for a few yards around it. Carcasses up to the size of a deer are generally dragged downhill as the condors feed. Once I saw 20 condors feed on a young calf which was wired to a stake. Soon after vigorous feeding commenced the carcass moved down the slope steadily, attended by several struggling condors, until it was 200 yards

downhill from its original site. At one point the group passed next to the trunk of a large live oak tree where the foliage was only four feet above the ground. On a barren gentle slope several condors scattered the remains of a calf over a distance of 50 yards. Eben McMillan saw tracks indicating that one condor had dragged a steer head which weighed 20 pounds. The path of dragging is easy to follow for it is marked by tufts of hair and occasional bones as well as by feathers.

After a group of condors has fed on a calf, sheep, or deer, the hide has but few holes and the bones of the appendages are often pulled out through these openings (plate 12). Frequently the leg bones are still articulated but are lying outside of the hide, the distal bones encased by the inside-out skin of the legs. The skin of the tail, too, is often pulled inside out although its tip may remain attached to the bone. On the carcass of one sheep the skin of the tail was inverted and pulled out through the anal hole. After 20 condors had fed on the carcass of a four-day old calf, the hide was intact except that the skin of the anterior half of the muzzle was missing, the ears and one foreleg were missing, one hindleg was ripped, and there were holes about three inches wide in the belly, in the scrotal region, and at the anus. I had difficulty in turning this hide right side out.

The distinctive bones which most frequently are found separated from the carcass are the scapula and the lower jaw. The jaw is probably removed in the process of eating the tongue and lower gums. The gum of the roof of the mouth may be the major piece of meat remaining on a consumed carcass. Although the tongue and most of the lower gums were gone from the carcass of one young calf, the delicate hyoid bones were still in place and neatly cleaned. The skin of the tip of the nose of calves and sheep is usually eaten. On large carcasses the chin may be the only part of the head which is skinned out. The eyes are normally taken by ravens or other birds before the condors commence to feed.

Even in carcasses of small calves and deer the skull may remain in the hide and it may remain attached to the axial skeleton. The turbinals and other cartilaginous parts may be nibbled. Frequently the axial skeleton is several yards from the hide. The hind legs are usually still joined to the pelvis. Many times not a single rib is disarticulated although the ribs are well cleaned of meat. Often the cartilaginous portions of the ribs and vertebrae of young animals are nibbled. The bones of young calves become disarticulated and are scattered much more than those of older animals. The maxillaries may be separated from the skull and the epiphyses of the long bones are usually scattered. Sometimes the sheaths of the hoofs of calves are pulled off. On one carcass of a calf the hoofs appeared to have been nibbled.

With the occasional exception of the intestine and stomach, all viscera are usually missing from carcasses on which condors have fed. Among the scattered remains of one sheep I found the intestine, fairly intact. The intestinal contents remain in the abdominal cavity of the carcasses of large cattle.

One day I flushed five condors from the remains of two ground squirrels on which they had been feeding. The caecum and much of the intestine of both squirrels were among the parts which were scattered for 20 feet (plate 13). The tails were separated from the backbones and the skin was inside out for an inch or two at the base. The skulls were fairly well cleaned, and they were unbroken except for one zygomatic arch. There was little left of the wet shredded skin. All but one of the legs were separate from the spine and skinned to the paw. The ribs were spread wide, several were missing, and a few were broken. Once I saw a golden eagle, and another time a turkey vulture eat the carcass of a poisoned squirrel and leave the stomach and part of the intestine. Joseph Keyes of the Fish and Wildlife Service told me that this is a common habit of condors and turkey vultures.

Casts and pellets.—In every condor nest that I entered I found bones or bone fragments and other indigestible parts of mammals on which condors had fed. Some of these items, and their maximum dimensions (in millimeters) measured at right angles to each other, are listed below:

Tarsal or carpal of cow (*Bos*)	43 x 30 x 25
Epiphysis of long bone	50 x 40 x 4
Intervertebral cartilage of calf, with epiphyses of adjacent centra	40 x 37 x 15
Section of shaft of rib of *Bos*	127 x 18 x 8
Proximal end of rib, including both heads (*Bos*)	73 x 35 x 20
Lower jaw of calf, with teeth	87 x 22 x 15
Molar of *Bos*	62 x 31 x 25
Incisor of *Bos*	65 x 15 x 12
Distal phalanx of hoof of *Bos*	57 x 33 x 29
Sheath of hoof of calf, entire	50 x 30 x 13
Skull of ground squirrel (*Citellus beecheyi*)	58 x 30 x 18
Section of hide (horse?)	65 x 65
Tip of ear of fawn, hair complete	100 x 35

I collected about 300 of these castings in and below condor nests. Dr. R. A. Stirton kindly examined this collection and found that practically all the identifiable bones were of cattle, although horse, sheep, deer, jack rabbit, and ground squirrel were represented. The bones were clean of flesh and showed no evidence of corrosion by digestive fluids. The wrist and ankle bones (carpals and tarsals) of cattle were by far the most common parts. About 15 teeth of cattle were included in the collection. Probably condors pull these teeth from the alveoli in tugging at the tongue and gums although this act would require very strong pulling. Only two pieces of heavy hide were found. Some small and rather delicate bones, such as the lower jaw of a ground squirrel and the upper jaw of a jack rabbit, were unbroken and still held all their teeth. In the stomach of a South American condor Murphy (1925:190) found a hoof and a few bristles of a pig, two leg bones and some cartilages of a seal, and bits of kelp as well as 10 large pebbles. Coles (1944:227) investigated many nest caves of turkey vultures but found no bones or animal remains in them.

In condor nests the cast hard parts are scattered as if regurgitated singly. I found no bones in pellets. Presumably nesting adults and their young regurgitate the indigestible parts after swallowing them, although I did not witness this action. At one nest which had apparently not been used previously by condors, I found the molar of a cow and a section of a rib near the egg about one month before it hatched, and before the chick could move about I found other casts at the mouth of the cave. Some of the objects, then, are surely cast by the adult, but they accumulate most rapidly in the vicinity of the chick. In one nest six bones were removed from within a few feet of the chick when it was one month old. Two weeks later eight more bones were found there. The bones were no smaller when the chick was one month old than they were later.

Approximately 30 bones accumulated during one successful nesting. Many bones were found below the nests rather than in them. In one nest cave I found nearly 100 bones, but this cave had been used for nesting several times.

In at least three nests which were in Vaqueros or Sespe sandstone, both Tertiary formations, I found whole or broken shells of bivalve molluscs. Sidney Peyton found similar shells in another nest many years ago. According to J. W. Durham, these shells could not be older than Pleistocene, and some of the shells, judging by their luster, might be only a few years old. The species represented (identified by J. W. Durham) were: *Chione californiensis, Aequipecten aequisculcata,* and *Tivela stultorum.* The shells of *Tivela,* the Pismo clam, were the most weathered and the most common in the nests. At present these species occur on the coast, 20 or 30 miles from the places of collection. Within five miles of the nests there are Quaternary deposits which may contain similar shells, but it is probable that at least some shells were brought from the shore of the ocean by condors. As there are no records of California condors being seen near the seashore during the past 40 years, the shells in the nests may be at least 50 years old. A. S. Taylor (1859c:18) reported finding mussels in the stomach of a condor killed at Monterey.

On occasions condors disgorge pellets which consist mainly of vegetable fibers. When one juvenile was 25 weeks old, I saw it cast up two pellets 20 hours after it was fed. The bird stood with its head lowered, the bill open and pointed posteriorly; it then moved its head up and down several times and the pellets dropped. Beneath this bird I found three pellets. Two were of loose composition, brown in color, and they contained twigs up to one inch long as well as fibers of leaves. The pellets were roughly cylindrical, the largest being 40 millimeters long and 20 millimeters in diameter. The third pellet was dark green and firm, about 25 millimeters long, and it consisted of finely shredded leaves. Three weeks later I found a similar green mass, wrapped around a twig, below the perch of the same juvenile. I saw this bird eat the leaves of manzanita and prickly phlox.

In one nest I found a brown pellet similar to the others except that it contained some animal hair and no twigs. The nestling may have eaten dried oak leaves which blew into the cave. Another time, a few inches from an egg, a loose pellet of finely shredded leaves mixed with hair was found. A firm, bright green pellet, 9 millimeters by 20 millimeters in size

and containing some hair, was found at the entrance of a nesting cave and doubtless was disgorged by an adult.

J. R. Pemberton (MS) saw an immature condor near Sisquoc Falls regurgitate five pellets in succession early one morning, more than 12 hours after its last opportunity to eat. The pellets were composed mainly of grass. Young condors were seen pulling at grass at a nearby pool. Beneath a favorite perching ledge near another pool I found pellets similar to those described. Immature condors perched on that ledge after visiting the water hole and nibbling at grass, leaves and roots.

Time and manner of feeding.—As condors depart from and return to the roosting area in a gradual manner, and as they are most scarce near the roosts at midday, one would expect that they would arrive at and leave the feeding area in a gradual manner, and that they would be most numerous at the feeding area at midday. This situation exists when there is suitable food in the area where the condors habitually feed and when the weather is favorable for flight. The accompanying diagram (figure 9) indicates the fluc-

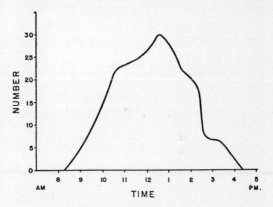

Figure 9. Numbers of Condors seen on the ground or in the air near the carcass of a steer at Kern Mesa, Kern County, on September 16, 1940.

tuation in the numbers of condors seen near the partly consumed carcass of a steer on one day of observation. On this occasion, the condors could be seen departing from and returning to the roost on a mountain several miles away. Although the first condor arrived at 8:30 a.m., none landed near the carcass until 9:27 a.m. Not over five condors fed at the same time, although 30 were on the ground within 50 feet of the carcass at 12:30 p.m. The presence of a large group through most of the day is common when the carcass is large and of low acceptability or when coyotes or eagles prevent the condors from feeding for long periods.

Pemberton's experience in Cuyama Valley was that the condors did not descend to food (sheep) until about two hours after the first one appeared in the area. Probably the birds spent this interval in searching for carcasses more suitable than Pemberton's bait. When the finding of desirable food requires no search, condors may descend within a few minutes after they arrive near the food. One windy morning in December, not far from a roost, the first two condors which passed over a ridge and sighted the carcass of a deer immediately landed (7:30 a.m.). Near Cholame, three immatures descended to a carcass without hesitation as soon as they arrived (9:15 a.m.). This carcass had been fed upon, presumably by the same birds, on the previous day. Where condors were feeding on squirrels I often saw individuals land within 10 minutes after arriving over the area and I saw them commence feeding within two or three minutes after they landed.

Condors may not descend immediately to a carcass even though it is suitable and easily found. About 10 of 22 condors fed on the fresh carcass of a young calf which I had placed near their roost and 19 condors roosted near this food. In the morning a few soared low over the carcass at 8 a.m. and several before 9:30 a.m., but none landed until 10:45 a.m. and vigorous feeding did not commence until 1 p.m. It may be that the hunger of the birds increased as the day advanced or that a coyote was present near the calf in the morning.

Where trees, boulders, or cliffs are present near food, condors usually perch on these before flying down to the ground. Sometimes they wait for one hour or longer before feeding. Where there are no elevated perches the birds land on the ground near the carcass and then either walk to it immediately or wait for a long period. In the observation related in the preceding paragraph, 13 condors were on the ground near the carcass for about one hour before more than two or three fed. The initial landing may be as far as 50 yards from the carcass. I did not see a condor make its initial landing on top of a carcass although golden eagles often did this. Throughout the period when many condors are on the ground near

food there are landings and takeoffs of individuals, small groups, or all of the birds, at irregular intervals. Frequently condors leave a carcass, land several hundred yards away, and remain for many minutes as if waiting or resting.

The first parts of a fresh carcass to be eaten are the eyes, tongue, and anal region. Pemberton's motion pictures of a group of condors feeding on a sheep show that one tugs at the tongue, then gives way to another and pecks at the anus, displacing a third condor there, and then pulls at the axilla. The first condor to approach the sheep earlier that morning plucked out the eye. John H. Storer told me that when condors ate the fresh carcass of a calf which he was observing, they first fed at the eyes and anus, even though the carcass was cut open. At one fresh carcass which I watched the first condor pecked at the anus and then pecked at the belly. I flushed 11 condors from the fresh carcass of a cow and found that it had a four-inch hole at the anus, that the lips and tongue had been nibbled, and that the upper eye was missing. The holes in the hides of calves on which condors have fed are most frequently at the anus, axillae, groin, and abdomen. Either the meat beneath these parts is choice or the hide is difficult to penetrate elsewhere.

Pemberton observed that condors nibbled rapidly in cleaning meat from the bones of a sheep. My own observations were made at too great a distance to observe this detail. When ground beef was fed to a nestling about 20 weeks old, the bird worked its bill open and closed rapidly. At the same time, it worked its tongue in and out so that the food was carried back to the throat. The distal four centimeters of the tongue of a condor are thick, with a U-shaped trough on the dorsal side. Each of the dorsal edges of the "U" bears about 35 hard spines which are directed posteriorly. These spines increase in size posteriorly, the largest spine being about three millimeters long. In eating, the young condor occasionally approximated the lateral margins of its tongue so that the food was grasped by the spines and was drawn back to the throat. The muscles which retract the tongue are about a centimeter in diameter and are evidently powerful.

Condors normally feed by pulling meat from the carcass with the bill. Small animals, such as ground squirrels, are held down by one or both feet. When the meat is not readily pulled from a large carcass, the condor stands with its tarsi flat on the ground and pulls back strongly several times in succession with a movement of the whole body. The bird gives one or two jerks per second. As many as 20 successive jerks may be given before the bird releases its grip. Evidently the gripping power of the bill is great. On occasions the tugging condor stumbles backward as it loses its grip or as the meat tears loose. A condor may stand on top of a large carcass while feeding.

When feeding alone, a condor is watchful and it pauses every few seconds to look about. In feeding on a squirrel one adult kept its head down for from two to five seconds and then looked about for an approximately equal period. I watched a single adult feed at a large carcass for one hour. The maximum interval without looking about was 20 seconds. Occasionally the bird stepped back from the carcass as if to look up at the sky.

Joseph Keyes told me that he had seen both condors and turkey vultures carry the remains of squirrels in their bills for a short distance in flight when disturbed. Others have seen turkey vultures fly with food (Bent, 1937:21) but I did not see condors do this.

When condors complete feeding by early afternoon, they may stand idly in the vicinity of the carcass for an hour or more, as if waiting for other members of the flock to complete feeding and join them in the flight back to the roost. Less than 20 minutes after 30 condors commenced to devour a sheep which Pemberton (MS) was watching, several of them walked away from the carcass and stood quietly. Soon others ceased feeding and stood nearby. About one hour after the feeding commenced 20 condors flew from the vicinity of the sheep, and the last few birds left within 10 minutes. At one large carcass where 10 condors fed, commencing at 10 a.m., several of them went to a water hole 200 yards from the carcass two hours after feeding began. Some eventually returned to the carcass. They departed toward the roosting area two or three at a time over a period of 2½ hours commencing at 2:30 p.m. When condors do not feed until late in the day, they do not stand about for long after feeding, but they take off for the roost, a few at a time, as they finish their meal.

Amount eaten.—According to Belle J. Benchley (letter, February 29, 1940), a California condor kept at Balboa Park for several years usually ate 1½ or 2 pounds of meat per day, but the quantity was variable. Because of its greater opportunity for activity, a free-living condor may require more food than a captive. Pemberton saw at least 30 condors consume one sheep. The birds could hardly have eaten more than 2 pounds apiece. Over a period of two days, I saw 22 condors consume a calf which weighed 85 pounds. Assuming that the skeleton and hide weighed 20 pounds, the birds ate about 3 pounds apiece. An adult doe was consumed by two golden eagles and 28 condors in one day. Again the birds ate an average of about 3 pounds apiece, including the viscera. Well fed free-living condors may require an average of at least 2 pounds of food a day.

The rate of feeding varies with the hunger of the birds and the exigencies of the situation. Two adults left a fresh calf carcass 15 and 30 minutes after they commenced to feed one morning. One fed a juvenile immediately. The 30 condors photographed by Pemberton were essentially finished with feeding in 19 minutes. Yet, I saw one adult feed for more than 20 minutes at a single squirrel carcass. Another individual fed alone at a cow carcass for one hour at midday. As the entire feeding activity for a day may be accomplished in less than one hour, condors are able to spend a great deal of time in searching for food.

Where condors are feeding on the carcasses of ground squirrels, they usually remain on the ground about 10 minutes and then fly to another location. Rarely does one remain at the same spot for as long as half an hour. Assuming that a condor gets one-half pound of food from one squirrel, an average of four or more squirrels a day would have to be eaten. Actually many more have to be found, for most of the accessible squirrels have already been partly consumed by other birds.

The idea is prevalent that condors may gorge themselves to such an extent that they cannot take off from flat ground. More than 100 times I have seen condors take off from flat ground in a light breeze after feeding without interruption, but I did not encounter any that could not fly. Both Wilson (1928:159) and Perry Sprague have captured an adult condor by running it down with an automobile. On both occasions, the bird could not fly even after it regurgitated. Probably these condors were unable to fly because of some condition other than overfeeding. Eben McMillan (letter, July 10, 1949) told me that a condor which he flushed from a carcass regurgitated as it rose in air. A piece of food hung several inches down from its bill and dropped when the bird was 200 feet above the ground. On occasions condors might regurgitate to lighten themselves for a quick takeoff.

Condors forage daily when the weather permits but they do not seem to suffer if they do not feed every day. A few times when a large group of condors was seen close to a carcass all day, only a fraction of the number fed. The effects of the pressure of hunger become apparent the day after the first day without food. The longest periods spent in incubation and brooding by the members of one pair were more than 40 hours in length. When many of a group of 22 condors did not feed one day, apparently because of the presence of a coyote, most of these birds fed vigorously on the following afternoon. The day after 28 condors consumed the carcass of a deer the weather was stormy and unfavorable for flight, but the following day a large group devoured the five-day old carcass of a sheep in the same vicinity. Not far from the roosts in winter, I saw over 20 condors at an old carcass one day and again two days later, but on the intervening day none fed there. On the few occasions when I saw what was apparently the same group of condors feeding vigorously on two successive days, the birds had been flushed on the first day before they had finished their meal. Condors can survive for several days without feeding. J. S. Appleton of Simi once kept a slightly wounded adult condor for a week. As the condor would not eat, Appleton released it and the bird flew away. P. S. Sprague kept a flightless adult, which regurgitated everything it ate, for 10 days before it died.

Method of finding food.—As the food is usually of large size and situated in the open, no more than a human sense of sight is required for finding it. In addition, ravens and turkey vultures indicate, to humans, the location of carcasses, and perhaps condors watch these birds. In areas where condors fed on ground squirrels, I frequently saw a condor fly straight to a group of turkey vultures, either in air or on the ground. In the squirrel country I often investigated the spot where an adult had landed but found only stinking burrows and no carcasses. I believe that these landings were for convenience or resting, for the behavior of the birds did not suggest that they had smelled a dead squirrel in a hole. Once

I came on an immature condor standing by a burrow where a squirrel was eight inches down in the hole but visible from above. As condors often fly less than 50 feet above the ground in foraging for squirrels, this squirrel may have been seen from the air. If condors have a sense of smell, it is normally of little importance in finding food.

When a group of condors appears to be foraging, they scatter in various directions over a large area and occasionally gather in small groups or, more rarely, in one big group. These groups soon break up and the birds scatter again. Often a single bird flies straight to a circling group. The whole action suggests that condors are aware of one another and that they may find food by cooperative effort. The basic impulse seems to be that of following other condors, but the following tendency does not prevent the quick dispersal of a group.

Relations between condors at food.—Fighting, chasing, and other evidences of social dominance are more common near carcasses than near roosts or water. One condor often gives way to another at a choice portion of a carcass. On the ground immature condors may be chased by adults, but I did not observe the reverse. Adults chase other adults but immatures chase only immatures, frequently chasing those which are obviously younger. Rather than one bird trying to keep all others from the food, the attacking bird seems to dislike certain individuals and pursues them. One condor may walk 50 or even 100 feet away from a group at a carcass in order to chase another. Once I saw an adult walk 30 feet from a carcass toward a standing group of six. Half of the group started away when the attacker arrived several feet from them. The attacker, wings flapping and neck outstretched, ran at one bird. This bird then jumped, flapping, into the air and the pursuer reached up toward the flying bird with its bill.

Some chases on the ground continue for 10 or 20 yards including one or two sharp turns. Often the chase continues into the air. The pursued bird may commence walking back toward the carcass as soon as the attack ceases. Immatures are especially persistent in returning. Most encounters result in no actual contact. However, John Storer told me that he saw two adults fight vigorously near a carcass, one hanging onto the skin of the neck of the other with its bill, and both kicking, flapping, and rolling on the ground.

The feeding of a large group of condors in a vigorous scramble is not their usual method. When this action occurs, the birds are especially hungry or the carcass is particularly choice. Generally an eagle or coyote has kept the condors from the carcass for an hour or more. Pemberton photographed 30 condors feeding on a single sheep in Cuyama Valley on October 8, 1938. His helpers had toured the vicinity and picked up all the carcasses except Pemberton's bait. An eagle kept the condors from feeding for most of the day but it was finally crowded off the sheep by 14 condors. I watched a flock of 28 condors feed all at once on a deer carcass. A pair of eagles kept the condors from the carcass until late afternoon. Then the eagles departed and the condors commenced to feed. Adults and young mixed in the melee as the struggling and flapping group of condors moved down the slope at a steady rate. Occasionally one which had been crowded away from the carcass walked around the group as if looking for an opening and then rushed in again.

When one of a feeding group jerks a scapula or other large piece from a carcass, this bird may scramble away followed by several others. A few then feed on the separated part, sometimes having a brisk tug of war. These actions explain the numerous feathers and scattered bones which mark the route along which a carcass is dragged. When many condors are feeding on a single carcass at once, there seems to be little watchfulness.

In squirrel country, where the food is small but scattered, condors feed in groups of one to five over a distance of two or three miles rather than all feeding at the same spot. I do not know of an observation of two groups feeding simultaneously at separate large carcasses in the same area. Evidently the flock tends to feed together when the food is large.

Relations with other animals at food.—Ravens, turkey vultures, golden eagles, and coyotes feed on the same carcasses as condors and thus compete with them for food. These animals usually commence feeding earlier and finish feeding later in the day than condors. In areas of rolling grassland far from the condor roosts, turkey vultures may arrive one-half hour or one hour before the condors and depart about two hours after them. Normally these vultures roost much closer than the condors to the food.

The largest flocks of ravens and turkey vultures that I saw in condor feeding areas consisted of about 50 individuals. Anderson (1935:70) saw at least 30 ravens, two turkey vultures, and seven condors over one carcass. Pemberton (MS) saw about 50 ravens, one eagle, and six condors circling over a carcass. Turkey vultures are rare in the range of the condor in late fall but they usually return in February. I did not see more than two eagles or two coyotes at a time near condor food. Mountain lions act as providers of food more than as competitors. There are black bears in parts of the range of condors, and these occasionally consume carcasses which condors might otherwise eat.

Ravens may feed within three feet of adult condors. Nevertheless, they often jump from a carcass as a condor approaches, fly out of the way as the condor descends to land, or hop away as it walks toward them. Occasionally a condor pecks at a raven and causes it to fly. One time when I was watching a juvenal condor at a carcass, a raven landed near it. The condor ran at the raven and caused it to fly. Then the raven hovered over the condor, swinging from side to side in the air, and the juvenile reached up at the raven with its bill. Turkey vultures, too, may drive ravens back. Pemberton (MS) suggests that inasmuch as ravens are wary, the sight of ravens near a carcass may encourage a condor to land. When there is some alarm, the ravens usually depart before the condors and the turkey vultures depart after the condors.

Condors at food are not approached as closely by turkey vultures as by ravens. Turkey vultures may fly from a carcass as a condor soars low above it or jumps up onto it. When a condor walks toward a carcass, the turkey vultures usually walk away. Seldom does a turkey vulture allow a condor to approach closer than five feet. Turkey vultures usually do not feed on a carcass at the same time as condors. Yet, on one occasion when 10 turkey vultures were feeding on a horse, a single juvenal condor stood a few feet away for many minutes as if reluctant to approach. When a condor lands near turkey vultures at a squirrel carcass, the vultures may leave the carcass and stand about 10 feet away until the condor finishes feeding. Occasionally other turkey vultures land by one which is waiting so that six or seven vultures are gathered near one condor. A few times I saw a condor leave a squirrel and walk or run toward one or two turkey vultures which stood nearby and drive them into the air. In one instance, a turkey vulture ran about 10 yards in a curve, the condor pursuing. Then the condor returned to the squirrel.

Golden eagles are present in every area where condors feed. One afternoon in December, I saw an eagle feeding on the carcass of a deer after the last condor had left the area. The condors had not yet found the carcass. At 7 a.m. the following morning an eagle was on the carcass and a second was perched close by. Soon a condor landed 100 feet from the carcass. An eagle immediately flew at the condor, chased it 100 yards in the air, and then returned to the deer. This action was repeated with another condor a few minutes later and several times later in the morning. One of the eagles chased four condors for half a mile while the other remained at the carcass. The eagles also chased ravens which approached. At 1:30 p.m., 16 condors landed on the ground 100 yards from the deer, but they quickly took off when an eagle darted among them. Ten minutes later 12 condors were on the ground, but again they were driven off. At 2:30 p.m., 14 condors landed and were chased off. The pursuing eagle struck one condor on the back with its talons, but the condor did not seem to be injured. Many times the attacking eagle did not come within 50 feet of the pursued bird. The condors twisted and dodged in fleeing. On some occasions when a condor soared about 50 feet above the carcass, the feeding eagle crouched with its wings and tail spread as if to hide the food. At 3:30 p.m., 23 condors perched on the slope near the deer. Some flew off but landed again. Forty minutes later the group of condors approached to within 20 yards of the carcass and did not leave when an eagle chased two or three of them in succession. The eagles then departed and the condors rushed to the carcass. Evidently the condors had grown bolder as the day wore on. It was cold and a storm was approaching.

About three weeks later at the same locality I watched an eagle at a carcass for three hours. At 5:15 p.m., four condors circled over the eagle and one landed only six feet from it. The eagle departed immediately and the four condors fed. Again the condors were bold late on an overcast cold day.

Pemberton (MS) saw an adult condor eating at the opposite end of a sheep from an eagle just before a group of condors crowded the eagle off. In the squirrel country I saw an eagle and an adult condor

standing 20 feet apart on the ground. The eagle walked to the condor and pecked at it. The latter retreated several feet and stood calmly. I found parts of the carcass of a squirrel at the spot.

The order of decreasing dominance of birds at a carcass is golden eagle, condor, turkey vulture, and raven, the greatest difference being between eagle and condor and the least difference between turkey vulture and raven.

Condors pay little attention to cattle roaming in the pasture unless the birds are in danger of being stepped on. Once I saw a cow repeatedly visit a calf carcass on which several condors were feeding. When the cow sniffed the carcass, three condors walked about 10 feet away from it and did not return until the cow left. Then the cow walked through a group of five condors. They parted and walked away rapidly, keeping about 10 feet from the animal.

Coyotes may visit carcasses in the middle of the day and thus encounter condors. On one occasion, I saw at least 10 condors fly from the ground near a carcass as a coyote approached. As this occurred late in the day (4:50 p.m.), the condors perched in trees nearby but did not return to the carcass that day. At another carcass where I saw up to 30 condors on the ground, one or two coyotes fed for a few minutes several times during daylight. Once when a coyote approached to a distance of 100 feet from three condors, the birds flew from the carcass and landed 100 yards away. The coyote ran toward the condors and they took off. At another carcass 20 condors took off as a coyote trotted toward them. One condor landed 40 feet from the coyote but immediately took off again. The group landed on the ground three minutes after the coyote departed. On occasions young or sick condors might be caught by coyotes. There are few coyotes in the areas where condors feed on poisoned squirrels because the coyotes are easily killed by the poison.

At the mouth of a squirrel burrow, only six feet from where a young condor had been feeding, I once found a rattlesnake. As snakes are common where there are squirrels, a condor might be bitten as it probes at a carcass in a burrow.

Effects of disturbance.—Condors on the ground near food flush at a much greater distance than when they are perched in trees or on cliffs. In open country, the first of a group of nine condors left a carcass when a car stopped half a mile away. The car drove slowly toward the remaining birds. The last adult flushed at a distance of a quarter of a mile, the last immature condor at 200 yards, and the last turkey vulture at 200 feet. On another occasion, a car stopped 250 yards from 17 condors at a carcass on flat ground. Two minutes later the birds commenced to leave, a few at a time, until only three immatures remained. The last of these flushed when approached to a distance of 150 yards. Dyer (1935:7) tells of seven condors leaving the carcass of a horse when men on foot approached to a distance of about 120 yards. To avoid disturbing feeding condors, unconcealed persons should not approach within one-half mile of them.

Condors which are flushed in treeless areas may land about half a mile away, but often they take off again within a few minutes. Those flushed from food late in the afternoon usually depart toward the roosts so that all are out of sight within 10 or 15 minutes. If flushed from food in the morning, they generally circle and rise and head for another feeding area. Ian McMillan told me that 14 condors were flushed from the same carcass twice in one day on Cholame Ranch in summer. The first time they were flushed by a man on horseback so that they probably were not strongly alarmed. Pemberton (MS) flushed 14 condors from the bait near his blind one morning when he entered the blind, but 11 condors landed there again a few hours later. The following day 19 condors landed at the same place. In both instances the birds were apparently disturbed so that they departed before they commenced to feed.

When food is plentiful, there is a tendency for condors to avoid a carcass from which they have been flushed. A few times I flushed a group of condors from the carcass of a calf before they had consumed much of it and then I moved the calf several yards to another location. The condors did not return to the carcass during the next one or two days, although once they ate at the carcass later. Within three days after Dyer (1935) flushed seven condors from a horse, none returned to the carcass, although condors flew over the area each day.

Condors do not avoid man-made structures if people are not in evidence. Once several condors fed within 500 yards of the house at Hopper Ranch. I saw three condors feeding half a mile from a large house and barn in open country. Joseph Keyes used an old wooden cabin as a blind and photographed feeding condors at close range. The birds paid no apparent attention to a tent which I set up near a pool where they drank.

Many persons have attempted to photograph condors by placing carcasses out in areas where they forage. Pemberton attempted baiting more than 30 times before he was successful in photographing the feeding of a group. Many of the failures in baiting attempts were caused by slight disturbances of the birds, but most failures were due to the fact that the condors found more desirable food elsewhere. Pemberton did nothing to disturb 30 condors which fed on his bait, but the next day none even flew over a carcass at the same spot although at least 15 condors were seen at a distance. Many times observers have given up waiting after one or two days and condors have devoured the bait subsequently. On the other hand, many baits which I placed out in areas where condors foraged every day were not eaten by condors within a week or more. Often not even turkey vultures or ravens took the bait. It is impossible to predict accurately and consistently that condors will eat a certain carcass on a certain day, regardless of how choice the bait and how elaborate the preparations. This is one of the reasons why putting out carcasses near condor roosts is not a practical conservation measure.

Food Supply

Pleistocene time.—To supply food for condors there must be an abundance of suitable animals at accessible locations and there must be active agencies for killing these animals. As remains of *Gymnogyps* are abundant in the Pleistocene deposits at Rancho La Brea, the food supply at that locality and time must have been good. Doubtless condors fed on mammals which had become trapped in the asphalt and had died there. In a census of the mammals represented in one collection of bones from Rancho La Brea, Stock (1929) found that the trapped mammals were 91 per cent carnivores and 9 per cent herbivores. The dire wolf (*Canis dirus*) and the sabre tooth cat (*Smilodon*) made up 90 per cent of the carnivores. A bison (*Bison*) was twice as numerous as the next most common herbivore, a horse (*Equus*). If then, as now, condors usually fed on large herbivores, the bison may have been the principal item of food. Large carnivores, such as the dire wolf, sabre tooth cat, and American lion, may have been the chief agencies which killed the herbivores. Today the carnivores are less formidable and the ungulates are smaller.

Early historical time.—With the decline of the large Pleistocene mammals, part of the population of condors may have shifted their foraging area to the seashore. Remains of condors have been found in ancient shell mounds near the coast at two localities. In 1806, Lewis and Clark (1905, 4:81) said of the condor: "We have seen it feeding on the remains of a whale and other fish which have been thrown up by the waves on the sea coast. These I believe constitute their principal food. . . ." Cooper (1870:497) wrote that condors were "said . . . to feed on dead seals and whale meat." Taylor (1859c:19) mentions seeing condors feeding on the carcass of a whale on the seashore near Monterey. Cooper (1871:757) relates that, in 1861, many whales were killed at Monterey and that the carcasses washed ashore.

It is not surprising that California condors would feed on the coast, for the South American condor does so today. Recently (1951), in the course of a day's drive along the coastal highway of Perú, I saw more than a dozen of the latter birds foraging over the ocean shore in areas where dead sea birds and the bones of whales were common. Probably the food supply along the Pacific coast shore has long since become inadequate for condors. However, the seacoast of California still furnishes a good living for many turkey vultures.

No evidence has been discovered which suggests that condors were driven from Oregon or northwestern California by a shortage of food there. It is probable that some factor other than lack of food caused them to disappear from these areas. In every other region from which condors have disappeared there has been a diminution in the amount of food available to condors. This scarcity of food, in combination with the existence of better food conditions at other localities, probably caused movements of the population to the more favorable regions.

Before the extensive introduction of livestock into California, condors in the interior must have subsisted on the carcasses of big game animals. The fact that condors are best adapted to feeding on large carcasses in open foothills suggests that they may have fed on antelope (*Antilocapra americana*) and to a lesser extent on dwarf elk (*Cervus nannodes*). Bison did not range into areas inhabited by condors within historical times. Antelope and elk were numerous and widespread in the Sacramento and San Joaquin valleys in the early 1800's. In 1855, when a few condors were still present in the Sacramento Valley, Newberry (1857:66, 71) found that antelope had become rare. By 1870 the large herds of elk and antelope were gone (McAllister, 1923:49; A. K. Fisher, 1920:35). The disappearance of condors from the Sacramento Valley occurred at about the time of the rapid depletion of the elk and antelope but was not necessarily caused by this change.

Mission era.—Cattle, sheep, and horses were introduced into California long before the native game had commenced to dwindle. From 1769 to 1820, twenty-one missions were established in California between San Diego and Sonoma (Cronise, 1868:17, 18). With few exceptions, the missions were within the range of the condor. Each mission owned large herds of livestock. About 1825, the approximate number of animals owned by some of the missions was as shown in the following table (*ibid.*:16).

Mission	Cattle	Sheep	Horses and Mules
San Francisco	76,000	79,000	3,800
San José	62,000	62,000	2,300
San Carlos	87,000	7,500	1,800
San Antonio	52,000	48,000	5,400
San Miguel	91,000	47,000	6,100
San Luis Obispo	87,000	72,000	9,200

The other missions owned similar herds. According to R. F. Miller (1942:5), in 1825 there were in California more than one million sheep at the missions and about as many more kept by ranchers. The largest cattle ranches in the condor range today have about one-tenth as many cattle as one of the former missions.

The number of carcasses available to condors must have been greatly increased when the cattle were slaughtered for their hides and tallow only. According to Cronise (1868:61), the annual export of hides and tallow from California increased from a single cargo each year in 1822 to 30,000 hides and 700 tons of tallow in 1832. The threat of the Mexican government to secularize the missions caused the slaughter of about 100,000 cattle in 1834 (*ibid.*:61). This was the year that the last specimen of the condor was taken on the Columbia River. If condors had previously migrated northward in search of food, they no longer had to do so.

That carcasses of domestic stock furnished much food for condors in the nineteenth century is corroborated by several authors. Grayson, in writing of the condor between 1846 and 1857, said that it approached "in large flocks the near vicinity of the Missions, where it contended with the coyote for the offal and carcasses of cattle slaughtered for their hides and tallow" (Bryant, 1891:52). Cooper (1870:497) stated that the condor was "most abundant in the hot interior valleys . . . where the large herds of cattle furnish abundance of food. . . ." Evermann (1886: 607, 608) provides a picture of conditions in southern Ventura County in 1881: "One of the great industries . . . is wool growing; the valleys and hillsides are covered with flocks of sheep, from a score to several thousand in number; and nearly every cañon has its corral. . . . In and about these corrals are . . . carcasses of sheep that have died of disease or starvation, bodies of dead lambs and the refuse of the sheep which the herder has slaughtered. . . ." In visiting such a canyon near Santa Paula, Evermann flushed a condor from the carcass of a pig.

Land grants period.—Commencing in 1775, the Spanish government made large grants of land to soldiers, and the succeeding Mexican government continued this practice (Cronise, 1868:19). These grants were recognized by the United States after it took control of California in 1846, so that many of the old grants persisted as huge cattle and sheep ranches. Of cattle raising conditions in California in 1868, Cronise (*op. cit.*:370, 371) wrote: "In no country are cattle raised at so trifling cost. They get no shelter and no feed except the wild pasture of the mountain ranges. As the Spanish grants, seldom less than four thousand acres, and often twenty thousand or more, are being subdivided, the wild ranges grow shorter; and as farmers become numerous they will be able to obtain legislation compelling the herdsmen to keep their stock from trespassing. This restriction is working notable changes and increasing the cost of cattle raising. . . ." Of Santa Barbara County, Cronise (p. 113) said: "As recently as 1864, thousands of cattle were slaughtered for their hides and tallow, but they have increased in value two hundred per cent since then, owing to the increased cultivation of land in other counties." The basic cause of the change from stock raising to farming in areas away from the ocean or large rivers was the advent of rail transportation which allowed farm products to be moved to market.

In 1868, most of the land in the stock raising counties in southern California was still in great Spanish and Mexican ranchos. These counties, except Los Angeles County, were sparsely populated. The land grants had already become subdivided in the central coast counties (Santa Cruz, Santa Clara, San Mateo, Marin, Napa), and the chief industries there were dairying and the raising of fruit. It is not surprising that condors were common in the southern counties and rare in the central coast counties.

The era of the huge ranchos operating with a minimum of cost and labor and utilizing much land ended, for the most part, about 1900. The trend is exemplified by the sequence of events in southern Ventura County. According to Herbert Guthrie of Somis, resident of that region since 1870, the original De La Guerra grant extended from Simi to the ocean and was entirely in livestock. This ranch was succeeded by the Las Posas (about 1882 to 1895) which had 60,000 sheep. Then the ranch was subdivided and the better lands were used for the growing of grain, then beans, then orchards. In some other areas, the shift has been made only from the raising of cattle and sheep to the raising of grain.

Sheep raising.—Bancroft (1890:53) states that by 1862 there were over 2,000,000 cattle in California, but the droughts of 1862 to 1864 greatly reduced the number of cattle and caused increased emphasis on the raising of sheep. The peak of the sheep industry occurred in 1876 when California was credited with over six million head (R. F. Miller, 1942:6). The accompanying table indicates the numbers of cattle (not including work oxen and dairy cows) and sheep in California, and in the major counties where condors ranged, as shown by the censuses of 1880 (U. S. Dept. Interior, 1883) and 1940 (U. S. Dept. Commerce, 1942). This table shows that there has been a great reduction in the numbers of sheep, and in the proportion of sheep to cattle, in the condor counties. Most of this change occurred before 1910 when the sheep industry reached a low point (R. F. Miller, *op. cit.*:8). Thereafter, little change in total numbers of sheep in California occurred, but in Kern, Los Angeles, and Santa Barbara counties there was a sharp decrease in the 1930's. Even during World War II when sheep production for the state increased about one-third, there was a decrease in several of the counties within the range of the condor.

Comparative Numbers of Cattle and Sheep in 1880 and 1940

	Cattle		Sheep	
	1880	1940	1880	1940
California	451,941	2,056,234	4,152,349	1,707,422
Kern Co.	32,989	92,899	152,041	28,438
Los Angeles Co.	7,061	24,324	330,350	12,939
Monterey Co.	19,149	72,503	126,644	9,381
San Diego Co.	10,124	44,924	148,252	3,805
San Luis Obispo Co.	22,677	66,389	143,107	11,292
Santa Barbara Co.	5,528	50,116	132,923	5,685
Tulare Co.	7,090	103,121	127,176	21,959
Ventura Co.	2,490	20,476	114,013	9,400

In Cuyama Valley, where Pemberton observed condors feeding on sheep in 1936, 1937, and 1938, there have been no sheep since 1938. Carl Twisselman of Temblor Ranch told me that he and several ranchers on the Carrizo Plains had shifted from the production of sheep to the production of cattle during the war.

The raising of cattle instead of sheep has diminished the supply of food for condors. According to figures given by Bancroft (1890:55, 56, 60) for 1880,

four or five sheep could be grazed on the same acreage as one cow, and the annual mortality for sheep was about 10 per cent contrasted with 5 per cent for cattle. Thus, on the same range, sheep furnish eight or ten times as many carcasses as cattle. In addition, sheep provide food for condors in areas where cattle cannot subsist because of the poor forage and scarcity of water. There are often more than 1000 sheep in a flock. Wherever I encountered large flocks of sheep, I found carcasses. In a barren area north of Bakersfield where condors were feeding, I found nine carcasses of sheep within a few hours.

Increased horticulture.—Grinnell (*in* Hornaday, 1913:23) suggests that the forage range of condors has become restricted by the development of agriculture in the valleys. Figures given in the census of 1935 (U. S. Dept. Commerce, 1937) for the proportion of the area of California in farms are as follows: 1850, 3.9 per cent; 1860, 8.7 per cent; 1870, 11.5 per cent; 1880, 16.6 per cent; 1890, 21.5 per cent; 1900, 28.9 per cent. There has been little increase since 1900. The area surrounding Santa Barbara was a sheep range in the 1880's and a cattle range in 1900. Condors nested nearby. Today the area is mainly covered with citrus orchards and condors are rare. Stock was formerly raised in many of the areas now covered by Los Angeles and its surrounding cities and orchards.

This trend of reduction of the forage range of condors has been offset, to some extent, by the fact that the increase in the value of farming land and livestock has caused the utilization for grazing of areas which would otherwise have no stock. Between 1941 and 1946, the growing of cotton and potatoes supplanted grazing in many parts of the southern San Joaquin Valley. Most of this development was too far from the foothills to cause any reduction of the feeding area of condors. During the war there was a great increase in the acreage of wheat on the Carrizo Plains and on the plains northeast of Bakersfield, but these areas are not entirely lost to condors for livestock is permitted to graze on the stubble. The pastures of the foothills of the condor range may never be cultivated because of lack of water and the steepness of the slopes. Undoubtedly changes in land use have caused changes in the range of condors, but it is doubtful that the amount of suitable forage area has ever been critical for the existence of the species.

Ranching methods.—Ranchers and old-timers in

many areas where condors forage, or used to forage, told me that cattle are no less abundant today than 40 or 50 years ago. This is true of the area where condors formerly occurred in San Diego County. The principal difference between the old days and the present is that now the ranches are smaller and the cattle are better cared for. In the old days, when cattle were sold by the head rather than by the pound, lean cattle and overgrazed lands were the rule. Old style methods are still used at a few ranches, such as the Cholame Ranch in southeastern Monterey County. On that ranch in summer, I saw many lean cattle and horses on badly overgrazed land and I seldom failed to find at least one fresh carcass. The arrival of condors at Cholame Ranch in 1945, 1946, and 1947 followed closely the time of marking and branding the cattle. I saw condors feeding on two steers which had evidently died of castration injuries. Such losses are avoided by modern practices. The Tejon and San Emigdio ranches operated in the old manner not many years ago but under modern management they have become efficient.

The old methods of ranching produced much more food for condors than modern methods. Now, the carcasses of cattle are generally burned or buried. On Tejon Ranch I have seen the carcasses of as many as four anthrax-killed cattle being burned at the same time. Within a few weeks in 1948, Eben McMillan burned four carcasses on Carrizo Plains. One of these had been fed upon by a group of condors. The vaccination of calves for blackleg is now routine. Ailing cattle are brought in from the range and treated rather than being left to die. Bancroft (1890:56) tells of 10,000 cattle which died of disease in Kern County in 1879. Today, outbreaks of disease seldom kill more than a hundred head. This trend of reduction in the number of carcasses available to condors will continue.

Droughts.—Droughts have had a great influence on the production of livestock and of food for condors in California. Cronise (1868:371) states that in 1856, 70,000 head of cattle were lost in Los Angeles County because of drought. Eugene Percy told me that his grandfather had 10,000 sheep in southern Ventura County in the 1870's and that only 300 survived the drought of 1877. In interviewing ranchers from San Diego County to Tulare County and northern Monterey County, I heard again and again of the drastic effects on livestock of the drought of 1877. In that year, 2,500,000 sheep were said to have been lost in California (Bancroft, *op. cit.*:60). As this drought occurred at about the time that many condors were supposed to have been killed off by the poisoning of carcasses, perhaps the drought rather than the poison was responsible for any sudden decrease in the population. Stephens (1895:82) tells of a drought which destroyed much stock in the Tejon area in 1894. At that time he saw a flock of 26 condors. Although droughts brought with them an excess of food for condors, there was a scarcity of food for several years afterward because, in those days, the herds had to be reestablished by increase of the remaining stock. These sudden changes in the food supply must have caused marked distributional shifts in the condor population.

Today droughts do not cause such far-reaching effects as in the past. Food can be brought in for cattle. If drought persists, the cattle can be shipped to other areas and brought back when the drought has ended. This is exactly what happened in the winter and spring of 1948 on the Cholame Ranch, Pinole Ranch, and several other large ranches in the condor range, although many ranches had to sell most of their cattle. Cattle were few at Cholame Ranch in the summer of 1948 and condors were not seen in that area for the first summer in three years. Modern stock raising methods benefit condors in that the effects of droughts are not so drastic or so prolonged as in the old days.

The disappearance of condors from the Sierra San Pedro Mártir is not difficult to explain in terms of drought and shortage of food. The high meadows were used for grazing when condors were not uncommon there in 1905 and earlier. Deer were fairly abundant when Salve Melling commenced to run cattle in these meadows in 1908, but by 1925 the deer had been reduced to a half or third of their former number (S. Melling, *fide* Grinnell, MS). Droughts caused a reduction in the number of cattle on this summer range. The year 1925 was the third dry year in succession and the land was badly overgrazed (Grinnell, MS). When Carroll Scott (MS) visited these mountains in 1935, he was told that there had been a succession of droughts for 10 years and that formerly there were three or four times as many cattle in that area.

Present supply of cattle.—At the present time the distribution of cattle changes with the season. On large ranches cattle remain in the lowlands in winter and move up into the hills as the grass in the lowlands dries up. Many mountain pastures are used only in summer. One of these pastures is the group of "potreros" on the ridge between Sisquoc Canyon and the Cuyama Valley. These potreros are well situated for the foraging of condors. In the mountainous ranches of central Ventura County, cattle are present all year. Seasonal changes in the forage range of condors may be correlated, in part, with changes in the location of the herds of cattle.

Where cattle stay in the mountains all year, the mortality is highest in winter during the season of calving (December to March). Eugene Percy of Hopper Ranch estimates that the average annual loss among his herd of 200 cattle is about eight. In the winter of 1943-1944 there was much snow and Percy lost about 70 head. Many of the carcasses were eaten by condors.

Perhaps the most consistent cause of death of cattle on the range today is anthrax. I was told by Carl Twisselman of Temblor Ranch that 78 cattle died of anthrax in Bitterwater Valley in the summer of 1942. In the summer of 1940, screw worms killed many cattle in the condor range. On Tejon Ranch many cattle died of hemorrhagic septicemia in the winter of 1936-37, according to Perry Sprague. In the San Pedro Mártir when a few condors were still present (1925), many cattle died of blackleg (S. Melling, *fide* Grinnell, MS). In the spring of 1949 and 1950 many cattle from southern Monterey County to the Cuyama Valley were killed by larkspur poisoning.

Present supply of sheep.—Today the large flocks of sheep within the range of condors are more or less transient. The mortality among sheep is highest in the lambing season, from November to February. At this season most of the sheep are in the lowlands near alfalfa fields and are inaccessible to condors. A few of the lambing grounds east and north of Bakersfield may be accessible to condors in winter. Commencing in March or April when the grass has started to grow and the lambs are able to travel, the sheep are moved into the foothills and from there into the mountains and even to the Mohave Desert. Some of the areas where condors find sheep in late spring or in summer are: Antelope Valley, Cummings Valley, Tehachapi, Temblor Range, and Carrizo Plains. In fall the sheep are brought back to the lowlands.

There is much variation in the time and direction of movement of sheep from year to year depending on the availability of forage. It may be that the seasonal distribution of condors is partly determined by these movements of sheep. The dispersal of the large numbers of condors in Ventura County in spring commences at about the time that the sheep start up into the hills, and the gathering of condors in that region in winter commences at about the time that the sheep reach their lambing grounds. Before 1900, when sheep were numerous in southern Ventura County, the gathering of condors there in winter would be of obvious advantage to them.

Deer.—Condors obtain part of their food within the boundaries of the Los Padres National Forest. Cattle graze in this forest, but less than half of the area is suitable for grazing and condors seldom range over the best grazing areas (lower Sisquoc Canyon, Avenales Ranch, Lockwood Valley, and others). Deer are abundant in parts of this forest. I saw herds of as many as 60 deer in spring.

It is probable that each year many deer are killed by mountain lions and that some of the carcasses are fed on by condors. I found only one fresh lion kill but I saw a lion stalking deer in the Sespe Game Refuge, and I found the tracks of lions in several areas near condor roosts. In a single season, Charles Tant killed at least eight lions in this national forest, but the country is so rugged that it is doubtful that the lions will be eliminated. A lion kill probably furnishes more food for condors than a coyote kill. Lions generally take only one meal from the carcass of a deer and then depart, perhaps to return later (Grinnell, Dixon, and Linsdale, 1937:359), but coyotes generally remain near a carcass until it is consumed. Indeed, coyotes may consume lion kills (*ibid.*:521).

It has been suggested that condors may feed on deer which have been wounded by hunters and which die later. This is a possibility as there are thousands of deer hunters in the national forests within the forage range of condors in late summer. Most hunters believe that a wounded deer nearly always works down the slope. If this is true, wounded deer would probably die in the bottoms of canyons where they would be much more accessible to coyotes than to condors.

Ground squirrels.—Between May 4 and August 31, 1946, I saw condors feeding on poisoned ground squirrels at several localities between Bakersfield and Porterville. The largest number of condors that I saw foraging for squirrels was 14. In June, I flushed 10 condors which had been feeding on poisoned squirrels in Shale Hills, western Kern County. Everett Horn, Bufort Fox, and Finas Bradshaw each told me that in the spring of 1935 they had seen condors feeding on poisoned squirrels at a ranch several miles east of Delano. Joseph Keyes said that he had seen condors eating squirrels in the Bakersfield area many times since about 1926. The largest number of condors that Keyes had seen there was 17 (in 1945). Keyes, Fox, and Bradshaw said that condors and turkey vultures seemed to follow a few days behind the poisoning crew and, within limits, I found this to be true.

Near Bakersfield poisoning commences about the first of May, after the last rain, and proceeds from the lowlands to higher ground. The poisoned grain kills many rabbits as well as squirrels. This source of food is of considerable value to condors. There is a steady supply of squirrel carcasses beginning at about the same time each year and lasting about four months. Much of the poisoned area is barren and has no other food during this period. The poisoning near Bakersfield commences just after most of the sheep leave the area. The food is widespread so that condors do not tend to concentrate in one small part of their range. It may be the poisoning of squirrels which has been responsible for the northward extension of the condor range since the 1920's.

Trapped carnivores.—I have heard several reports of condors feeding on coyotes, bobcats, lions, and other carnivores which had been trapped, and I saw evidence of feeding by condors on two carcasses which had been removed from traps. As there are many state, federal, and county trappers working within the forage range of condors, the number of animals trapped is great, but most of the carcasses are discarded in areas which are unsuitable for condors.

Summary.—In the Pleistocene the abundance of large carnivores and ungulates provided many carcasses for condors. With the decline of these mammals, condors were forced to feed on carcasses of sea animals near the coast and to feed on smaller native game in the interior. Commencing about 1820, large

herds of domestic stock near the missions produced an abundance of food for condors. The mission era was followed by the era of huge ranchos on which stock was raised with little care so that there were many carcasses. Repeated droughts in the 1860's and 1870's hindered cattle raising and encouraged the raising of sheep so that there were vast herds of sheep and consequently there was much food for condors.

With the development of railroads in California, many areas formerly used for grazing were cultivated, land prices rose, and the ranchos became subdivided. As some foraging areas became unfavorable, the condors moved to other areas. The increased value of cattle led to modern methods which greatly reduced the number of animals dying on the range and caused a curtailment of sheep raising. These trends reduced the amount of food for condors so that the birds were forced to feed on the carcasses of squirrels provided by poisoning operations in order to supplement their diet of domestic stock.

As the changes in the supply of food have been gradual, and as the former numbers and distribution of condors are poorly known, it is not possible to prove that specific changes in the food supply caused specific changes in the numbers and distribution of condors. However, I believe that with the exception of the killing and molesting of condors by man, the change in the supply of food has been the most important factor determining the distribution and numbers of condors within the last century.

It is not improbable that scarcity of food has been a factor limiting the condor population at times in the past. It must be remembered that it is not the day to day supply of food which might act as a limiting factor, but it is the minimum supply which occurs at the most unfavorable period of a cycle of many years. The reproductive rate is so low and the number of condors so few that a week of food scarcity could cause a permanent reduction in the population.

There is little which can be done effectively to increase the number of carcasses in the range of condors. Efforts to increase the food supply should be directed toward facilitating the utilization of available carcasses.

Drinking and Bathing

Watering places.—In the Sespe region, a favorite water hole for condors is located on top of the cliff above the big cave in Hopper Canyon (plate 14). When full, this pool is about 20 feet long and 10 feet wide. The bottom of the pool and the adjacent banks are mainly of sand. During the season of greatest use of this water, the sand is covered with the footprints of condors for 60 feet back from the foot of the pool. I found a few tracks as far as 120 feet upstream. Most of the pool is not over three inches deep. The maximum depth is about 10 inches. The water is always clear but often it is not running. The high open location of this water hole allows condors to land and to take off easily. On the cliff below the pool there are many ledges, points, and potholes which are used as perches or roosts by condors.

This pool usually contains water from early January to the middle of May, depending on the time of rainfall. In 1941 there was still some water on June 7. In the dry year of 1946 there was no water in the pool on March 12, but the pool was full and running one month later. As this water hole dries up, condors commence to use a group of pools 600 yards down the canyon and a few hundred feet lower in elevation. On some days in late spring both watering places are used.

The lower watering place consists of three main pools at different levels in a cascade 50 yards long and 30 feet high (plate 15). Each pool is situated near the edge of a sharp drop in the bed of the creek so that condors can take off down the canyon without difficulty. Adjacent to the water there are flat open areas of sandstone, and there are many points on the rocks where condors perch in approaching or leaving the pools. As compared with the water hole above the big cave, the lower pools are more difficult of access for condors because the slopes and chaparral are close to the bed of the creek.

In size, the three main pools are from about 5 feet by 9 feet to 10 feet by 10 feet when they are full. The maximum depth of the water is about 2 feet, but in the parts which the condors use, the water is only an inch or two, or at the most 6 inches, in depth. Apparently because the lower two pools have more extensive sandy-bottomed shallow areas than the top

one, these lower pools are the favorites of the condors although the top pool is the most accessible to them. The water is always clear but is not running in summer. At that time, the pools are partly filled with green algae and they contain many water bugs and a few snakes (*Thamnophis*). All year there is some water accessible to condors at this place.

In August, 1940, while condors were still frequenting the watering place just described, I occasionally saw a few condors standing about half a mile from it near three potholes which were situated on a gentle sandstone slope. Upon investigation, I found that one of the holes was half-filled with sand which formed an incline down to a bowl-shaped depression two feet in diameter. This depression held clear water, but the condors must have had to reach down at least six inches over the vertical sides of the hole in order to drink. The sand around the water was covered with condor tracks.

Three times in October, 1939, one of the pair of adults at nest 1 was seen to land at a pothole 100 yards from the nest in an area of bare sandstone. The hole contained murky water eight inches deep and an incline of sand entered the water at one end. Five days after the last time that a condor was seen there, the pool was dry.

Although condors are not particular in their requirements for a drinking place when they are pressed for water, clear pools at the tops of waterfalls are preferred. In spring I saw two condors at the top of a high, intermittent waterfall in Sespe Canyon. In December, 1939, I saw two adult condors drink in clear running water at the top of a fall 70 feet high in Santa Paula Canyon. In that canyon there are at least three falls which seem to be suitable as drinking places for condors and the water runs all year. Sidney Peyton and others told me that in 1917 they saw condors drinking in a pool at the top of a waterfall in Coldwater Canyon, a tributary of lower Sespe Canyon. That fall runs all year and is favorably situated for drinking.

In Santa Barbara County the best known watering place for condors is a pool near the brink of Sisquoc Falls. In July of 1937 Pemberton saw as many as seven condors at once near that pool, but in several days of watching in July of 1939 and 1940, I saw a maximum of three condors a day visit that water. For six feet back from the brink of the falls the stream is about one foot wide and an inch deep. Then the stream widens into a circular pool 10 feet long. The pool is about two feet deep at the center but much of the marginal area is less than four inches in depth. I found the pool to be free of sand but, according to C. S. Robinson, there was a sandy beach there in 1936. As three sides of the pool are obstructed by slopes, trees, and chaparral, condors can fly to the water hole only from the falls side. However, condors perch and walk about on a clear area which extends several yards on each side of the lower part of the pool. There are many perching places on the cliffs nearby. The water is clear and cool, and the stream runs well all year.

The only other place that I saw condors drink was on Cholame Ranch. In June, 1946, six condors, after feeding on a carcass, drank in the overflow of a cattle watering trough on flat ground. There was a muddy area 50 yards long and the only water was that in the cattle tracks. In that dry region it is probable that condors drink at water troughs. Near Castle Mountain, Don and Alta McMillan saw 16 condors perched around a water trough one morning in August, 1945. Some of the birds were perched on the trough itself. Carl Twisselman found a dead condor near a water trough on the Temblor Ranch. Ernest Still found a dead condor in a water tank near Annette. The region near Castle Mountain, the Temblor Range, and the Carrizo Plains seems to have less water available to condors than any other area where they forage. Nevertheless, in that region condors occur most frequently in summer. In the tributaries at the head of the San Juan River there are several open perennial pools which appear to be accessible to the condors which roost near McChesney Mountain.

In the foothills of the east side of the San Joaquin Valley I did not see condors drink, but in summer I flushed many condors from a carcass which lay in the water of Cottonwood Creek. Water was running in Little Creek at the time that I saw condors feeding in that vicinity. Near Fountain Springs I saw several condors descend in the vicinity of a water trough in the late afternoon. The Kern and Tule rivers and several creeks run through the open foothills in this part of the forage range of condors.

To summarize, condors prefer to drink clean water at the tops of waterfalls in the vicinity of their roosts, but when necessary they will drink from stagnant pools in potholes, from water troughs, or from cattle tracks. The supply of water is apparently most critical for condors in the region of the Temblor Range, but there is no indication that the presence or absence of water controls the distribution of condors in that area.

Activity at water holes.—At Hopper Canyon the number of condors which visits the water holes is greatest in the morning before the birds depart to forage and in the afternoon shortly after they return from foraging. On the average, neither morning nor afternoon seems to be favored, although on some days the activity is confined to one period or the other. Even in hot weather in summer, many individuals do not drink before departing from the roosting area and many do not drink after returning in the afternoon. When a half dozen or more condors were present in Hopper Canyon, I rarely could account for more than half of the number at the watering places at any one time. On some days in summer, when several condors were in the area, I discovered no activity at all near the usual water holes. The schedule of drinking is irregular even when the weather is fairly uniform. Incubating adults can go without drinking for two days. These facts suggest that condors need not go to water more than once a day, even in summer. The time of drinking depends on the thirst of the bird and the availability of water.

Spallanzani (1784:173) found that a pet eagle could go for several months without water, but when it had water, it drank. Possibly condors have physiological adaptations which enable them to get enough water from fresh meat and metabolic water to satisfy their minimum requirements.

Condors tend to drink shortly after feeding. On a warm dry day in June I saw six condors, all that were present, go to a water hole two hours after commencing to feed on a carcass. From one to four condors were near the water for two hours. Some fed again but did not return to the water before departing for the roost. One afternoon in June I saw 20 condors feeding on a calf. Before the last few left the carcass, at least eight of the group were at a water hole two miles away. There were at least eight condors near the water for almost two hours. Condors returning from foraging frequently make their initial landing

Plate 12. The hide and leg bones of a calf which six Condors consumed. The axial skeleton lies in the background. Photograph taken 8 miles east of Famoso, Kern County, May 31, 1946.

Plate 13. Remains of two ground squirrels on which Condors fed in Kern County on May 12, 1946.

Plate 14. A favorite bathing pool in Hopper Canyon in spring. This pool, about 20 feet long, is above the big cave shown in plate 7. The outlet is at the left. The wet sand around the pool is covered with the tracks of Condors.

Plate 15. Pools in Hopper Canyon used in summer. Three pools at different levels are shown.

near a water hole.

Most of my observations of drinking and bathing were made in Hopper Canyon in March and April. In those months I saw condors drink as early as 6:35 a.m. and as late as 5:45 p.m. In these extreme instances the temperatures were 43°F. and 48°F. Cool weather did not prevent drinking. Several times I saw both adults and immatures drink when the sky was heavily overcast. One morning in summer I saw three birds go to a pool at 8:50 a.m. although that area had been covered by fog until 8 a.m. The humidity must have been high. I observed drinking in every month of the year.

There is no more hesitation in landing near water than at any other perch. On some occasions I saw a condor land, drink, and take off again within four minutes. Drinking is a short process. A few times I saw one condor drink, walk away from the pool, and return to drink again five or ten minutes later. Occasionally I saw a bird drink at one spot, move to another part of the pool, and drink again.

In drinking, a condor stands at the edge of a pool or wades into the water a few steps, then places its bill to the surface of the water, nibbles about three times, raises its head quickly, and nibbles a few more times as it looks about. Usually the dipping movement is accomplished in 1½ to 3 seconds and the periods of looking about are from 3 to 10 seconds in length. The dip may be repeated as many as 10 successive times at one spot although two or three sips often seem to satisfy the bird.

Drinking is normally in water from one to three inches deep. At Sisquoc Falls the foot of the pool is preferred for drinking and condors frequently drink where the water is running out briskly. The foot of the pool has the advantage of being close to the brink of the cliff. After drinking, condors may bathe or may perch near the pool with other condors rather than depart immediately.

At water, as elsewhere, one condor often gives way to another. Occasionally one approaches another which is drinking; the second backs away and then goes to another part of the pool and drinks.

The bathing of condors is more frequent and thorough in the afternoon than in the morning. Probably this is because the feathers become soiled and disarranged in feeding. I did not observe bathing earlier in the year than March or when the tempera-

ture was below 50°F. Condors may bathe vigorously on overcast days and on days of dry winds. The latest bath that I witnessed was at 5:10 p.m., in April. I saw no thorough bathing before 9 a.m. although I saw immatures wading as early as 6:30 a.m. Condors bathe in water from one-half inch to about six inches in depth.

Bathing varies in method and thoroughness. Often the bird merely bows forward and twists its body so that the side of the ruff or breast is dipped in the water. This action may occur in very shallow water. Frequently the neck is given a sidewise flirt as the side of the ruff is dipped. The entire action is usually repeated about three times, at least once on each side, before the condor leaves the pool. At other times, the breast is dipped or rolled from side to side in the water. At the same time the anterior edge of the wings may be dipped or the partly extended wings may be sloshed up and down in the water from two to five times.

In one frequent type of bath the condor walks into the water to the depth of its heels, then crouches with its wings partly extended and places the side of its extended neck on the water. Then the neck is swept sidewise and brought sharply upward, throwing water onto the back and the wings. This action is repeated three or four times in succession. Occasionally the condor lowers its breast into the water and then moves its wings up and down alternately as in shaking. Sometimes one dips its head in and out of the water quickly and thus throws water onto its back.

An entire bath, including walking into the pool and out again, may be accomplished in five or ten seconds. Once I saw an immature stand in a pool for four minutes, occasionally dipping its breast in the water. A condor may repeat the bath several times at intervals of a minute or two, standing several feet from the pool between baths. When this occurs, the bird usually bathes with increasing vigor and in increasingly deeper water at each return to the pool. In one observation, an adult returned to the pool eight times in 18 minutes. The initial baths lasted about 15 seconds, the final baths about 30 seconds. At first only the breast was dipped. Later the wings were sloshed in the water. On the last two trips the condor walked an additional 10 steps upstream in the water, soused its body to the level of its back, flapped its wings in the water, and splashed water several feet into the air.

Normally immatures do not bathe as vigorously as adults.

In entering a pool for a bath a condor usually walks slowly, as if searching for a suitable spot. It may drink or pick up an object from under water. I saw one immature bird keep its head under water for one and one-half seconds. Upon completing a bath a condor usually runs out of the pool with its wings up. It may fly out of the pool and perch close by. Occasionally one fans its wings or shakes before leaving the water. In walking from the pool after taking a bath, one adult put its breast to the ground and gave its neck a twist, hardly hesitating in its forward motion to do so. This action was repeated after four successive baths so that there was a conspicuous amount of wet sand in the ruff. Usually, upon leaving a pool, a condor perches near the edge of a cliff as if to be ready for a quick departure.

The shortness of the time of bathing, the quick departure from the pool, and perching at an advantageous point between baths are probably part of the innate caution of condors which prevents them from being caught at a disadvantage in the water. On occasions I saw a soaking wet condor chased into the air by another. The wet bird seemed to fly well enough but it perched quickly when the pursuit ceased.

Within a few seconds after completing a bath, condors usually shake themselves, fan their wings, and shake their heads. These actions may be repeated several times. After bathing they sun and preen for long periods while perched in the vicinity of the pool. One evening I saw eight drying themselves at the same time.

The vicinity of water holes in the roosting area is a gathering place for immature condors. In Hopper Canyon I saw as many as 12 immatures perched near the pool above the big cave when at least 26 condors were present. Several times I saw from four to six immatures in the water at the same time. Of seven condors Pemberton (MS) saw at the water hole at Sisquoc Falls, six were immatures. Immature condors generally arrive at the water holes earlier in the day than adults and leave later than adults. The extreme times of drinking are greater for immatures than for adults. The immatures wade a great deal but I do not believe that they actually drink or bathe any more frequently than adults. Finley (1910:8) relates that his pet juvenal condor seemed to be fond of wading and bathing. Holmes (1897:58) reports a similar trait in another captive juvenile.

Only a few sites are well suited for the drinking and bathing of condors. In addition, the birds are very cautious when performing these actions. Therefore, the protection of frequented watering places from disturbance is highly essential to the welfare of condors.

Mating

On more than 30 occasions I observed sexual display in condors. The earliest observation was made on October 1 (1940) and the latest on April 13 (1946). In each month from October to February the action was seen but once or twice (December). Most (22) of the observations were made in the Sespe region in March. This is the month when most eggs are laid.

The mating actions of a pair of captive South American condors (*Vultur gryphus*) have been described to me by Mrs. Belle J. Benchley and Ken Stott, Jr., of the Zoological Society of San Diego. These condors usually commence to display about one month before the egg is laid. The display of *Vultur* is similar to that of *Gymnogyps* except that in the former both sexes are said to display in a similar manner, while in the latter only one member of a pair, presumably the male, displays actively. A unilateral display may be of benefit to *Gymnogyps* in sex recognition because the sexes look alike. In *Vultur* the male has a distinctive comb.

Stott (letter, September 20, 1949) says that a captive pair of king vultures displayed in a manner similar to that of *Vultur,* both sexes participating actively. Audubon (1834:51) gives a brief account of the courtship of the black vulture. The male opens its wings and lowers its head as it approaches the female, and it repeats this action several times. Audubon's account indicates that the display of *Coragyps* is similar to that of *Gymnogyps*. The display of the turkey vulture has apparently not been described in the literature.

At the start of the courting action the California condor faces its partner, which is usually from three to six feet distant but may be as far as 15 feet away. In the display attitude the "male" holds its wings out to the sides with the primaries hanging approximately vertically. On occasions the distal primaries are held out at an angle of about 45 degrees. In *Vultur* the distal primaries are usually held horizontally, according to Stott. *Gymnogyps* holds these primaries horizontally in sunning. In the display attitude the tail is unexpanded and the tip of the tail drags as the bird moves about. In sunning the tail is expanded. In display the naked neck is bent forward and downward so that the top of the head and the back of the neck are presented toward the display partner. The body is inclined somewhat forward and is not erect as it is in sunning.

Several features of the display attitude were not clearly seen, for the observations were made at long distances. The bill seemed to be held close to the posterior end of the ventral cervical apterium. Possibly this apterium and the neck are inflated and the displaying bird hisses. According to Stott, during the display of *Vultur* the bird inflates its neck, hisses, and makes a guttural clucking sound, and the red coloring of the head and neck becomes more intense.

The displaying *Gymnogyps* turns slowly from side to side about the vertical axis. Sometimes the swing is about 30 degrees to each side, frequently it is about 90 degrees, and occasionally the bird turns 180 degrees or even a complete circle. The swaying action is usually centered toward the display partner but it may be directed as much as 90 degrees off to one side. The displayer turns slowly with many short shuffling steps. A turn of 180 degrees was accomplished in five seconds. Frequently the "male" waddles toward the "female," then turns about and waddles directly away for several feet, then returns again. At other times the displayer walks back and forth in front of its partner. The attitude is seldom maintained more than 30 seconds, but the display may be repeated after a short interval. Once I saw an adult display three separate times within five minutes. In *Vultur* the displaying bird also walks back and forth and it may turn slowly in a circle.

Generally the "male" *Gymnogyps* crowds its partner back by walking into it while in the display attitude. On three occasions I saw the displayer put one foot on top of the lowered head of its partner as if about to mount, but mounting did not occur. In one instance this action was repeated several times, but the foot slipped off the head of the "female" each time.

The "female" usually seems to be unimpressed by the display and appears to be annoyed rather than submissive. When crowded, the "female" normally responds by pecking or nibbling at the back of the naked head and neck of the "male." Once I saw the pursued bird peck at the base of the throat and at the bend of the wing of the pursuer. Again, the "female" snapped at the displayer and the latter drew back. Once the partner was seen to put its head under the bend of the wing of the displayer. Stott told me that in *Vultur,* when the male pushes the female, she may peck at him or pass under one of his wings.

Often posturing ceases before the display partner is touched. The action may cease when the "female" pecks at the displayer, but usually the pursuit continues. For instance, on March 11, 1941, I saw the pursued bird turn around and walk away from the displaying one; the latter followed and crowded the "female" from the rear. The pursued bird occasionally turned to face the aggressor, but it was again pushed and it had to hop and flap in order to maintain its footing on the cliff. Finally the displayer forced its partner off the edge of the cliff; then it ceased posturing. Nearby, later that day, I saw a similar pursuit which ended when the heads of the pair became locked and the birds fell from a ledge.

The role of the "male" is generally that of the pursuer. Several times I saw it accompany or follow the "female," either walking, or flying, or in shifting from one perch to another, before or after the display ceremony. On December 31, 1939, I saw a pair alight on a hillside. One bird displayed three times. The two condors walked 100 feet up the slope together, occasionally stopping and seeming to rub their heads together. They took off, one a few yards behind the other, and soared away in company. Again, two adults flex-glided in a joint flight, matching turn for turn, seldom over a dozen feet apart, and alighted in a dead tree. The lower bird climbed to a higher branch where the other adult was perched and then it displayed briefly. The pair roosted together in the tree. These instances indicate that display may occur after the pair is formed. In fact, at one nest I saw display between a mated pair on October 1, 1940, while a chick was still in the nest.

Only once did I observe posturing by the same individual at successive perches. On April 9, 1946, within one-half mile of a nest which had been abandoned a few days earlier when the egg became broken, one adult landed in a pothole and another joined it. Then one soared to a second pothole and the other followed. Several times they seemed to rub their heads together. One displayed briefly. Both soared to a third cave where they stood for nearly one hour, their heads often together. One displayed, both disappeared into the hole, and several minutes later they soared away together. Not improbably the pair was seeking a site for a nest.

Another observation indicating that the pair selects the nesting site was made on March 17, 1941, close to a nesting cave which had been used in 1939. The pair was perched on a stub. One flew to a pothole and was followed by the other. A few minutes later one followed the other to another pothole and then followed it to a tree. Then one flew to the mouth of the old nest. The other landed near it. Several minutes later one took off and the other soon followed and circled with it. There was no display or contact between these birds.

With one exception, whenever display was observed, the "male" singled out a particular individual from a group as its partner or the pair was initially isolated from other condors. The exception occurred on March 15, 1941, when I saw two adults land a few yards from a third. The last displayed, walking toward the two and crowding them back. The displayer pursued one, then the other, until both of the pursued adults hopped to lower perches. In this instance the displayer apparently performed before two different birds. Once I saw an adult display before a subadult.

Courting may occur wherever condors are perched together. I saw the ceremony performed once on a sparsely stubbled hillside, several times on branches of conifers, and a few times in potholes or atop large boulders. Most frequently the action occurred atop a high cliff near a water hole and roosting ledges which many condors used in winter and spring. Display was never observed when there was the slightest disturbance.

With few exceptions the display was observed within one-half mile of a known nesting site and never farther than that from apparently suitable nesting cliffs. Many weeks were spent in watching adults at their nest sites but I saw display between a nesting pair only once (October 1). Evidently postnuptial display is rare in *Gymnogyps.*

Display may occur at any time of the day when condors are active. It was seen as early as 8:45 a.m. and as late as 5:05 p.m. Two condors may perch together for a long time before display occurs. On March 30, 1941, I saw two adults perched a few feet apart in the top of a tree at 4:30 p.m. Both were quiet until 5:18 p.m.; then one displayed and the other took off. No seasonal difference was noted in the manner of the display or in the reaction of the display partner. Perhaps the "male" was less persistent in the fall, for in the four observations which were made in the fall the display was not repeated.

The actively displaying bird is usually at a lower level than its partner. Never was it seen at a higher level. On three occasions in which the pair was in a tree, the partner was from one to five feet higher than the displayer. Twice I saw one display toward another which was perched a foot above it on a small boulder. The relative heights of the adults may have some significance in regard to dominance. In the courtship of night herons the "dominant" bird usually keeps its head higher than that of the "subordinate" one, and the subordinate bird normally initiates the ceremony (Noble, *et al.,* 1938). The male condor might establish his dominance over the female by means of display.

Usually the displaying condor and its partner do not seem to notice other condors which are perched nearby, and the bystanders do not seem to pay attention to the active pair. Other condors are not stimulated to display by the sight of a posturing one. Two quiet adults jostled by a courting pair did not retaliate. On another occasion, I saw the displayer approach its partner by walking around an intervening condor. The third condor, a subadult, snapped at the passing adult and then stood quietly a few feet from the active pair during the display. I saw an immature condor follow a pair, which flew in a joint flight, and then perch above them and watch the display.

According to Stott, at the zoo in San Diego the immature of a previous year pecked the displaying pair of South American condors. Its presence during the display period seemed to inhibit the successful mating of the adults in consecutive years. By removing the young before the time of mating, successful breeding in three successive years was brought about.

Many of the reactions occurring between the members of an active pair and other condors may be related to social dominance and not to sexual activity. On one occasion when five condors were perched near a pool, an adult alighted on the back of a displaying condor. The latter jumped forward suddenly but no further action ensued. Another time, when five adults

were standing side by side, one displayed, crowding another about and bumping into the perched birds. The pursued adult dashed at the three inactive birds and drove them into the air. Again, when three adults were perched together, one drove another into the air and then displayed to the remaining one. Once I saw the displayer drive a quiet bystander into the air, reaching after it with its bill, and then chase it vigorously in the air.

Chasing flights might be a part of courtship. By its missing feathers, I identified the pursuer in one aerial chase as an adult which I saw displaying earlier in the day. One member of a mated pair was seen to chase the other, but this occurred in August when a chick was in their nest. Chases were observed most frequently in winter and spring. However, at that season the largest numbers of birds were observed roosting in the same area so that opportunities for encounters were frequent. In the breeding season condors might be especially irritable and thus more apt to chase others.

On one occasion I saw an adult, not the display partner, pluck at the feathers in the anal region of a posturing condor. Later that day I saw one adult stalk another as if to display and then put its head under the tail of the pursued bird. The latter gave a jump and the aggressor was left with a pinch of down and a four-inch feather in its bill. Possibly pecking of the anal region is related to mating.

Only once did I observe an action which appeared to be copulation. At noon on February 12, 1946, an adult landed on the point of a cliff a quarter of a mile from the site of a nest used later that year. A second adult landed and the pair stood several feet apart for over an hour. Then one walked around the other, head down, one wing half raised, and sprang upon its back. The upper bird flapped as if to gain balance, then both stood with their wings folded for half a minute. The upper adult held its head low and flapped gently, then it hopped down onto the rock, took off, and perched nearby. The lower bird remained perched quietly. Half an hour later both soared away together. No display occurred on this occasion. About one month later an egg was laid near the site of this action. Possibly in *Gymnogyps* copulation is not immediately preceded by display. In the captive *Vultur,* Stott says that display precedes copulation, that copulation lasts for several minutes, and that afterward the male resumes its display while the female sits quietly.

Of the four types of display in birds mentioned by Lack (1940:281), the display of condors is apparently to be classed as "epigamic display, or display between the sexes to promote copulation. . . . There is direct evidence that epigamic display stimulates ovulation . . . and indirect evidence . . . that it helps to synchronize the two sexes in copulation, since most such display occurs when the other sex fails to respond adequately."

Conspicuous colors and structures are exhibited during the sexual display of many animals. The effectiveness of display may be increased by revealing the colors suddenly. The colors of the condor which one would expect to be used in display are: the white patches under the wings, the orange head, the red skin of the ventral cervical apterium, and the red eyes. The white patches are prominently displayed to the partner, and the turning of the displaying bird causes these patches to be more or less flashed. In *Vultur* there are white patches on the dorsal surface of the wings rather than on the ventral surface. That bird might present its back to its partner more than does *Gymnogyps*. The parts presented most closely to the display partner are the crown, occiput, and hind neck. This action seems logical for the male *Vultur* because that bird has a conspicuous caruncle on its head. However, in *Gymnogyps* the back of the neck is gray and the crown and occiput are less brightly colored than the rostral region. Possibly, as in *Vultur,* the neck of *Gymnogyps* becomes red during display.

The most highly colored structure adorning *Gymnogyps* is the red ventral cervical apterium. One might expect that in display this apterium would be distended in the manner of the red throat bladder of frigate birds. In front view the sight of this apterium is largely obscured from the display partner by the lowered head of the displayer. In *Vultur* this apterium is not brightly colored, yet it is said to be distended during display. Possibly the eye of *Gymnogyps* is somewhat protruded during display, for the eye of the chick is slightly protruded in the threat attitude.

The display attitude of the "male" condor bears more resemblance to the threat attitude of the chick than to any other posture. In some birds the male employs the same action in display as in threat. The threat attitude of the chick resembles the display attitude of the adult in that the head and neck are lowered in front of the body, the unexpanded tail is held stiffly and is raised slightly above the plane of the back, and the wings are held somewhat out from the body. In threat, and perhaps in display, the condor hisses. Threat differs from display in that the ruff covers the neck, the bird does not turn from side to side, and the wings are but slightly extended.

The similarity between the mating display of *Gymnogyps* and *Vultur* is perhaps an example of the situation described by Lorenz (1937:254) in which "an instinctive action, common to . . . closely related species has caused some of them to evolve colors and structures serving to make their movements more conspicuous." The caruncle of *Vultur* may be such a structure, and perhaps the colors of the heads and the white wing patches of both condors are such colors. Lorenz makes the hypothesis that "in all such cases the releasing ceremony is phylogenetically older than the structures used by it." This reasoning suggests a basic relationship between the two condors. Analysis of the display patterns of all the Cathartidae might help to elucidate their systematic relationships.

Condors probably do not breed until at least their sixth year of life. Only adult-plumaged birds have been found breeding and condors apparently attain this plumage at 5 or 6 years of age. A captive at the National Zoological Park first "bred" when 12 years old, according to Dixon (1924:192). The first egg of a captive *Vultur* at San Diego was found when the female was evidently 8 years old, although there were signs of mating the previous spring (Belle J. Benchley, letter, December 12, 1949).

It is probable that the members of pairs usually remate several times, for isolated nest sites have been used again and again over periods of many years and pairs have been seen at all seasons. To determine whether condors mate for life, one would have to mark a pair and observe it every spring for many years. Lack (1940:271) believes that there is no reliable evidence for life mating in any falconiforms.

Nests and Eggs

Nest characteristics.—I investigated fifteen nest sites and received first-hand information concerning additional sites from Sidney Peyton, Frank Arundell, Fred Truesdale, and others who had found condor nests many years ago. Some accounts in the literature, and even data accompanying eggs, are known to be inaccurate or purposely false. For example, the locality "not far from Monterey" given by Sharples (1897: 21) was actually on the San Luis Rey River in San Diego County. Collectors falsified information in order to emphasize the danger and difficulty of procuring condor eggs and to prevent competition.

With one exception, all condor nesting sites of which I have definite knowledge are in the Upper Sonoran Life-zone and between 1500 and 4500 feet in elevation. The exceptional site, not discovered until 1950, is at 6500 feet elevation in the Transition Life-zone. Probably in Sespe Canyon or in the Santa Monica Mountains there have been nests as low as 1000 feet above sea level. There have been nests within six miles of the coast near the southern boundary of Monterey County and probably also in the Santa Monica Mountains. Until the finding of the nest in Tulare County, 120 miles from the coast, no nests were known to be more than 40 miles from the sea. Again excepting Tulare County, all the known nesting has occurred within a belt 400 miles long and 40 miles wide reaching from Santa Cruz County to San Diego County (figure 2). Most of the nesting today occurs in Ventura and Santa Barbara counties within an area 80 miles in length. The most important breeding area from which condors have disappeared is the southern Santa Lucia Range near the Monterey County line.

For condors, the nest is "a mere place" (Nice, 1937:212), the place normally being a cavity in a cliff or among boulders. Nests have been found in granite, coarse conglomerate, and various kinds of sandstone. The cavities may be potholes, caves, or clefts in cliffs, or they may be formed by boulders which lie close together. In one instance the site was a cave-like hollow in a big tree (*Sequoia gigantea*).

Occasionally nest caves are open at both ends. The Finley (1906:138) nest was formed by a slab of rock leaning against a perpendicular face of granite making a space about two feet wide and six feet long.

The Peyton nest figured in Bent (1937:plate 2) was under a large boulder and open at both ends. However, I do not know of an instance of two entrances being used by the nesting adults, although turkey vultures may use two entrances (Coles, 1944:221).

Nests are located some distance above the ground level or at least above steep slopes so that the condors have space in which to descend in flying from the nest. One frequently used nest cave is 25 feet down from the top of a rough-faced, but nearly vertical, sandstone cliff about 200 feet high. Great height on a smooth-faced cliff would be disadvantageous, for the juvenile cannot fly at the time it leaves the nest.

Great height above the bottom of a canyon is not essential for a condor nest. The site of nest 9 (plate 19) is only 50 feet above a gradually sloping stream bed. Another nest site is in the very base of a cliff almost 300 feet high, but it is above a steep slope. The site of nest 13 (plate 20) is in the lowest of a series of several thick ledges. Most nests are lower in canyons than the most used roosting perches. The low position has the advantage of protecting the nestling from winds.

Near every nest there are large trees, or at least ledges and points on the cliffs, where the adults can perch and roost. Some nests have an outer shelf where the young bird may perch and be fed. At one nest this shelf was 15 feet long and five feet wide, even though the nest cave itself was spacious. Pothole nests are generally small and seldom have an outer shelf (plate 16).

The size of the entrance to pothole nests may be small. The opening of one Truesdale nest (Dawson, 1924:1724) I measured and found to be 15 inches high and 17 inches wide. In contrast, a nest cave 20 feet deep was 10 feet by 12 feet at the entrance, and another cave was 6 feet by 6 feet as far back as the egg.

The size of the nest cave is various. The smallest nest that I examined was 18 inches wide, 25 inches high, and 4 feet deep. In another cave the egg was 30 feet from the entrance, and in two other caves the egg was more than 15 feet from the entrance. In nest 1 the egg was seldom over 2 feet from the entrance. The floor space of nest caves, considering only the part apparently used by the condors, varies from about 6 to 90 square feet. In two nests I could stand erect within a few feet of the egg but the clearance directly above the egg was less than 3 feet. In the Finley nest the back of the adult hit the roof and side when the bird stood up (Grinnell, MS).

In every rock nest which I examined, the site of the egg or young chick was a level area of silt or sand an inch or more in depth. Small rock particles, oak leaves blown in by the wind, or twigs and acorns carried in by woodrats were mixed with the sand. In some nests the adult had to walk several yards over a jumble of rock slabs in order to reach the egg.

Wherever I could determine the location of the egg, it was between walls from 16 inches to 2½ feet apart. The egg in the Finley (1906:138) nest was between walls about 2 feet apart. These facts suggest that the incubating adult may receive the same sort of tactile stimulus from the walls surrounding it that many other birds receive from the sides of the nests which they construct.

The darkness at the location of the egg is various. In nest 4, a shallow cavity, the reflected light from the darkest recess measured 3.2 foot candles by Weston exposure meter at the brightest part of the day in October. Direct sunshine did not reach into this nest. At another nest sunshine reached the site of the egg for half an hour at midday. On the other hand, the egg or chick in nest 9 could scarcely be seen from within the long cave.

I do not know of any nest caves which have an unprotected opening to the south. Condors might avoid these caves because storms are usually accompanied by southerly winds which blow rain into south-facing cavities.

The main physical requirements for a condor nesting site seem to be: location in cavity in rock (or large tree trunk), suitable roosting perches nearby, fairly easy approach from the air, space below for taking off, protection from storms, winds, and direct sunshine, space enough to hold two full grown condors, level soft area where walls are about two feet apart, and perches available for young bird when it leaves the nest. The principal features of some of the nests which were examined in the course of this study are given in the following paragraphs.

Description of nest sites.—The site of nest 1 is in east-central Ventura County at an elevation of 4300 feet and half a mile from the head of an extensive canyon where many condors nest, roost, drink, and occasionally feed. The cave is a pothole a third of the way down a vertical 50-foot cliff (plate 16). The cliff is of soft sandstone and contains concretions of various sizes. The opening of the nesting pothole faces west-northwest and is roughly pentagonal in shape, the maximum height being 33 inches and the maximum width 22 inches. Directly opposite the opening the hole is 39 inches deep. A flattish rock lies about one foot within the entrance (figure 12); otherwise the floor is level. The south chamber of the cave extends 4 feet from the edge of the opening and the north chamber is 1½ feet in length. The nearest trees suitable for roosting are 600 yards down the canyon from the site of the nest.

The site of nest 2 is at an elevation of 3000 feet and within a few hundred yards of roosts and a water hole used by many condors. The tunnel-shaped cave, half way up a 50-foot sandstone cliff above a steep slope (plate 17), is 2 feet high, 1½ feet wide, and 4 feet deep. Outside the cave is a gently sloping shelf 4 feet long. The shelf is open at the outer end but is bounded by the cliff on one side and by a low wall on the other side. A favorite perch of the nesting adults was the top branch of a big-cone spruce 100 yards from the nest and 30 feet below it.

The site of nest 4 is a red sandstone outcropping about 100 feet high (plate 18) situated at an elevation of 1800 feet near the junction of a long descending canyon with a larger canyon. There is a water hole for condors one mile from this site but few condors frequent the area. A triangular shelf, 6 feet on each side, slopes gently outward from the northeast face of the cliff. This shelf is enclosed on two sides by walls which slant inward, especially at the base, so that the inner corner is well protected but not dark. The outer edge of the shelf is fenced with the basal branches of shrubs. Because of the brush, one cannot see into this nest from any nearby point. The adults had to ascend several feet up the rocks before they could take off. The favorite perch and roost of the adults was a sheltered ledge at the tip of the outcropping about 100 feet from the nest and 20 feet below it.

The site of nest 9 is at an elevation of 2800 feet and within 100 yards of a waterfall where condors drink. The cave is 100 feet above and 50 feet to one

Plate 16. The setting of nest 1 (1939) as seen from the west. The mouth of the cave is slightly left of center in the face of the main cliff. The outjut of the cliff at the right was a favorite landing place of the adults. The tip of the ledge at the left on the level of the nest cave is the point from which the adults usually went to the nest.

Plate 17. Site of nest 2 (1939). The cave is in the center of the main rock exposure. A favorite perch was on the tree top at the extreme right.

Plate 18.   Site of nest 4 (1940) in the rock outcrop at upper left.

Plate 19.   Site of nest 9 (1941). The egg lay 30 feet from the entrance to the cave which is at the right of the center.

Plate 20. Site of nest 13 (1946). The cave is slightly above the center in the main cliff.

Plate 21. Adult preparing to take off from the entrance of a nest cave. Note the inability to grasp with the feet.

Plate 22. California Condor egg in place in the nest cave. Photograph
by Don Bleitz.

Plate 23. Nest site 95 feet above ground in the cavity of a big tree (*Sequoia gigantea*). Juvenal Condor
standing in entrance in the fall of 1950. Photograph by Ed Harrison and Frances Roberts.

side of a stream and is in a sloping sandstone cliff about 40 feet high. A section of the thick outer layer of the cliff has slipped downward and the space between the outer and inner layers of rock forms a cave (plate 19). The entrance is in the form of an oblique triangle 5 feet wide and 8 feet high. The egg was near the end of the silt-covered floor 30 feet from the entrance. A favorite perch of the adults was the top of a green canyon live oak 60 feet from the entrance of the nest and 20 feet above it.

The site of nest 13 is at an elevation of 3800 feet in a sandstone ledge 100 feet high. This ledge is 1000 feet below the highest similar ledge on the same ridge (plate 20). The nesting cavity is formed by the space between several large boulders which have become jammed in a notch at the top of the cliff. The cavity is 10 feet from the top of the cliff and has an opening (about 4 feet square) away from the face of the cliff. However, the adults entered and left the nest via an inclined rock which led to an opening on top of the cliff. As there are no trees close to this nest site, the adults roosted in a group of conifers a quarter of a mile from the nest and 300 feet above it in elevation.

A nest site discovered in 1950 by Claude Rouch, Jr., a logger, is situated 95 feet above the ground in the trunk of a big tree (*Sequoia gigantea*). The tree is about 170 feet tall and 15 feet in basal diameter. The nesting cavity is estimated to be 5 feet high, 3 feet wide, and 2½ feet deep (plate 23). This hollow was formed by fire which burned out the base of a large branch. A piece of wood caught just inside the lower lip of the hole allowed litter to accumulate and form a level floor in the cavity. A thick stub branch 3 feet below the nest entrance was the principal perch of the young condor soon after it left the nest. A pine tree growing opposite the nest hole and 30 feet away allowed men to ascend and photograph the nest. Except for being made of wood, this nest site has all the essential features, such as steadiness, accessibility to condors, ease of take-off, protection of nestling, and presence of perches, found in cliff nests.

Frequency of use of nest sites.—The nesting history of individual condors cannot be traced in a satisfactory manner. It is impractical to capture condors and mark them in a permanent and conspicuous fashion. A pair may use several nests, some of them unknown to the observer. The fate of the young in their first year of life is difficult to determine. The eggs have

little pattern by means of which one may judge whether the same female laid them. It is not improbable that unscrupulous persons may steal condor eggs even today. Some people who have nesting information keep it secret or give out false data. Accordingly, the known history of the nesting of any pair is fragmentary.

Two adults and an immature condor were seen near the Finley nest early in 1905 but no nest was found. In March, 1906, the nest was found. The chick was taken from the nest in summer. An egg was taken from the nest on February 10, 1907. In June of that year adults were seen near the site of the nest but the nest cave was empty. An adult was found incubating in the nest on May 9, 1908, and presumably the egg hatched. A young condor, perhaps not a young of the year (specimen, M.V.Z.), was killed near the nest in December, 1908. No subsequent nesting is known for that area. These data indicate that the pair may nest at the same place in successive years if the egg fails to hatch or if the chick does not survive, and that laying of a second egg in the nest if the first is taken may not occur in the wild in the same season. These conclusions are confirmed by other observations.

Sidney B. Peyton told me of a nest cave from which an egg was taken in the spring of 1915 and 1916. Near that site, in the previous summer, a hunter had seen an adult which appeared to be feeding a young bird. There was apparently nesting there in 1918 but not in 1917 or 1919. In 1917 and again in 1920 two adults and an immature condor were collected in that vicinity. An egg was in the nest in 1922 but it was broken by a falling rock. A collector took an egg within half a mile of that site in 1922 and a chick from the latter nest in 1923. At various times before 1921 Peyton found evidence of nesting at two other sites near the 1915 nest. Bent (1937:2) visited the Peyton nest site in 1929. He thought that the site might have been used since 1922. In all, there were at least eight nestings at four or more sites within a distance of half a mile. Condors may still nest in that exceedingly rough area.

Fred Truesdale of Paso Robles told me of the history of another nest area. Four or five sites within a distance of half a mile were used by the condors. An egg was taken in 1908, 1909, 1913, 1917, and 1920, as well as Truesdale could recollect (1946). The earliest and latest dates of collection were February

27 (1908) and May 12 (1909). In 1911, Dawson (1924:1724) discovered a chick in a pothole where Truesdale had taken an egg in a previous year (probably 1909). In another year an egg was left because ice on the rocks made it inaccessible. Another egg was stolen while Truesdale was away getting a camera to photograph it, and yet another egg was broken by the adult condors. In all, there were at least nine nestings within 15 years and the same hole was used three or four times. More than one nesting per year was not discovered although the suitable nesting area was moderate in size and was searched again and again in some years. Not improbably condors still nest in this area on occasions.

A collector of eggs told me of an old nest which he said had been used 12 times between 1897 and 1921 but which had not been used since. Chester Carden collected an egg from that nest in 1902. According to Carden (letter of November 4, 1902) condors had nested there three times in 12 years. I visited the nest site in 1939 and found a late nestling there. There was evidently no further nesting by 1946.

Two other collectors told me of a nest site which, to their knowledge, had not been used for more than 20 years. In 1940 I found no evidence of recent use of this site but a chick was in the nest in 1946. Because condors may nest at old sites which have not been used for many years, the protection of former nesting areas which are still apparently suitable for condors is justified.

Nest 1 was used in 1939 but showed no evidence of previous use. By 1946 it showed no evidence of further use although condors nested at a similar site three-fourths of a mile away.

Nest 2, where a chick was raised in 1939, was not used in 1940 or 1941, but in 1946 it contained an egg and evidence of nesting between 1942 and 1945. Less than one-half mile from nest 2 a chick was raised in 1941 (nest 9). Within 300 yards of the latter nest, an egg is said to have been stolen in 1940 and there was nesting in 1945.

In 1940 I found a chick in nest 4 and I found evidence of previous nesting in the same small canyon. In 1946 there was no evidence of further nesting at that site although there had apparently been nesting nearby in 1945.

I found nest 5 while investigating an area where forest service men had noted a pair of condors in

1932 and 1935. A nestling was raised there in 1940 and was last seen shortly after it left the nest. The site was used again in 1941 but the egg failed to hatch and became broken. In 1946 the site showed evidence of a nesting between 1942 and 1945 and condors nested half a mile from the site in another canyon (nest 13). Several times in June, 1943, an observer saw one or two adults and an immature near nest 13. This indicated nesting there in 1942.

There is little evidence of regularity in the frequency of nesting. The Finley nest was used three years in succession when the egg or young was taken. I do not know of another example of nesting at the same site in more than two successive years and many collectors have discovered a nest site to be unused in the year after an egg or young was taken. Nest 2, relatively undisturbed, was used three times in seven years. To my knowledge, there is no record of a series of more than two undisturbed nestings at the same site in alternate years although presumably nesting would occur every other year if the chick survived. Pairs of condors, like golden eagles, may have two or more nesting sites which are used at various times.

Eggs.—Bent (1937:3) gives the average measurements of 46 condor eggs as 110.2 by 66.7 millimeters, the longest egg being 120 millimeters in length. Harold Hill (MS) found one egg to be about 5⅜ inches (131 millimeters) in length. Generally, the surface of the shell is irregularly covered with tiny pits and excrescences. In color, the shell is usually a very pale but distinct green or blue. Two eggs taken from one locality were smoother and whiter than typical eggs so that the collector (Truesdale) had difficulty in proving that they were genuine. A good full-sized color plate of the egg of a condor was published by Bendire (1892:plate 4).

Alexander Taylor (1859a:539) found that one whole egg weighed 10½ ounces and its contents alone weighed 8¾ ounces. The shell held 9 fluid ounces of water. Less than 12 hours after a fresh egg was removed from the nest it weighed 9½ ounces and its contents weighed 8 ounces, according to the notes of the collector.

In shape, the egg of a condor is a slightly ovate ellipsoid. For two eggs I calculated the volume using the formula for an ellipsoid ($V = \frac{\pi}{6} ab^2$), and allowing one millimeter for the thickness of the shell and membrane. I compared the calculated volume with the volume of water held by the eggshell. For an egg measured by myself the calculated and measured volumes were 241 and 249 cubic centimeters. For the egg described by Taylor (*loc. cit.*) the volumes were 256 and 266 cubic centimeters. The measured volumes were less than 4 per cent greater than the computed volumes.

Many damaged or infertile eggs have been reported. The egg taken by Howard in 1895 (Shields, 1895) was addled and had a small hole in one side (H. Robertson, letter August 24, 1934). Sharples (1897: 21) reported the taking of an addled egg which was slightly broken at the tip. Gallaher (1906:57) reported finding an egg with the contents dried up. M. C. Badger (verbal) found an egg with a broken tip in 1917. Frank Arundell found a "stale" egg in June, 1920 (B. W. Evermann, MS). Perhaps some collectors have claimed that eggs were addled in order to justify their taking them.

Other eggs have become broken from various causes. In 1941, the work of a trail crew within 50 yards of one nest presumably caused the failure of the egg. Finally the egg became punctured and ants consumed the contents. In March, 1946, I found an egg in another nest. On my next visit, one month later, the egg was broken and part of it lay in the nest. There were bones of an embryo in both of these eggs. In the same spring I found two other broken eggs below nesting caves. At least one of these caves contained part of the eggshell. Possibly the dryness and coldness of the spring of 1946 contributed to the failure of these three eggs.

The incubation period at nest 1 was at least 42 days. Harold Hill (MS) found that after at least 32 days of incubation an egg had an air space occupying about one-fifth of its volume and, judged by the appearance of the chick when it was first seen (15 days later), the incubation period was about 42 days or longer. I saw an adult in another nest 53 days after I first discovered the egg. However, this egg did not hatch; six days later it was broken and no adult was in the nest. The egg of the South American condor is similar in size to that of the California condor. The incubation period of the former bird, in captivity, is about 56 days (San Diego Zoo).

The extreme egg dates known to me are February 10, 1907, and May 25, 1920. Data accompanying one egg (M.C.Z.) gives June 15, 1899, as the date of collection, but Redington (1899:75) gives April 17, 1899, for the same specimen. Finley's chick hatched on March 22. If the incubation period exceeds 42 days, the egg must have been laid before February 10. There is no way of determining the accuracy of collectors' data which indicate that some eggs taken in May were fresh.

After the egg hatches the eggshell apparently becomes crushed beyond recognition. I removed a shell, crushed but fairly intact, from near a chick three days old. Large fragments of eggshell were present near the chick five days later.

A condor (presumably always the same one) laid many eggs at the National Zoological Park. The bird was received as a young of the year in 1903. It laid at least one egg almost every year from 1919 to 1936 or later. The incomplete data indicate that all eggs were laid in March and April. The earliest date of finding an egg was March 6. Most of the eggs became broken in the nest. Many were removed and deposited in the United States National Museum (nine there in 1949). Two eggs were placed in an incubator and two others under a hen; the eggs proved infertile. In 1928 and in 1929 two eggs were laid. One was found on April 21, 33 days after the first was found broken. Another was found on April 15, 41 days after the first was discovered (taken then?). These data indicate that a condor can lay until at least 32 years of age and that it is possible for a second egg to be laid about one month after the first is lost. The South American condors at the San Diego Zoo have laid and hatched a second egg after the first was taken or broken. For free-living California condors, the laying of a second egg after the first is taken is unknown. If second layings occur, egg collectors should have discovered this fact long ago.

The collection of the eggs and young of condors in the past, especially around 1900, is sufficient to account for a significant decrease in the population. I have records of nearly 60 eggs, not including those laid in captivity, which are in collections at the present time. These eggs were taken between 1859 and 1922 in a more or less legal manner. Nineteen were taken between 1900 and 1902. Probably at least 25 eggs for which I have no data are in collections. I have data for 17 young condors which were taken from the nest. One was taken in 1865, one in 1923, and the others between 1896 and 1909. One man, W. B. Whitaker of Piru, took at least five young. The three condors which survived at the National Zoological Park until several years ago were purchased from Whitaker for $75 apiece.

At one time the main objective of several collectors was the obtaining of condor eggs. A few persons even tried to sell the eggs of swans as those of condors. In an open letter, H. R. Taylor (1895c:100) offered $250 each for three condor eggs. In 1905 Taylor said (letter April 2, 1905) that his collectors had taken nine eggs for him. Through several articles in The Nidiologist, Taylor strove to emphasize the rarity of condors and their eggs so as to increase the value of his collection.

Although he already had seven condor eggs, John E. Thayer bought another from Fred Truesdale for $300 (letters December 3, 1909, and September 21, 1910). As far as I know, a higher price has never been paid for the egg of a condor. Some collectors' catalogues have listed the trading price of the egg of a condor at $500. This price does not represent cash value but merely the worth of the eggs in relation to that of the other eggs which oölogists are constantly trading back and forth. A few years ago Lawrence Stevens of Santa Barbara bought a perfect egg taken in 1895 for $25. The Cohen collection which included a first class condor egg was sold for $200. An egg taken illegally in recent years would have to be sold at a "fence" price. Unfortunately, most newspaper accounts state that condor eggs are extremely valuable. In the Los Angeles Times of May 14, 1939, a price of $750 each was publicized in an article entitled, "Eggs: $9,000.00 a dozen." In the same newspaper for August 8, 1949, condor eggs are said to be worth $500 to $1000 apiece. Obviously this erroneous and deplorable publicity tempts people to seek condor eggs.

Behavior of Nesting Adults

The principal stages in the nesting behavior of adult condors are:

1. Incubation
2. Care of nestling
   a. Early nestling (brooding)
      (1) Continuous brooding
      (2) Brooding at night only
   b. Middle and late nestling
3. Care of juvenile (out of nest)
   a. Flightless juvenile
   b. Volant juvenile (somewhat dependent)

Most of my data concerning the behavior of nesting adults were obtained at nest 1. Observations of the adults or young of nest 1 were made on 107 days between March 23, 1939, and March 24, 1940. At that nest, the lengths of these stages were as follows:

1. At least 42 days
2. a. About 5 weeks (commencing May 4)
   b. About 15 weeks
3. a. About 10 weeks (commencing about September 25)
   b. About 7 months

Figure 10. Duration of the stages of the nesting cycle in the condor.

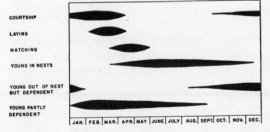

After a few days of observation at nest 1, I could recognize each member of the pair by certain missing remiges and by the color of the head and plumage. Their sex was unknown. I called the supposed female *A* and the supposed male *B*. The young bird I called "chick 1" while it was in the nest and "juvenile 1" after it left the nest. The same system of designating young was used at other nests.

At nest 1, the behavior of the adults indicated that the egg was pipping on May 3, although it appeared from a distance to be intact at 6 p.m. Twenty-four

hours later I first glimpsed the chick. For purposes of analysis, I assumed that the incubation stage ended when *A* relieved *B* on the afternoon of May 4.

Extreme times of arrival and departure; incubation and brooding stages.—During the incubation and brooding stages the adults alighted near nest 1 in order to enter it after a bird had been flushed from the nest, to return after a recess from incubation or brooding, or to relieve the guard. The observed schedule of the adults during the incubation and brooding stages is shown in figure 11. With rare ex-

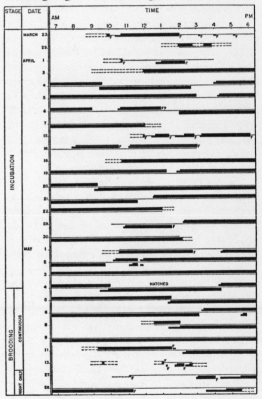

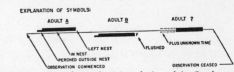

Figure 11. The observed visits of the adult Condors to nest 1 during the incubation and brooding stages.

87

ceptions, the adults did not arrive at the nest before 9 a.m. or after 5 p.m. The earliest exception occurred on April 16 at 7:52 a.m. when A arrived after a night during which no adult was in the nest. Otherwise, the earliest arrival of A was at 10:20 a.m. on May 2. The earliest observed arrival of B was at 8:50 a.m. on April 6 during a strong wind, but the bird did not land. However, three times during the incubation stage I saw B relieve A before 10 a.m., the earliest landing being at 9:06 a.m. The latest that A was seen to land was at 4:18 p.m. on May 4, the day that the egg hatched. B was twice seen to arrive equally late when returning to the nest after being flushed, and once it arrived at 5:25 p.m. (May 6) when returning to the nest after a recess. B tended to arrive at the nest earlier and later in the day than A.

The earliest observation of an adult departing from nest 1 (9 a.m.) occurred when A left to follow B in a strong wind. The next earliest instance (9:15 a.m.) occurred when A departed after being relieved by its mate. The latest observed departure (6 p.m.) occurred when the adult was inadvertently flushed from the nest. The next latest departure (5:51 p.m.) occurred two days after the egg hatched when B departed after being in the cave with A for many minutes.

Waiting interval.—Before entering nest 1, the adults perched nearby for an interval of time (shown by the half-width horizontal bars in figure 11). This habit of waiting is evidently part of the innate caution of adults in approaching the nest. Even adults which roost within sight of their nest wait close to it before entering. In the incubation and brooding stages B usually waited longer than A, the comparative average intervals being about 12 minutes and 6 minutes. The extreme intervals for A were 2 minutes and 16 minutes, only one interval being over 9 minutes. The longest interval for A occurred following a night when no adult was in the nest. The extremes for B were zero and 39 minutes. The two longest intervals for B occurred when A remained in the cave while B was perched nearby, but in five similar instances B waited not over 9 minutes and once it flew directly to the cave without waiting.

The average waiting interval was about 20 per cent longer when an adult returned after having been flushed from the nest than after it left without being disturbed. Once when an adult was flushed from the top of the cliff and later flushed from the nest, both

times returning and entering the nest, the second waiting interval was twice as long as the first as if the bird were more cautious after being flushed the second time. The activity of men, when not sufficient to flush the bird from the top of the nest cliff, prolonged the waiting interval.

The following is a summary of the average duration (minutes) of waiting intervals observed at nest 1 in the incubation and continuous brooding stages.

Interval	Average
All (instances: A, 12; B, 13; ?, 4; total 29)	9.6
Adult not previously flushed (16 instances)	8.4
Either adult previously flushed (13 instances)	11.1
Same adult returned after being flushed (4 instances)	8.0
Guard changed	6.7
After recess	5.6

After the brooding stage the waiting intervals at nest 1 were generally much longer than before, the comparative average intervals being about 10 minutes and 68 minutes. Even excluding three intervals of over 2 hours, the average interval was almost five times the previous average. The transition from a short to a long waiting interval occurred in the course of the stage of brooding at night only. The increase in the waiting interval was apparently caused by increased cautiousness and decreased attachment to the nest. For the middle and late nestling stages, as before, the waiting interval was shorter for A than for B, the comparative averages being about 42 and 97 minutes (9 instances for A, 8 for B). In these stages B was more cautious than A.

On June 11 B was discovered to have an injured leg, but the injury did not appear to influence the waiting interval. Neither were long intervals caused solely by the presence of the observer, for I observed intervals of more than one hour when I was at least one mile from the nest. At other nests, too, an adult sometimes perched nearby for a long period.

In the middle and late nestling stages the shortest observed waiting interval for A and B occurred when they arrived at about the same time, unusually late in the day. Presumably they were in a hurry to feed the chick and to reach their roost. Another time when both were present the waiting interval was also short. These actions suggest that the presence of the mate reassures the waiting adult so that the waiting interval is shortened. On the other hand, once when both adults were present, the waiting interval was long because some interaction diverted the bird from entering the nest.

The waiting interval, as observed at several nests, was highly variable. Some of the factors which seem to influence the waiting interval are listed below.

Disturbance by man (difficult to evaluate)

Cautiousness of adults (age, sexual, and individual differences)

Experience of adults (familiarity with surroundings)

Ease of approaching nest (weather, landing places, obstructions)

Readiness to feed chick (psychological drive; recency of eating)

Activity of chick (sounds, begging, visibility to adult)

Presence of mate (reassurance or diversion)

Time of day (urgency of other activities; remaining daylight)

After juvenile 1 left the nest, the interval between the landing of the adult and the feeding of the chick was much shorter than in the nestling stage, in spite of greatly increased caution of the adults. Probably the begging action of the youngster outside of the nest had a greater influence on the adults than the presence of the chick more or less hidden in the nest. In addition, except for the first few weeks after the youngster left the nest, the parents could land near it much more easily than they could land in the nest. The approach to juvenile 2 after it left the nest was more difficult than when it was in the nest. On occasions the parents occupied several successive perches before reaching the youngster and the waiting intervals were long (15 to 100 minutes for three instances).

BEHAVIOR OF ADULTS IN APPROACHING AND LEAVING THE NEST OR YOUNG

Incubation and brooding stages.—The adults usually approached nest 1 from the direction of roosts and water holes which were situated two miles from the nest. Occasionally one was seen perched on a high cliff a mile from the nest before approaching. The direction of the aerial approach was fairly straight toward the nest cliff, but it was greatly influenced by the wind. Usually the adult first passed over the nest less than 150 feet above the ground.

The interval between the arrival of the adult over nest 1 and the landing of the bird was about 3 minutes; once it was 9 minutes. This interval tends to be short on calm days and long at nests which are difficult to approach from the air. Disturbance prolongs the interval. On two occasions at nest 1, the flushed adult circled for half an hour while men were in the open but it landed within 5 minutes after the men concealed themselves.

The adult arriving at nest 1 descended in large circles, sometimes soaring half a mile or more down the canyon and returning. Before landing it commonly flew back and forth in front of and over the nest cliff from two to seven times. Then it landed on the edge of the cliff above the nest (plate 16). In more than half of the observations, the adult first landed within 10 feet of an outjut on the top of the cliff about 60 feet south of the nest.

Generally the adult remained at the spot where it first landed for from 2 to 6 minutes (occasionally 20 minutes), then it moved to another perch. Immediately after landing the bird looked around quickly and within a minute or two it turned and faced outward from the cliff. Every few minutes it turned to face a new direction. Usually it walked a few steps before leaving the top of the cliff. Occasionally it flew to a second perch on top of the cliff or flew directly to the nest. Most frequently it flew to a broad ledge 25 feet north of the nest. On this ledge it normally remained from one-half to 3 minutes. The two longest periods observed (8 minutes) occurred when *B* was on the ledge while *A* remained in the nest. When the initial landing was on the ledge rather than on the top of the cliff (9 instances), the maximum time spent there was longer (16 minutes for *A* and 10 minutes for *B*).

Soon after landing on the ledge near nest 1 the adult commonly hopped atop a boulder about two feet high. Within one minute the bird flew the 35 feet to the nest. Just before flying it usually held its neck stretched toward the nest for about five seconds. On occasions the bird hopped down to the tip of the ledge nearest the nest (25 feet) before flying to the nest hole. *B* once had difficulty in landing downwind. First it "missed" the cave and landed atop the cliff. It returned to the ledge and tried again. Again it missed, then flew 200 yards downwind, circled back, and landed on the ledge. Again it flew toward the nest, turned suddenly, and made good a clumsy landing, beating its wings against the face of the cliff. Because of tall trees near another nest, the adults often had to maneuver for several minutes before landing. One soared for three minutes and traveled more than half a mile away from the nest in moving from one point on the cliff to a perch a few yards closer to the nest.

In the incubation and brooding stages an adult was seen to land near nest 1 on 40 occasions (A, 13; B, 18; ?, 9), and one was seen to enter the nest 33 times. They first landed on top of the cliff 75 per cent of the time (A, 60 per cent; B, 80 per cent). The cliff-ledge-nest sequence was used about half the time. The ledge-nest sequence occurred half again more frequently than the cliff-nest sequence. The most used sequence of perches was what one would expect from the physical arrangement of the cliffs. The top of the nest cliff offered a high unobstructed perch relatively easy to land on or to take off from, and it was a good lookout position. The ledge was lower and somewhat obstructed but from there the adults could see the nest cave and could walk to a point only 25 feet from it.

Before crouching to take off from nest 1 the adult looked up and down the canyon, its neck stretched out of the cave. The initial course was always down the canyon, regardless of the direction of the wind or the location of men. Usually it soared at least one mile before commencing to circle.

The place of roosting of the adult off the nest at night during the incubation stage is uncertain. I saw no indication that it roosted within one mile of nest 1. Both adults roosted near another nest in August, but on two nights in May none roosted near that nest and the relieving adult approached as if from a roost about three miles away.

Middle and late nestling stages.—In these stages an adult was seen perched 41 times (A, 15; B, 12; ?, 14) near nest 1. The sequence of use of perches was more uniform than during the earlier stages; perhaps this was because the weather was more uniform. Except for one instance, they first landed on top of the nest cliff. The cliff-ledge-nest approach was followed 17 of the 19 times that one entered the nest.

Occasionally, when disturbed, the adult waited on a distant perch before flying to nest 1. For example, on August 7, B remained perched on a cliff one-half mile south of the nest for 40 minutes and then flew to the nest cliff. An adult had been flushed from the nest three hours earlier. A few times when the adult

was mildly disturbed on its first approach, it returned about half an hour later and landed.

More frequently than in earlier stages the initial landing was on the favorite outjut on top of the cliff at nest 1. If the adults did not land there, they nearly always soon moved to that point. More frequently than before A walked between perches on top of the cliff; often it walked 30 yards. Perhaps because of its leg injury, B usually flew between the same perches. In walking, the birds paused periodically for a few seconds or minutes and looked about.

After August 1 the adults usually dropped down (from 6 to 10 feet) from the top of the cliff above the ledge to the boulder on the ledge, instead of flying from the outjut of the cliff to the ledge. In addition, the birds normally went to the point of the ledge nearest the nest before flying to it. This method of approach was rare before June 1. Possibly these changes in the manner of approaching the nest can be ascribed to learning. However, in each of five observations near nest 2, the final approach of the adult to the nest was different. In a single day the parent once flew to the nest from a shelf 20 feet above it, again flew from a tree to a bush to a ledge and then to the nest, and again flew from a large tree to a small oak 30 yards from the nest before flying to the nest. At that nest, the adults had formed no habit of using a certain sequence of perches. As compared with nest 1, the air currents at nest 2 were weak and variable, there were many obstacles to flight, and there were many suitable perches.

At two nests the adults landed a few feet away and walked in, although they could easily have landed directly in the nest. One nest was at the end of an open ledge about 15 feet long, yet the adult landed on a very narrow ledge apart from the long ledge and walked to it. At these same nests the adults also walked out instead of taking off directly from the nest.

The crop of an adult is normally distended when the bird arrives to feed the chick. In addition, the neck and cheeks may be greatly swollen as if this condition were correlated with preparation of food for the young. Preening, scratching, and other general actions are performed by birds waiting near nests. At nest 1 the side stretch and sunning were not seen to be performed by the adults, but at some other nests I saw adults alight and sun after they were flushed. At nest

Plate 24. Adult on the point of the cliff near a nest. The wings are held high after landing.

1 only the injured adult was seen to sit for more than a few minutes, but I saw an adult sit within a few feet of another nest for as long as 45 minutes at a time. Of course birds which roost near nests perform the common post-roosting actions there.

On occasions the activity of the adults from the time of roosting to the time of entering the nest was observed. Once both adults roosted near nest 2, changed perch once or twice between 7:30 a.m. and 8:15 a.m., soared briefly with other condors, landed near the nest, and then waited until 10:23 a.m. before one adult flew to the nest. In one observation at nest 4, both adults commenced soaring at about 10:40 a.m. In the course of the next two hours they soared together and separately, then perched near a water hole one mile from the nest, and then soared straight back toward the nest and landed before one entered the nest. In two instances at nest 13 one adult entered the nest soon after leaving its roost, but in another instance both adults left the vicinity about one hour before one returned and entered the nest. On occasions adults may depart to forage before either approaches the nest.

After feeding the chick in the morning the parent usually departs as if to forage. I saw one circle up out of a canyon as if to commence foraging after feeding the chick as late as 12:50 p.m. After feeding the chick in the afternoon the parent generally goes to roost. At nest 5, I saw an adult feed the chick as early as 11:40 a.m. and 12:50 p.m. and then remain near the nest the rest of the day and roost there. At nest 2 an adult went to roost after feeding the chick at 3 p.m. Adults leaving nest 1 after 3:30 p.m. usually headed for roosts.

After leaving nest 1 an adult occasionally perched or roosted in a group of big-cone spruces about 600 yards down the canyon from the nest. There were no closer suitable roosting trees. At other times the adult headed for a roost two miles away. The pair roosted on cliffs within 200 yards of nest 4 on three consecutive nights that I watched. At nest 2 the pair roosted in a tree 100 yards from the nest on three or four evenings that I watched. Adults leaving the nest at any time of day may perch near the nest for half an hour or more as if resting, then proceed on their way.

Flightless juvenile stage.—For one month after juvenile 1 left the nest it remained perched below the nest cliff. The adults used the same perches as before in approaching the young bird, but in addition they had to perch in a small dead oak, on a low boulder, and on a manzanita bush. When juvenile 2 was perched in a small live oak surrounded by brush and trees, the flying and alighting abilities of its parents were taxed. Within 23 minutes before arriving in the same tree as the youngster, one adult perched in six separate trees, all of them under 25 feet tall. The perches, none more than 50 yards from the juvenile, were arranged in a crude spiral centered on the young bird.

GENERAL ACTIVITIES OF ADULTS IN THE NEST

Incubation and brooding stages.—A was slightly more adept than B at landing in the small entrance of nest 1, but both adults often made very neat landings, scarcely touching the rim of the cave. Over a period of six months I discovered no significant change in the manner or skill of the adults in landing in the nest. Variations in landings were apparently caused by differences in the air currents.

Upon landing on the lip of nest 1 the adult usually remained perched for 10 to 30 seconds and looked back over one or both shoulders before folding its wings. Normally it looked back again, stretching its neck, before stepping into the cave and walking slowly toward the egg with its head held low. Often the bird paused upon reaching the egg and stretched its neck back toward the entrance for a final look out. The interval from landing on the lip of the nest to sitting on the egg varied from 20 to 90 seconds. This interval did not decrease as incubation progressed.

Even when not disturbed, the sitting adult often rose and stood close to the entrance of the nest for as long as 15 minutes. On occasions it peered out of the cave as if looking for its relief, or it moved the egg. Perhaps the bird stood to relieve the tedium of sitting. In the brooding stage the adult frequently rose but remained well inside the cave with its lowered head near the chick. In walking about in the nest the adult moved slowly, taking about three-fifths of a second per step.

After the egg hatched the brooding adult frequently rose on its tarsi as if annoyed by the movements of the chick and immediately sat again. On a few occasions I saw this up and down movement performed from three to six consecutive times at intervals of three to 10 seconds. Sometimes the sitting bird rose on its tarsi, shuffled about, and sat facing the opposite direction.

The normal locations of the adults in nest 1 is indicated in figure 12. Usually *A* sat facing northward

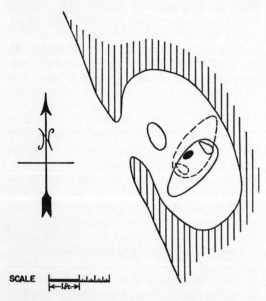

SCALE

Figure 12. Diagrammatic section of nest 1 showing the approximate normal location of adult A (solid line) and B (broken line) in relation to the egg (solid black).

and *B* sat facing southward. Each adult occasionally sat facing in the direction characteristic of the other, but *A* maintained its normal position much more constantly than *B*. For example, in three days commencing April 18, *A* was observed 20 hours and *B* 13 hours. *A* sat facing only northward while *B* sat facing opposite to its normal direction for three periods averaging 105 minutes. The normal position of *B* was disadvantageous in that the bird had to stretch its neck in order to look out of the cave. On two days when *A* was constantly disturbed it sat opposite to its usual direction and close to the entrance of the cave, as if to watch the photographic blind without leaving the egg.

A seldom rose except when disturbed by man or in order to leave the nest or to move out of the sun. *B* frequently rose without apparent cause. In three days of observation *A* rose without apparent cause only once in 20 hours, while *B* rose six times in 13 hours and remained standing as long as 16 minutes.

The longest period that *B* remained sitting on the egg without rising was 2½ hours. *A* sat on the egg steadily for 3½ hours on two occasions and for 5¼ hours on another (April 19). Altogether, *B* seemed less attached to the egg than *A*. In the last two days of incubation the frequency of rising of both adults was doubled. On the day that the egg hatched *B* rose and sat again at least eight times in the course of one turn of 4½ hours, never staying up longer than 3 minutes.

Just before sitting, the adult in nest 1 usually nudged the egg with its bill. *A* generally turned 180 degrees and sat quickly after performing this act. Occasionally each adult, but especially *B*, rose immediately after sitting and sat again within half a minute. As the bird settled down, its head and body worked back and forth or from side to side three or four times. The egg seemed to lie at one side of the body so that it was covered by the wing rather than by the ventral cervical apterium. No wearing of breast feathers by the egg was noted.

The adults in nest 1 moved the egg a few inches when shifting their own positions. One day when the adult was continually disturbed, it moved the egg about 18 inches northward to a point 15 inches from the outermost edge of the nest. I observed another nest on 12 different days and found the egg always within six inches of its normal position. In no nest did I find the egg in a definite concavity made by the adults, although digging activity observed at nest 1 may have formed a ridge around the egg.

In order to move the egg several inches, the adult in nest 1 stood facing the egg with its head lowered, put its bill over the egg so that the lower mandible touched the far side, and drew the egg slowly toward its feet. The action was similar to that of some ground nesting water birds in moving a displaced egg back to the nest. After moving the egg the adult normally paused and raised its head, then moved the egg a lesser distance.

For several minutes after the adult sat on the egg the bird turned its head frequently, but less often than when outside the nest. Rising for any reason was preceded by frequent turnings of the head. On occasions the sitting adult seemed to doze, its head resting on its body and throat. The head of the brooding bird often drooped forward and downward to a vertical position. Finley (1908*b*:61) mentions finding a brooding adult asleep in the nest.

The adult rarely preened more than several seconds at a time while sitting. Occasionally one wing was shrugged or raised several inches. The bends of the wings rested on the floor when the bird was relaxed. The wings often sagged low after the bird rose. Rising was slow and hesitant.

Several times I saw the sitting adult put its bill or entire head under one wing as if arranging the egg or chick. This action was rarely observed until three days before the egg hatched, and it may have been stimulated by the motions of the chick in pipping. During incubation the head was usually thrust behind the shoulder and kept under the wing for 5 to 10 seconds. During brooding the head was usually thrust down in front of the shoulder, disappearing behind the forearm, and sometimes it remained out of sight for several minutes.

A summary of the activity observed on May 5, the day after the egg in nest 1 hatched, will illustrate some of the foregoing points. In 7 hours of observation I saw A rise four times, twice with its bill near the chick, once to defecate, and once to leave the nest. Six times I saw it put its bill beneath the wing for periods of 10 seconds to 3 minutes. In the following 4 hours I saw B stand 13 times, not counting several times that it merely rose on its tarsi. It put its bill beneath its wing at least eight times for periods of 5 to 30 seconds.

The incubating adults in nest 1 often shifted position as if to keep the naked head and neck out of the sunshine. If the bird was at the same location in the cave each afternoon, the sun would cause it to rise about the same time. For example, on April 18, 19, and 21, A rose at 4:53 p.m., 4:44 p.m., and 4:51 p.m. after a long period of sitting. In each instance it moved the egg and then sat with its head out of reach of the sun. Possibly condors nest in caves in order to avoid the heat of sunshine. In most nests sunshine cannot reach the vicinity of the egg.

When brooding, the adults in nest 1 often sat for half an hour or more with their naked parts in the sun. However, they fidgeted and kept the chick well covered at about 5 p.m., when the sunshine was strongest in the nest. The activity of the chick may have been stimulated by warmth or by feeding at this time. Sunshine was not the only cause of this activity, for late one afternoon after fog obscured the sun B

changed position frequently.

On occasions during the incubation stage I saw the adult in nest 1 nudge or nibble the sandy floor with its bill, or pick up and drop a billful of sand four or five times in succession. Two days before the egg hatched I saw A rake sand toward the egg with its bill for about one minute. The next afternoon this bird dug extensively, as if ploughing up the floor of the nest and building a ridge of sand around the egg. A stood, reached out and took a bite of sand, then pulled its neck back and dropped the sand near its body. This action was repeated approximately 50 times in four minutes at a maximum rate of three bites each five seconds. Ten minutes later the bird raked sand toward its legs. An hour later it dug for another 10 minutes. At times it took two or three bites before bringing the sand toward its feet. Once it laid the side of its head flat on the floor and scraped sand from beneath its wing and tail toward its feet and the egg.

Several times in the course of the first week of brooding the sitting adult was seen to bite at the floor and then put its head under the wing which sheltered the chick. This action was repeated about 20 times at intervals of three to five seconds on one occasion. Subsequently I saw no digging activity in the nest. The digging was evidently correlated with the time of hatching of the egg at nest 1. Herrick (1934:138) tells of a bald eagle digging in its nest. "After settling down to brood, the mother eagle reached out with her bill and dug into the earthen floor of the nest, shoveling its substance about her on all sides and about the eaglets under her. . . ."

On all (nine) occasions when I saw an adult defecate in nest 1, the bird had been in the nest for at least 17 hours. Usually it rose as if only for the purpose of defecating and sat again within two or three minutes. If it stood longer, it defecated just before sitting. The act did not tend to occur at any particular time of day. There was no attempt at sanitation. The excrement struck the walls and the floor and was projected in any direction. In every nest excrement lines the walls to a height of about 18 inches. This deposit is produced by adults for the chick does not raise its rump to defecate throughout most (or all) of its nest life.

There was no conspicuous excrement on the cliff below nest 1 until two weeks before the egg hatched.

The chick contributed greatly to the amount of excrement. Two months after the egg hatched, there was a white band from two to four inches wide extending three feet below the lip of the nest. The adults were not seen to defecate in the nest when they entered only to feed the chick.

RELATIONS BETWEEN THE MEMBERS OF THE PAIR

Sharing of incubation and brooding.—The adults take turns at incubation and brooding (figure 11). Of 462 hours that nest 1 was known to be occupied by an adult during these stages, *A* was in the nest 55 per cent of the time (see Appendix, table 2). In the incubation stage *A* was in the nest 70 per cent of the time. The longest turn of *A* was 46 hours and 5 minutes (commencing May 2) while the longest turn of *B* was 26 hours and 19 minutes (commencing April 20). No significant increase in the duration of the turns was apparent as incubation progressed. I observed four turns of more than 20 hours at least four weeks before the egg hatched.

In the brooding stage *A* was in the nest only 27 per cent of 159 hours recorded. The longest turn of *A* was 21 hours and 8 minutes (commencing May 4) and the longest turn of *B* was at least 40 hours (commencing May 8). Judged by these observations, the share of the sexes in incubation and in brooding was reversed. However, comparatively few observations were made in the last three weeks of the brooding stage. Later *A* fed the chick more often than *B*. The fact remains that during the first week of brooding *B* was bolder than *A*, and *B* remained in the nest for longer periods than *A*. *B* performed a greater share of the continuous brooding than of the incubation.

The incubation schedule seemed to depend largely on the success of *B* in finding food. In general, *A* entered the nest when it found that *B* had departed, and *A* ceased its turn only after *B* entered the nest. *B* departed from the nest when it became hungry and entered the nest after feeding.

A was known to be in the nest at least 11 nights and *B* at least nine nights. The sharing of night duty was about the same as the sharing of total time in the nest and followed the same trends. *A* performed 75 per cent of the night incubation, 25 per cent of the night brooding, and 55 per cent of the total night duty. Whichever adult happened to be in the nest at

about 3 p.m. usually remained for the night.

Early in the incubation stage *A* was observed to be in the nest on three successive nights, although it was out from one to 6½ hours each day. In the late incubation stage *A* once remained in the nest for two successive nights without leaving the nest at all during the day. *B* performed this feat once during the continuous brooding stage and, according to Pemberton (MS), once in the stage of brooding at night only. I noted only two instances of regular alternation of the sexes (*A-B-A*) in nights spent in the nest.

Changing guard.—At nest 1 a change of guard was observed 13 times (see Appendix, table 3). On two days the guard was changed twice, at about 9:40 a.m. and 4:15 p.m., *A* being in the nest on the preceding and succeeding nights. On at least six days and probably on 10 days of observation, the guard was changed but once.

A tended to relieve the guard later in the day than *B*. When there had been no disturbance, *A* entered the nest between 3:20 p.m. and 4:30 p.m. in three of five observations, while *B* entered between 9:15 a.m. and 10:00 a.m. with the same frequency. This difference indicates that when *A* returned from foraging it relieved its mate, but when *B* returned it usually roosted overnight before relieving its mate.

When *B* landed near the nest to relieve the guard, *A* rose and stood at the entrance of the nest, but sometimes (brooding stage) *A* sat again before *B* entered. Usually, after *B* entered, *A* pushed past it and took off, and *B* sat less than one-half minute later.

Two days before the egg hatched *B* left the nest as if for a recess, and *A* entered during its absence. *B* returned one hour later, entered the nest, and sat on the egg while *A* was still in the nest. Eventually *B* departed leaving *A* to continue its turn.

Absences from the nest; incubation and continuous brooding stages.—In four clear instances at nest 1, one or the other adult left the nest and later returned to resume sitting. These recesses averaged 71 minutes (extremes 45 and 99 minutes) and commenced between 9 a.m. and 3 p.m. On each occasion the adult had been in the nest continuously for at least 16 hours and 40 minutes before leaving. Presumably the birds left the nest to drink. On the two occasions when *B* left for a recess, *A* entered the nest before *B* returned.

When the adults were not disturbed, the observed

periods when the nest was unattended were as follows:

Date		Minutes absent	Adult leaving
April	4	85	B
	5	80	A
	6	99	A
	19	45	A
	21	61	B
May	2	43	B
	2	18	A and B
	6	16	B

The average absence was 56 minutes, the extremes 16 and 99 minutes. A entered the nest at the end of each period. These data suggest a trend of decreasing periods off the nest toward the end of the incubation period. The egg was continuously attended for at least 30 hours, and perhaps for more than two days, before it hatched.

The duration of these undisturbed absences was rarely exceeded by absences occurring after an adult was flushed from the nest during the soaring hours of the day. The longest periods that the egg was known to be unattended during the day were 103 and 138 minutes. When the adult was flushed from the nest one evening (April 15), the egg was unattended for at least 14 hours (overnight).

With a single exception (on the day of hatching), B left the nest from 16 to 85 minutes before A entered. The behavior of B in leaving did not suggest that it had seen its mate flying in the vicinity. How, then, did A know that the nest was empty? Once when B was flushed from the nest, A entered 42 minutes later. Twice when A was flushed from the nest, B entered less than 80 minutes later. These actions suggest that the adult not in the nest was seldom more than one hour of flight away, and that it discovered that the nest was empty by recognizing its mate in the air or by returning to the vicinity of the nest from time to time and looking into the cave. At nests where the sitting adult is not visible from the outside, the bird in the nest may occasionally come to the entrance (as it did at nest 1) and stand for a few minutes where a passing bird could see it.

Sharing of feeding the young bird.—The number of times that each adult was seen to feed the young bird at nest 1 was as follows.

Nestling 5 to 13 weeks old: *A*, 4; *B*, 6.
Nestling 14 to 19 weeks old: *A*, 7; *B*, 2.
Juvenile 24 to 28 weeks old: *A*, 6; *B*, 2.

In the first half of its nest life the youngster may have been fed more often by B than by A. Later A fed the youngster more than twice as often as B fed it. When both parents were perched near the nest or juvenile, it was always A which first fed the young bird (seven instances). One day I saw A feed the juvenile two times, 3½ hours apart, while B did not feed it at all. There was no apparent difference between the parents in the time of day, location in the nest, speed, or manner of feeding the nestling.

Behavior of nesting adults toward each other.—Whether in or out of the nest, the perched adults seemed to pay little attention to each other. Once both adults were in nest 1 for 20 minutes and did not touch each other. Near another nest the two adults perched on the same branch for three hours without interaction. A few days after the egg in one nest became broken, I saw the pair perched 100 yards from the nest. One tugged at the cheeks and nibbled the head of the other. The latter nudged the head of the first, then, holding its own head inverted, thrust its bill under the chin of its mate. Later each tried to nibble the ruff of the other at the same time. Finally the second took off and the first followed. A similar action was seen between the same (?) birds the previous fall shortly before the chick left the nest. I do not believe that this chick survived.

Several times after the brooding stage I saw both adults perched near nest 1 or near the juvenile after it left the nest. Whenever there was any interaction, A approached B and followed it in movements on the cliff, and B moved away as if annoyed. Finley (1908b: 59, 60) saw similar action near a nest containing a young chick. "She nosed him . . . but he responded . . . by moving away and she followed. This crowded him out where the limb was too small, and he jumped across back of her." The "male" soon took off and the other followed. At least twice I saw A leave the nest to follow B in the air but never the reverse. Once I saw B peck A as if in retaliation for nibbling. These actions seem to be evidence of social dominance between the members of the pair.

When both parents perched near nest 1 or the juvenile at the same time, A was usually the first to arrive. On two occasions the heads of the adults were similarly discolored with blood or dust as if both birds had fed on the same carcass and returned to the nest together. They landed from 10 minutes to one hour apart but left as long as three hours apart.

In approaching the nest or in leaving to forage the adults may fly together. Usually they soar from one-quarter to one-half mile apart, but at nest 4 on a windy day I saw a joint flight. The incubating adult left the nest and met its relief in air, and the pair swooped, dove, turned and flapped together for 20 minutes, one following or beneath the other, seldom over 100 feet apart. At this nest I saw a chasing flight when the chick was only half grown. One displaced the other on a perch, then chased it in the air for five minutes before both perched near the nest. At this same nest sexual display was seen two or three weeks before the chick was ready to leave the nest.

To summarize, the usual relationship between the members of the pair after the brooding stage seems to be as follows: The parents roost at suitable perches near the nest, sometimes within a few feet of each other. In the morning, if one feeds the young bird, the other may wait for it. Then the pair departs to forage. The two often fly together but rarely does one chase the other. They return from foraging either separately or together. One, perhaps the female, is more attached to the nest than the other and generally enters the nest first when both adults are present. If the birds return separately, the first to return feeds the youngster.

One adult generally follows the other in walking, shifting perches, or taking off, and on occasions it gently nibbles the head of its mate. At nest 1 this was the probable female. The other adult moves away from the first and seems to resent the nibbling. It may peck back as if in retaliation, but at other times the gentle nudging and nibbling is mutual. Chasing flights and sexual display may occur while the chick is still in the nest.

SUMMARY OF DIFFERENCES IN BEHAVIOR BETWEEN THE MEMBERS OF THE PAIR AT NEST 1

I. Differences probably due to sex.
1. A (the female?) performed most of the incubation.
2. During the incubation and continuous brooding stages, A normally remained in the nest until B entered, but B rarely remained until A entered.

3. A changed position, fidgeted, and rose from sitting in the nest much less frequently than B.
4. A usually commenced its turn in the nest after returning from foraging in the afternoon. B usually waited until morning before relieving A.
5. A was bolder than B during the late incubation stage. B was bolder than A during the early incubation and continuous brooding stages.
6. B performed most of the continuous brooding.
7. A fed the young bird twice as often as B fed it after the middle nestling stage.
8. A waited a shorter time than B between landing and entering the nest or feeding the young bird.
9. When both adults were perched near the nest or juvenile, A was the first to feed the young bird.

II. Differences probably due to social dominance.
1. In walking or shifting perches, A generally followed B and sometimes crowded B.
2. A took off to follow B more frequently than the reverse.
3. When A came close, B usually moved away.
4. A initiated mutual nibbling or nudging of the heads. B sometimes pecked in retaliation.

III. Differences due to individuality.
1. Usually A sat in the nest facing one direction and B sat facing the opposite direction.
2. B tended to land at the nest and depart from the nest earlier and later in the day than A.
3. In approaching the nest A walked along the top of the cliff more frequently than B.

RELATIONS BETWEEN THE PARENTS AND YOUNG

Time and frequency of feeding young.—In the course of the continuous brooding stage at nest 1, the apparent periods of feeding the chick occurred at about 10 a.m. and 5 p.m. After the brooding stage, in 12 of 17 observations in which an adult was seen to land near nest 1 and enter it, the landing occurred between 2:30 p.m. and 5 p.m. However, the birds were often disturbed and consequently did not enter the nest on their first visit of the day. Figure 13 shows the distribution in time of the observations which I judged to represent the first landing of the day for each adult.

Considering the roosting and feeding habits of condors, the bimodality of figure 13 indicates that

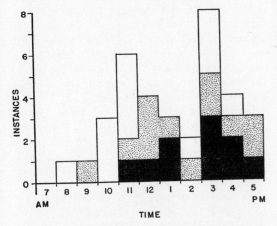

Figure 13. Times of day that the parents first landed near nest 1 during the middle and late nestling stages (35 instances). Black squares, adult *A*; stippled squares, adult *B*; white squares, adult not individually identified.

the adults most frequently returned from foraging at about 3 p.m. and fed the chick, but almost as often they roosted overnight after returning from foraging and fed the chick on the following morning when soaring conditions became favorable. Occasionally an adult was disturbed upon its arrival near the nest in the afternoon so that it waited until morning to go to the nest. Nevertheless, of six instances in which an adult was seen perched on the nest cliff when no person had been near the nest for at least one day, four instances occurred in the modal classes of figure 13 (two in each) and two instances in the 10 a.m. class. At various nests I saw adults visit the chick in the morning when there was no possibility of previous disturbance. At nest 1 there seemed to be no tendency for the same adult to feed the chick in the mornings and the other to feed it in the afternoons.

The two earliest landings seen at nest 1 occurred when an adult had been flushed from the nest the previous afternoon. After July 1 no landings before 10 a.m. were seen during the nestling stage, even though on three occasions an adult was flushed before it fed the chick in the previous afternoon. Perhaps

the drive to feed the chick diminished as the youngster grew.

At five other nests I saw an adult visit the chick a total of 15 times. All but two observations were made between 9 a.m. and 5 p.m. The earliest and latest instances (8:55 a.m. and 6 p.m.) occurred at nests where the adults roosted close by and did not have to fly far between the nest and their roosting place.

On at least six days of observation at nest 1 the chick was fed but once. On four other days I saw each adult enter the nest once. On three of these occasions I could not be sure that the chick was fed on the second visit (from 10 to 100 minutes after the first feeding), but on the fourth occasion the chick was well fed on the second visit (four hours after the first feeding). The chick was capable of taking two meals a day but took them with zest only if they were offered a few hours apart.

The same adult was not seen to enter nest 1 twice in any one day. Once an adult landed on the nest cliff one hour after it had left the nest, but this bird had not fed the chick on the first visit. At nest 2 I saw the late nestling fed three times at intervals of about one hour, but one adult had been disturbed and had left the chick after feeding it briefly. The adult which has not fed the chick might experience some physical discomfort, such as distension of the crop, which is relieved by feeding the chick. Perhaps it is psychological tension. The longest that one adult was known to go without feeding the chick was 78 hours or more. After this interval the bird was unusually persistent in returning to the nest although the chick had been fed by the other adult within 24 hours. When chick 2 had not been fed for 45 hours, the adult was unusually bold in approaching the nest. On occasions the adults entered the nest within one-half hour of each other although the chick had been fed within 24 hours. The need of the chick for food seemed to have no effect on the schedule of the adults.

Adults can retain food overnight before feeding the chick. At nest 2, I saw the chick fed at least 20 hours after the adults returned from foraging. Because of disturbance they did not feed the nestling in the afternoon but roosted near the nest. The following morning both fed the chick before departing to forage. This was the only observation made at any nest which suggested that both adults may enter the nest in the same morning.

With regard to feeding the chick in the morning, the situation seems to be as follows. The first adult to return from foraging feeds the chick. The second may enter the nest soon after the first departs, but the chick, satisfied with its first meal, will feed but little or not at all. Adults might become conditioned so that they tend not to enter the nest when their mate has fed the chick; then only one would attempt to enter the nest in the afternoon. In the morning the adult which did not feed the chick on the previous afternoon feeds it before leaving to forage. The adults may return from foraging so late in the day that they do not have time to go to the nest before roosting; then they visit the nest in the morning. Possibly food must be macerated in the crop for a certain period before it can be fed to the chick, but I saw an adult feed a juvenile not over 85 minutes after the adult had fed on a fresh carcass.

The times of landing of the adults near the juvenile after it left nest 1 were about the same as the times during the nestling stage (compare figures 13 and 14). The main difference was that in the juvenile

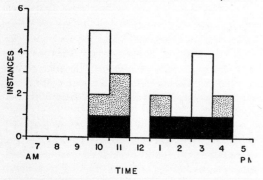

Figure 14. Time of day that the parents landed near juvenile 1 after it left the nest (17 instances). See legend for figure 13.

stage the parents tended to land earlier in the morning. Five of 17 observed landings occurred between 9:30 a.m. and 10:00 a.m. Such early arrivals were rare in the nestling stage. The adults may have landed earlier than before because the youngster was on an exposed perch where it could easily be seen and approached. On two of the five early visits the juvenile was not fed. The extreme times of landing near the juvenile were 9:30 a.m. and 4:20 p.m. The extreme times of departure after feeding the juvenile were

9:50 a.m. and 4:35 p.m. At other nests I saw a flightless juvenile fed on five occasions, all between 10:45 a.m. and 3:10 p.m.

In nine full days of observation I saw juvenile 1 fed twice on three days, but it was visited by an adult at least twice on two additional days. On the three days when two feedings were seen, they occurred 10, 20, and 200 minutes apart. On some days the chick was fed but once and one day it was not visited by the adults, although there was no disturbance. Apparently the juvenile is fed no more frequently after it leaves the nest than when it is in the nest.

Under undisturbed conditions, the maximum period between feedings is rarely over 24 hours. The longest period of starvation observed when there was no disturbance was 40 hours. Because of disturbance, chick 1 went without food for the following intervals:

Over 24   hours at 38 days of age
Over 54½ hours at 61 days of age
Over 53½ hours at 107 days of age
Over 44   hours at 115 days of age
Over 44   hours at 152 days of age

At nest 2 the chick went without food for 45 hours when it was about 18 weeks old. I noted no signs of weakness in these starved birds although an apparent "hunger streak" (Bond, 1942:81) was produced in the tail feathers of chick 1. Evidently a healthy nestling can stand more than two days of starvation when it is nine weeks old. This ability to go without food for long periods adds to the safety of the nestling from starvation when food is scarce or when the adults are kept from the nest.

Manner of feeding the young.—Several times during the continuous brooding stage at nest 1, I saw activity which seemed to be feeding of the chick. The action continued about 6 minutes. The wavering head of the chick reached upward and the adult held its bill vertically near the chick for several periods of 5 to 20 seconds each. Even in the first week after the chick hatched it seemed to be fed in about the same manner as later. The details of the feeding action were not clearly observed until the chick was 8 weeks old. Thereafter an adult was seen to feed the nestling 12 times, the activity was photographed three times, and at three other nests I saw feeding eight times.

Until it was about 15 weeks old chick 1 showed no reaction to the aerial approach of an adult. Thereafter it often held its wings out and peered upward and occasionally it gave a short series of grunts when the adult was flying at least 200 yards away. At about 18 weeks of age chick 2 spent much of the day on an open shelf outside of the nest cave. It reacted to the approach of an adult as far as a quarter of a mile away by spreading its wings, looking up, and flapping gently.

After juvenile 1 left the nest, it nearly always reacted to the aerial approach of an adult by begging, sometimes flapping rapidly. The increase in the reaction of the youngster may have been due to the fact that visibility of the surrounding air was much better from outside the nest than from inside. Flapping probably helped to inform the approaching adult of the location of the juvenile. This purpose is served by the location call in many birds. The head of the juvenile often followed the course of the soaring adult. After the adult landed, the juvenile continued to flap, and at times it grunted. Occasionally the youngster turned 360 degrees, begging at the same time, while awaiting its parent.

On occasions the juvenile pays no apparent attention to the approaching adult. Once juvenile 2 remained sitting until the adult perched beside it. It paid little attention to its parents when they were perched 20 or 30 yards away although once it commenced to beg three minutes before its soaring parent landed. Differences in hunger probably caused the differences in the reactions of the juvenile. When the youngster is not hungry, it may not beg when the adult approaches. This lack of response may inhibit the feeding reaction of the parent. I had no opportunity to observe whether juveniles would react to adults other than their parents.

When chick 1 was eight weeks old and had not been fed for more than 54 hours, it walked about and gently flapped when the approaching adult flew from one point to another on the nest cliff. Normally, until three months of age, this chick showed no anticipation of feeding until the adult landed on the lip of the nest. Thereafter, when the adult landed on top of the cliff the nestling often hissed, and when the adult landed on the ledge within sight of the chick, the young bird demonstrated vigorously by begging, hissing, and grunting. If the adult waited for several minutes before flying to the nest, the chick ceased begging and waited in the feeding attitude or resumed other activities.

Although I often heard a soaring adult before I saw it, nestlings were not seen to react to the approach of an adult until it was in sight. It may be that the bright red color of the distended ventral cervical apterium of the parent is a sign stimulus which releases begging action in the chick. As the young bird develops, it may become conditioned so that it reacts to other indications of the approach of an adult.

While the adult stood on the lip of nest 1 before stepping in, the chick remained well back in the cave in the feeding attitude, at times begging vigorously. At other nests, too, I noted that nestlings rarely moved toward the parent in order to be fed. When chick 2 was about 18 weeks old, an adult stood five feet from it for 20 minutes while the chick alternately begged and stood quietly; the chick did not approach the adult. On occasions the parent pecked sand from the floor just before feeding the chick.

The chick does not attempt to feed until the adult lowers its head and holds its bill approximately vertically a few inches above the floor. Then the chick thrusts its bill into the gape of the adult and the two heads lock in a feeding contact. Occasionally the parent is forced back a step or two by the struggling chick. The adult gradually raises its head until the chick can no longer maintain contact. Then the adult closes its bill. The nestling may try to force its bill into the closed bill of the adult. After the contact ends the adult slowly lowers its head and another contact commences.

In each contact the locked heads pump back and forth about four inches at a rate of two pumps per second. The pumping action seems to be caused mainly by the efforts of the chick, for it performs a similar movement in begging. On the other hand, in regurgitating when not feeding a chick, a condor moves its head downward with strong repeated strokes. Possibly, then, the adult contributes to the movement of the locked heads.

Until it was about three months of age, chick 1 remained in the feeding attitude throughout the period of feeding. In this posture it squatted low so that the base of its throat appeared to touch the floor, extended its wings to the sides with their tips resting on the floor, and crooked its neck with the bill slanting upward. Even after it left the nest, the juvenile squatted low on the perch with its body horizontal and its wings extended and drooping.

Before and between contacts the head of the chick pumps upward and forward, and the body bounces up and down in unison with this pumping and the beating of the wings. This action I consider to be begging. Feeding flaps are given in a short arc from about horizontal to perch level. The upward stroke seems more rapid than the downward stroke. The wings are held in a relaxed manner and the flapping often raises the dust in the nest. The rate of flapping may be very slow but occasionally it is as rapid as three flaps per second. Flaps usually occur in groups of about five with a pause between groups.

After the age of three months chick 1 often stood on its tarsi, or even on its feet, in reaching after the rising bill of the adult. At times the nestling growled between contacts. There was little or no flapping during contacts but much flapping when the bill of the chick commenced to pull out of the mouth of the adult. Then flapping usually continued until the next contact was made. On occasions the adult was struck on the head or back by one flapping wing of the chick. Once I saw the adult push the offending wing off with its bill and then peck at the juvenile. A few times I saw an adult put one foot on top of the head of a young bird during a feeding contact or when pecking at it.

Often the chick seems to be less eager for food at the first contact than in later contacts. Usually it shows little eagerness in the final contact as if its appetite is satisfied. The number of contacts required to satisfy the young bird is variable. In one instance a juvenile appeared to be satisfied after two contacts, but another time it continued to beg vigorously after five contacts. In a period of feeding from three to eight (usually five) contacts are made. Each contact lasts from 10 to 60 seconds (usually about 25 seconds). The normal interval between contacts is approximately 15 seconds. I discovered no change in the number and duration of contacts as the youngster grew, at least after it was two months old. As there is no increase in the number of feedings per day, it appears that as the young condor grows and the capacity of its crop increases the rate of transfer of food during each feeding contact must increase.

In nest 1, at the start of feeding the adult normally stood partly in the north chamber, facing southward, and the chick squatted near the back wall facing the left side of the adult. Even after it left the nest, juvenile 1 normally commenced feeding from the left side of the adult as if from habit. A juvenile which had been raised in a more spacious nest commenced feeding from either side or from the front of the adult. At other nests the feeding chick faced at right angles to the adult, and the adult stood between the chick and the outer edge of the nest.

In feeding contacts the longitudinal axes of the locked heads are about parallel. The chick normally inserts its bill at the corner of the mouth of the adult and thrusts it far back into the throat. Occasionally the chick holds its head inverted as it inserts its bill. While in the mouth of the adult the head of the chick is usually cocked 45 degrees, but it may be right side up or sideways. On occasions I saw that the tongue of the adult was out to the tip of the lower mandible during a feeding contact. The method of feeding is similar in the black vulture (Bent, 1937:33) and in the turkey vulture (*ibid.*:16).

While the heads are locked, the cheeks and chin of the chick ripple as if its bill were opening and closing, or as if its tongue were working back and forth with each pump of the head. Dark liquid may be smeared on the face and breast of the young bird or splattered on the head of the adult. When chick 1 was eight weeks old, I saw it withdraw a chunk of food from the throat of the adult and swallow it. At 14 weeks of age it pecked at pieces of food which protruded from the throat of the adult, and it picked up and swallowed chunks of food which had dropped to the floor.

After the last contact the adult turns away from the chick and goes to the entrance of the nest. It may pick up particles from the floor and drop them again or wipe its bill on the sandstone. When feeding the juvenile out of the nest, the adult normally holds its wings up as if for balancing. Between contacts the adult looks around or picks up spilled food. Either in or out of the nest, the adult usually takes off within two minutes after feeding the chick. The maximum post-feeding stay of an adult in nest 1 was six minutes. Once I saw an adult remain by a juvenile out of the nest for 18 minutes after feeding it; occasionally it preened the young bird.

In 13 typical feedings at nest 1 the adult was in the nest cave for 2 to 6 minutes (median 3 minutes). The stay was normally within these limits at other nests. The maximum period that the adult remained in the cave when chick 1 was fed was 11 minutes. Once *B* remained in the nest for 18 minutes, but it did not feed the chick. For the juvenile stage at nest 1, the interval from the landing to the departure of the adult was from 5 to 36 minutes (median 15 minutes) when the chick was surely fed.

The flapping movement of the chick seems to release the feeding action of the adult. Once *B* entered the nest 25 minutes after the chick had been fed. The chick assumed the feeding attitude and remained quiet. The adult did not feed the chick but soon turned away and faced out of the cave. Then the chick commenced to flap and the adult reentered the cave and fed it. Another time the chick continued to flap after the adult had fed it and had crouched to take off. The adult reached back with its head and gave the chick another brief feeding. Under similar circumstances at another nest, an adult returned from a perch a few feet below the nest in order to feed the begging chick. At times the adult may not return in spite of the begging.

Usually the chick ceases begging when the adult turns away after the last feeding contact, and it abandons the feeding attitude before or immediately after the adult takes off. After the adult leaves, the chick stands for several seconds with its wings out and drooping. Occasionally it makes wheezing sounds just after the adult flies. On an occasion when an adult was flushed before it had fed the nestling, the young bird jumped up and down and grunted for a few minutes. Again, when an adult was flushed halfway through a feeding, the chick came to the entrance of the nest and looked after the departing bird.

The tolerance of the adults for disturbance increases after they enter the nest. If the adult is disturbed while in the nest, it may hold its wings several inches out from its body and spread its tail, as if to hide the chick while feeding it. In one such instance, a photographer shouted continually trying to make the adult move out of the way. Three times the adult opened its bill and lowered its head as if to feed the chick, but each time it rose up nervously before making contact, and finally it left without feeding the youngster. On a similar occasion the disturbed adult turned back toward the chick and made another contact before taking off.

Food of the young.—When a chick was about 3 days old, and again when it was about 7 days old, one of its parents regurgitated when flushed from the nest or when prevented from entering. Presumably the regurgitated food was to have been fed to the chick. On the first occasion the disgorged food consisted of 2 ounces of meat in four chunks. The meat was soft and had a foul odor. In the second instance about one pint was disgorged. Most of the material was thumb-sized chunks of white tissue and soft red meat. Other pieces were: a white blood vessel 8 inches long and one-quarter inch in diameter, a strip of hide 10 inches long which bore slipping hair (deer?), and a chunk of fat 2 inches square and three-fourths of an inch thick. Once a chick about 3 weeks old regurgitated three chunks of meat. The largest piece was a section of muscle and white tissue 4 inches long, one inch wide, and three-eighths of an inch thick. The meat was of moderate tensile strength. Evidently the chick is fed solid meat before it is 3 weeks old.

The young condor kept by Finley (1910:6, 7) from the age of 15 to 27 weeks "was fed twice a day with about a pound of raw meat and given plenty of water." This bird was fed on clean fresh meat from the time that it was taken from the nest. It apparently became conditioned to the eating of fresh beef, regardless of its eating habits when fed by its parents, for Finley found that it refused meat which had been on the ground and would not eat squirrel, rabbit, or "stale meat" if fresh beef was available.

Other relations.—For at least one week after the egg hatched in nest 1 the adults brooded the chick as constantly as they had incubated the egg. When the chick was 2 days old it was first left alone. *B* departed from the nest before *A* arrived and the chick was alone for 16 minutes. After an adult was flushed from the nest, the chick was left alone for 45 minutes at 7 days of age, 53 minutes at 9 days of age, 4 hours at 23 days of age, and 5¼ hours at 24 days of age. Apparently when the chick was about three weeks old, the adults would not leave it alone for longer than about 5 hours.

I am not certain when the stage of brooding-at-night-only commenced and ended at any nest. Chick 1 was brooded continuously when it was 7 days old and was brooded at least at night when it was 24 days old. I visited nest 9 in the middle of the day when the chick was 3 weeks, 4 weeks, and 6 weeks old, but I did not find an adult brooding. Pemberton observed that chick 1 was not brooded one night when it was 5 weeks old, but on that occasion the adult had been flushed late in the day. Finley (1908b:61) states that when his chick was 34 days old he found an adult brooding. When flushed, the parent roosted nearby, and it visited the nest for one hour the next morning. This action suggests that the chick may be brooded at night when it is 5 weeks old. Chick 1 was not brooded at night when it was 8 weeks old. Brooding evidently ceases at about the time that the second down covers the nestling.

During the nestling stage at some nests one parent was seldom far away. At nest 4, where both adults roosted nearby, on three consecutive days in August the longest period that no adult was present was two hours on two days and six hours on the intervening day. Halfway through the longest absence I saw the pair soaring within one mile of the nest. Once at nest 5 an adult arrived and fed the chick only one-half hour after its mate had first left the area, and it remained nearby the rest of the day.

The brooding adults draw the chick toward themselves with the bill in about the same manner as they move the egg. Finley (1906:141, 142) removed a chick one day old from the nest and placed it near the sitting adult. "The old bird just sat with her head down and paid no attention to the chick under her nose, who had now grown too weak to even squirm." The chick was warmed and replaced near the adult. "For an instant she paid no attention to him, but just then he began to stir and wriggle." Then "putting her bill down she drew him gently near, crouching down at the same time and finally drawing him under her breast."

On rare occasions an adult stayed many minutes with the young bird. When chick 1 was about 13 weeks old B entered the nest 10 minutes after A had fed the chick. Soon B sat and the chick sat by its side and occasionally flapped. Several minutes later B stood and pecked at the side and tarsus of the chick and at a chunk of excrement in its down. The crop of B still bulged when it left the nest 18 minutes after entering. One hour later B returned to the nest cliff. The actions of sitting and pecking at the chick might be considered substitute activities inasmuch as the normal activity, feeding the chick, was not consummated.

A similar action occurred one month after juvenile 1 left the nest. Both adults were perched near the

young bird. A fed it and departed at 10:20 a.m. B did not approach the youngster until more than one hour later. Several times the juvenile begged. It poked, rubbed, bit, and pulled at the bill, head, and neck of the adult. B gently pecked at the wings, bill, head, and throat of the youngster and once put its closed bill between the mandibles of the juvenile. When the youngster bit its rostrum, B twisted its head away. The parent tolerated much plucking but occasionally gave a sharp peck as if in retaliation. Twice B hopped to the top of a boulder as if to escape the attentions of the youngster. The two were together for about 100 minutes and the crop and cheeks of the adult were bulging, but the juvenile was not fed. The sight of A feeding the chick may have inhibited the feeding reaction of B.

Another time an adult remained near juvenile 1 for 18 minutes after feeding it. Possibly the adult had emptied its crop but was kept at the spot by the begging actions of the young bird.

Mild disturbance inhibits feeding of the young. On one occasion an adult perched beside a juvenile for over 20 minutes. The juvenile begged and several times succeeded in getting its bill in the mouth of the sitting adult, but there was no feeding. At times the adult pecked sharply at the youngster. This adult then perched 100 feet from the juvenile and returned and fed it an hour later. James Fassero, an experienced photographer of golden eagles, told me that often when a man is near an eagle will come to the nest but will not feed the young.

Finley (1908b:65) removed a chick 15 weeks old from the nest and placed it on a ledge while the parents were standing near. The "mother edged down to her young. Then she began caressing him, pushing her head under his wing and biting him gently on the leg." In spite of the apparent tameness of the adults, Finley did not see them feed the chick.

A few times when an adult was seen to perch near a juvenile in the morning, before departing to forage, there was no begging and no feeding. The adults may have been attracted to the vicinity of the juvenile even when they had nothing to feed it.

The movements of the young bird after it leaves the nest are somewhat directed by the tendency of the juvenile to approach the parent in order to be fed. One instance of such "luring" occurred one month after juvenile 1 left the nest. It was perched on the top of a dead oak below the nest. The juvenile flapped vigorously as *A* walked along the top of the cliff above it. *A* dropped down to the ledge and walked to a point six feet from the juvenile. The youngster leaped to the slanting edge of the ledge and clung for a moment, then it scrambled up to the adult and was fed. This was the highest perch that the juvenile had gained up to that time.

Relations between parents and the volant juvenile. —The juvenile may be fed by an adult until the summer of its second year of life. Before that time it often follows an adult within the limitations of its flying ability. Even when the juvenile can fly well, the adult often approaches it in order to feed it. Adults may lead the juvenile to food. Young feed themselves to some extent while still being fed by adults. The juvenile may perch or roost near the nest site, not infrequently with one or both parents. It may be that adults chase the juvenile from the nest area during the mating season.

Some of these relations are illustrated by observations made near a carcass in Hopper Canyon on June 12, 1946. At 9:50 a.m. an adult and a juvenile circled over the carcass and alighted in a tree, the juvenile 50 feet below the adult. The juvenile gave feeding flaps, climbed to higher branches, took off, and alighted on the same branch as the adult. The young bird then begged vigorously and approached the adult but fell from the perch. Both were at the carcass 10 minutes later. The juvenile was chased from the carcass several times by two other immatures so that it could not feed. An adult left the carcass and perched in a tree and a juvenile soon perched 20 feet below it (same birds?). The adult descended to the juvenile, fed it, and took off 20 minutes later. The juvenile remained on the same branch at least five hours.

One morning in April I saw an adult and a juvenile land by a month-old horse carcass and feed gingerly. The adult soon left and the juvenile remained, but it was evidently kept from the horse by a group of ravens and turkey vultures.

At a certain isolated group of cliffs I often saw a juvenile, sometimes with one or two adults, between December and March. The morning of January 5 an adult went to the juvenile and apparently fed it. Then the juvenile nudged and pulled at the neck of the adult and the adult nipped back. Eventually the adult took off and the juvenile, apparently less than one year old, followed. Both rose about 500 feet and soared toward a feeding area.

In March, 1940, I approached juvenile 1, which was marked with a band, not far from the nest where it had been hatched the previous spring. Within a few minutes a pair of adults alighted in the roost trees which had been used by the adults at nest 1.

Philip Pringer (letter March 7, 1905) saw two adults apparently feeding a juvenile in Eaton Canyon in February, 1905. Grinnell (MS) saw an adult and immature perched side by side there about May 20, 1905. Condors nested close to that spot in 1906.

Near one nest I saw a juvenile begging and evidently being fed on March 23, and A. J. Wool saw a similar action there on August 15 of the same year. Harriet Boyce, lookout at Big Pine Mountain, saw a juvenile fed near her station on four separate afternoons in July, 1946. One day both adults fed the young bird. Other persons saw a juvenile fed at that locality the previous October, and I saw begging nearby in July of another year.

At one section of cliffs where there was apparently a nest in 1941, I saw an immature begging on August 10, October 7, and November 9, 1940. On each occasion the young bird took off and followed an adult. In one instance the juvenile was initially perched in a small pothole with two adults. A juvenile which could fly in August could not be a young of the year. At that same locality I saw two adults chasing a young bird vigorously for several minutes on January 8, 1941. Several times this juvenile flew toward a cliff near the nest site as if to perch, but each time both adults overtook the youngster and flew above it so that it could not land. Twice the juvenile landed but it took off within a few seconds after an adult landed near it.

A few times in summer and early fall, before young of the year were flying, I saw an adult remain perched near a volant juvenile for one hour or more after begging occurred, although there was no feeding. At times the juvenile pecked at or nudged the head of the adult and the adult pecked back. In July an adult roosted in the same tree with a volant juvenile. In the morning they wrestled with their heads and necks and the adult preened the young bird. When flying with an adult, a juvenile usually follows and alights after the adult. A few times I saw an adult alight after a juvenile and then feed it.

RELATIONS BETWEEN THE NESTING PAIR AND OTHER CONDORS

Nest 1 was close to a flight lane used by condors in leaving or approaching their roosts, but foreign condors were rarely seen within 200 yards of the nest and never were seen to land near it. The nesting pair noticed condors more than any other birds and seemed to watch nearly every one which passed within their field of vision. Once I saw these two condors circling near the nest with a third adult. Occasionally the bird leaving nest 1 joined others which were soaring a mile or more away.

In not one instance did I see an adult from nest 1 attempt to drive off another condor. Finley (1908b: 65) saw one member of a pair take off and chase one or two adults which soared high over the nest. Nest 2 was close to a group of popular roosting trees. One morning I saw at least 10 condors roosting within a quarter of a mile of this nest. On other occasions a perched member of the pair paid no apparent attention to an immature condor perched 100 feet from nest 2, or to an adult perched 100 yards away.

Nesting adults occasionally chase immature individuals. I saw one of the pair at nest 2 take off and chase an immature which was soaring with two adults a few hundred feet above the nest. Finley (1908b:64) tells of seeing one of the parents chase a subadult which perched a few hundred yards away. The subadult retreated but remained nearby and once perched on a tree about 40 feet from the nest. One adult drove the bird off but chased it only a short distance. Dawson (1924:1722) saw an adult pursuing an immature condor near a nest containing a downy chick.

The few observations of Finley suggest that a nesting territory is defended by condors. My own observations at several nests indicate no defense. Most of the opportunities for encounters were seen near nest 2 which was situated close to frequented roosts, while Finley's nest was in an area where other condors were rarely seen. It may be that pairs which seldom encounter other condors are more likely to drive them away than pairs which meet other condors every day.

To my knowledge, the shortest distance between two condor nests used simultaneously was about one-half mile. The same areas tend to be used for nesting over a period of years so that more or less permanent territories may exist, and these territories are so few that over a period of years other condors learn to avoid them. Immatures would be more likely than adults to wander into out-of-the-way places. It is unlikely that the area surrounding nest sites which are located close to roosting and drinking places used by many condors could be defended with any degree of success. Territoriality, if existent, is not pronounced in condors.

REACTION OF NESTING ADULTS TO DISTURBANCE BY MAN

In the first several months of this study the results of unintentional disturbances of condors were noted and analyzed. Through evaluation of this information it was found that on occasions, under favorable conditions of weather and at suitable times in the schedule of nest duties of the adults, a nest could be inspected at close range for a short period at midday without causing desertion by the adults or fatal cooling of the egg or young. Although the molestation of nesting birds was regrettable, it was necessary for the obtaining of many facts concerning the young as well as concerning the effects of man on nesting condors.

Old nests.—Early in the nesting season adults may be attracted to old nests when they are entered by man. In February, 1946, two adults alighted 100 yards from a nest cave when I entered it. The nest had been used in 1941 and again before 1945. In March, 1946, while I was in another old nest, an adult landed 100 feet away and peered at me. The nest had been used in 1940 but evidently not since. Neither nest was used in 1946, but possibly the adults nested nearby. I entered three other nests during the breeding season of the year after they were used, but no adults were seen.

Incubation stage.—The adults were extremely wary on the day that I discovered nest 1. While I was sitting 500 yards away, the adult in the nest was uneasy and remained standing at the mouth of the cave for as long as one hour at a time. It flushed when I moved 50 yards closer. Three times later that day, while I remained 500 yards from the nest, an adult landed on the nest cliff but did not enter the nest. When the incubating adult in nest 1 was moderately disturbed, it rose, came to the entrance of the nest, stood for 2 to 36 minutes (average 9 minutes), then returned to the egg. The interval spent standing depended on the severity and duration of the disturbance and on the boldness of the adult at that stage. In the first week of

April the adult stood at the entrance for 2 to 5 minutes whenever a man moved in the open 500 yards away. A shout from the same distance kept the bird at the entrance for 5 to 10 minutes. At another nest the adult was made to stand by shouting and whistling nearly one mile away.

In late April the incubating adult in nest 1 usually departed when a man entered a blind 100 yards from the nest, but it did not flush when a man left this blind. After mid-April I usually watched from an open-sided blind 250 yards west of the nest. Even on the day that the egg hatched, B stood when I entered this blind. Three days before the egg hatched B left the nest when I approached to a point 150 yards away.

At nest 1 there was a trend of increase in the tolerance of the adults for disturbance as incubation advanced. Aside from getting used to observers and photographers, the birds showed an increased attachment to the nest after the first week in April and another increase commencing three days before the egg hatched. The relative boldness of the two adults was not the same at all stages. At first A was more easily flushed than B, but during the last two weeks of incubation the situation was reversed. The tolerance of the sitting adult was variable and often unpredictable. The birds were more easily disturbed by persons approaching the nest than by persons walking away. Often they seemed more disturbed by men several hundred feet away than by men closer to the nest. This difference may have been due to the fact that the more distant men were above the level of the nest while the closer men were below that level.

Often the adult in nest 1 was more easily disturbed when approached the first time during the day than when approached later. One day A rose and stood at the entrance for 13 minutes when I approached to a point 350 yards from the nest at 11 a.m., yet that afternoon I approached in a similar manner to within 200 yards without causing the same bird to rise.

Shortly after sunrise the adult was less easily disturbed than later in the morning. Possibly the drive to incubate is greater at the lower temperatures of early morning. At about sunset the sitting adult was more easily disturbed than earlier in the day; it would rise when I left a distant blind in the evening although it had not risen when I entered the same blind at midday. On April 15 the adult did not flush when three men approached to within 100 yards of the nest and set up a blind, but it did flush when a single man approached to a point 250 yards away at 6 p.m.

Sounds, such as shouting, whistling, the breaking of brush, and especially hand-clapping, were more effective in bringing the adult to the entrance of the nest than any movements by men at the same distance. Probably sounds reverberated in the nest cave. Once I saw the sitting adult turn its head quickly in apparent response to the roar of an airplane several miles away.

While standing in the nest, the alarmed adult held its head low. The more severe the disturbance, the lower the head was held. After the disturbance ceased, the adult slowly raised its head. If the disturbance increased, the bird raised its wings and took off. If the disturbance was very mild, the sitting adult usually did not rise, but the frequency of the movements of its head increased. If it did rise, it stood inside the cave rather than on the lip and lowered its head but slightly.

Many factors may cause variation in the tolerance of incubating adults for disturbance. Some of these factors are: stage of incubation, previous length of time in the nest, time of day, previous disturbance, and egg temperature. Possibly coolness of the egg stimulates the drive to incubate. The adults at nest 1 usually entered the cave and sat with least delay after the egg had been unattended for a time. After a night off the nest A entered the cave about 8 a.m. and was extremely bold, but it flushed easily in the afternoon.

In gauging the effects of disturbance on condors, the varying thresholds for disturbance reactions must be considered. The accompanying table is an attempt to express the relative thresholds for common actions of the adults at nest 1. The table illustrates, for example, that normally a greater degree of disturbance was required to flush the adult from the nest than to prevent its landing on the cliff. With a certain degree of disturbance, the adult would land on the cliff but would not enter the cave unless the disturbance subsided (or the threshold was lowered by accommodation or other factors).

No Response	Relative Stimulus	Response
Land on cliff	xxxxxxxxxxxxxxxx	Not land on cliff
Enter nest	xxxxxxxxxxx	Not enter nest
Sit in nest	xxxxxxx	Stand in nest
Infrequent head movement	xxxx	Frequent head movement
Remain in nest	xxxxxxxxxxxxxxxxxxxxx	Flush from nest

One nest was visited twelve times on various days.

The adult usually flushed when a man first came into view 200 yards from the nest and 50 feet above it. Occasionally, especially when the nest was approached from the slope below, the bird did not flush until the man was 50 feet away. At this nest there was no apparent decrease in flushing distance as incubation progressed. The flushed adult either perched on some tree from 10 yards to 100 yards from the nest, flew back and forth near the nest, or (twice) left the vicinity and did not return during the next hour.

While a man was in this cave, one or both (four instances) adults usually soared nearby and on occasions they perched within 50 feet of the nest. One perched only five yards from a man, but it was more wary on two subsequent days. One adult approached somewhat closer and remained longer than the other. During the incubation period the appearance of the second adult when the nest is entered by a man is rare. Perhaps the adult off the nest roosted nearby. When perched near the invaded nest, the adults showed alarm for a few minutes but then they usually preened and sometimes they sunned or sat when within 25 feet of a man. The previous fall when a late nestling was present, these (same?) adults were very cautious.

Judged by three observations at this site the adult returned to the egg just as quickly (30 to 40 minutes) after a man had entered the nest as when the nest was not approached closer than 200 yards. On two occasions when the flushed adult was perched within 50 feet of the nest at the time the man left, the bird flew to a more distant perch a few minutes later and did not immediately return to the nest. Evidently the adults perched close to the nest because of the intrusion and not because of lack of alarm. If the nest had not been entered, the adults might have seemed as wary as those at nest 1.

At Finley's nest, the adult was flushed by the firing of shots across the canyon although a man shouting 20 feet below the nest had not been able to flush the bird. After more than half an hour the adult returned to the nest. When flushed again, it perched about 30 feet from men near the nest and then soared away (Finley, 1906). One month earlier, in the following year, this nest was visited by two other men. The adult was flushed by a yell from across the canyon but it entered the nest again while the men were close by. The men flushed the adult by yelling and by throwing moss into the nest. The bird returned to the egg and would not leave although it was shoved and poked with a stick for 15 minutes. Occasionally it gave a low hiss and struck at the stick, but generally it acted drowsy unless poked. When the egg was drawn out with a stick, the adult nosed it back under itself again. The adults at this nest were extraordinarily bold when the nest was invaded.

Brooding stage.—The day after the egg hatched in nest 1, *A* behaved the same as in the incubation stage and stood at the entrance of the nest for nine minutes when I left my blind. The next day it stood only 20 seconds in response to the same action by me. Soon after hatching the chick may be so inert that it does not elicit the change from incubation to brooding behavior of the adult. *A* was more wary than *B* during brooding. In the first four days after the egg hatched *B* was watched longer and subjected to more disturbing stimuli than *A*, yet *B* did not once respond by coming to the entrance of the nest while *A* did respond on at least three occasions. When *A* was flushed from the nest one week after the egg hatched, *B* entered before *A* returned.

On two occasions a photographer shouted from a blind near nest 1 in order to make the sitting bird rise so that the chick could be seen. The adult shuffled around sideways, keeping the chick hidden, and sat with its flank toward the man. When sunlight was directed on the brooding adult with a mirror, there was usually no reaction, but on occasions the adult drew its head in a bit and once it rose.

When the young chick is in danger, the adults become bold and are attracted to the nest. One week after the egg hatched in nest 1 the sitting adult almost flushed when I approached within 100 yards, but by alternately approaching and waiting, I reached a point only 40 yards from the sitting bird where I could watch it. One hour later I departed and the adult flushed when I was more than 100 yards away. Two days later the sitting adult flushed at 120 yards, but when a man climbed on top of the nest cliff both adults left a perch one mile away and soared toward the nest. One alighted 100 feet from the man. The man departed but an adult did not enter the nest until 40 minutes later. Finley (1906:139) found it necessary to whistle and yell from a distance of four feet in order to make a brooding adult rise from a chick one day old. The second adult landed 40 feet away. Three weeks later the second adult perched nearby soon after the first was flushed from the nest.

Persons unacquainted with the psychology of birds frequently misinterpret actions such as the foregoing as indicating tameness in nesting condors. Rather, these actions are innate responses to extreme alarm. These responses are strongest during the brooding stage. Certain essential activities, such as feeding the chick, are not performed when the adults are in a state of alarm.

The notes of one photographer tell of an adult condor which was captured in the nest when the chick was about three weeks old. The bird paid little attention to the chick when placed beside it; once it snapped at the youngster. When the adult was released at the mouth of the cave, it battled its captors in trying to return into the nest. Tyrrell (1938:469) lifted a brooding turkey vulture from a nest containing downy young. When released, the adult immediately returned to the nest and covered the young. This action was repeated several times.

When chick 1 was 24 days old, one adult was still bold and remained sitting in the nest while a blind was set up only 40 yards away. Finley (1908b:64, 65) succeeded in sneaking up to a nest without flushing the adult when the chick was five weeks old. After it was flushed, the adult perched nearby and remained overnight. The second adult did not appear until morning. Finley found that the parents became "tamer and tamer" as the chick grew older, but at nest 1, where the young bird was seldom closely approached by man, the adults became more wary. If Finley's birds had really been unconcerned, he would have seen them feed the chick.

Twice I saw an adult regurgitate because of disturbance. When one chick was about three days old, the flushed adult perched in a tree and swung its head toward its feet five times with vigorous regular strokes. A wad of meat was thrown down from the bill. Then the bird stood quietly. Four days later an adult landed at the entrance of this nest while a man was inside. It stood for a few minutes and then disgorged about a pint of soft meat. An adult captured in a nest by some photographers regurgitated about one pint of material. Brooding turkey vultures may regurgitate when disturbed (Coles, 1944:225).

Middle and late nestling stages.—In these stages, the adult which was flushed from the top of the cliff at nest 1 often turned back and soared over the disturbing men or returned once or twice at intervals of 5 to 15 minutes and soared over the nest area. Then it usually did not return until two or three hours later. If flushed in mid-afternoon, the adult did not return that day. After being disturbed at the nest site or before returning to it, the adult, on occasions, perched for 30 minutes or longer on cliffs half a mile from the nest. Soaring back and forth near the nest before landing was most prolonged when the bird seemed to be especially cautious in other actions. When an adult was prevented from landing, it normally soared about 200 feet over the nest area one or two times before departing, but at times it turned away before coming within 200 yards of the nest. If prevented from landing, the adult returned from 15 minutes to 2 hours (usually about half an hour) later and landed.

In early June B was about as tolerant of humans as when chick 1 was brooded only at night. Twice it landed on the nest cliff while unconcealed men were within a distance of 50 yards, but it soon soared away. By the end of June the adults were as wary as in the late incubation stage. The observation blind which I had used in early May did not conceal me well enough to prevent disturbance, and slight movements or sounds from a blind 50 yards from the nest caused perched adults to leave the nest cliff. The entry of the nest early in July by some intruding men may have augmented the caution of the adults. Up to that time no one had been within 50 feet of nest 1. By the end of July the adults were as wary as in the early incubation stage. They flushed from the top of the nest cliff when a man approached within 400 yards of the nest and would not land if a man was in the open 500 yards away. James Fassero, who succeeded in photographing the feeding of the chick in mid-August, said that the condors were much less wary than golden eagles which he had photographed.

The approximate variation in time of the threshold for disturbance reactions of the adults at nest 1 is indicated in figure 15. The threshold was judged by the average flushing distance of an adult perched on the nest cliff. The slightly increased boldness at the end of the late nestling stage followed the banding of the chick (August 20).

Even in the late nestling stage an adult may be attracted to the nest area by disturbance. In September, an adult soared low over two men at the base of

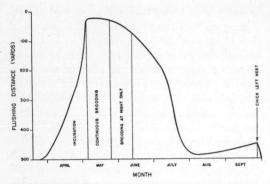

Figure 15. Variation in boldness of the adults at nest as shown by the average flushing distance of the adult perched on the nest cliff.

the cliff below nest 1 at 8:55 a.m. This was an extraordinarily early time for an adult to visit this nest. On the only two occasions when I approached within 20 yards of nest 2, an adult soared back and forth nearby and perched within 30 yards of me. Once the second parent alighted beside the first. When I was visiting nest 4, an adult landed only 15 feet away. As I retreated from the nest, the adult moved to perches farther and farther from the nest in the direction away from me, but it soared low over me when changing perches. The threshold for the fleeing reaction of adults is raised high by the sight of men close to the nest so that the adults may perch nearby, but when the men withdraw, the threshold is lowered and the birds tend to flee. Of course one can visit a nestling when both adults are off foraging without attracting the parent birds.

In the late nestling stage the adults at nest 2 were disturbed by my presence 500 yards away. They often circled low over me when they approached or left the nest and were reluctant to feed the chick if I was not concealed.

The apparent success of a nesting in a big tree near a logging road in Tulare County is due to the position of the nest and the fortuitous timing of disturbances nearby. Of foremost importance is the fact that there was no disturbance in the area during the periods of mating, nest selection, and incubation. The nest site is far above the ground and men in the vicinity are fairly well screened from the view of condors by foliage and tree trunks. It has been pointed out that condors are much more tolerant of men below them than men near their level. Photographs of the juvenile

indicate that it was being brooded at the time that the road was built. In the brooding stage the adults are the most tolerant of disturbance (see figure 15). As crews were small, logging work in the near vicinity was not continuous throughout the day nor continued into the evening. Thus there were long undisturbed periods when adults could go to the nest. The three trucks used traveled together, and as hauling and loading required several hours the disturbance from passing trucks was confined to two or three short periods of the day. Certainly this instance cannot be used as evidence that the activities of man near nest sites are harmless.

Flightless juvenile stage.—After juvenile 1 left the nest its parents became as cautious as at any previous stage of nesting. They departed from the nest cliff if a man stood in the open 500 yards away. Several times after an adult was flushed from near the juvenile in the morning, it did not return again all day. In earlier stages the adult returned within two or three hours. The disturbance threshold for feeding the juvenile was very low in comparison with the threshold for other activities. The photographing of this activity by Ed Harrison was a feat of nature photography.

The pair at nest 2 was more tolerant of men than the pair at nest 1. Twice an adult fed juvenile 2 while a man was in a poor blind 50 yards away. Nest 2 was located close to many roost trees and it had evidently been used before. Nest 1 was distant from frequented roosts and apparently had not been used before. The adults at nest 2 may have derived confidence from the "familiarity of the environment" (Nice, 1943:83). The adults at nest 1 had the opportunity to become used to men but some of this association did not instill confidence. Nest 2 was not entered until after the juvenile had left it and the chick was not closely approached by man.

When the flightless juvenile is distant from the nest, the adults seem to have no further interest in the nest site. In addition, they seem less attached to the young bird than they were to the nest. The adults showed no concern when I entered two nests while the juvenile was perched a few hundred yards away. When I approached close to a flightless juvenile away from the nest site, the maximum reaction of the adults was to perch 200 yards away or to soar back and forth 100 feet overhead.

Summary.—It is apparent that nesting adults are

keenly aware of any man in sight within 500 yards of the nest, and that they will not perform certain activities which have a very low disturbance threshold when men are near. At least they will not perform these activities with normal frequency. One cannot tell whether the normal action of a bird is being inhibited by the presence of the observer unless the normal action of that individual for that particular activity is known. As the environmental influences are many and unknown to the observer, the normal action of a free-living condor cannot be anticipated with certainty.

One man can keep a pair of condors from the egg all night or prevent the feeding of a chick for an entire day merely by exposing himself within 500 yards of a nest for a few minutes at one or two critical times of the day. Loud noises can alarm condors at distances of over one mile. Individuals or groups of persons moving about must keep at least one-half mile from condor nests in order to avoid disturbance of the parent birds. If the adults soar or perch nearby when a man is close to the nest, it is because of their concern for the nest or its contents and not because of their tameness. It is impossible to photograph nesting condors without disturbing them and causing serious deviations from their normal actions.

Behavior of Nestlings and Juveniles

Stages.—Extensive observations of a young condor were made only at nest 1. The chick was eight weeks old before it could be well observed from outside the nest. I observed six other nestlings at irregular intervals. At nest 1, the correlation between the development of the young bird and the behavior of the adults was as follows:

Feather Development	*Relation Between Adults and Young*
Natal down	Chick brooded continuously
Second down appeared	Chick brooded at night only
Juvenal feathers appeared	Chick fed in nest, not brooded
Feathers completed growth	Juvenile out of nest, flightless, entirely dependent
In juvenal plumage	Juvenile volant, somewhat dependent

These stages correspond approximately with the five stages in the psychological development of passerines recognized by Nice (1943:14), and the first three stages correspond with the three main stages of growth in raptors recognized by Sumner (1933:284, 285).

Location in the nest.—The chick stays close to the location of the egg for the first 3 weeks after hatching. Chick 1 was first seen to move toward the entrance of the nest at 24 days of age. In five visits to another chick before it was 4 weeks old I always found it within a few inches of the site of the egg. When chick 1 was 8 weeks old, it usually remained well back in the cave, often lying near the rear wall 3 feet from the lip of the nest, but occasionally it reached a low rock one foot from the lip. At 12 weeks of age the chick sometimes stood on this rock, and at 15 weeks it stood there for as long as 15 minutes at a time. At 19 weeks of age, chick 1 occasionally stood on the lip of the nest with its wings or forebody out of the cave. When chick 2 was about 17 weeks old, it spent most of the day on a shelf just outside the nest cave. In one nest Harold Hill (MS) saw a chick, about 20 weeks old, at the mouth of the nest cave, 20 feet from the site of the egg. To summarize, following the continuous brooding stage the chick gradually increases its scope of movement and perches at the outermost parts of the nest by the time it is ready to leave the nest.

General positions, activity, and locomotion.—Finley (1906:140) found that a chick one day old "could hardly kick, and he seemed to raise his head with difficulty. . . ." Photographs show the chick lying on its belly, the feet and tarsi approximately beneath the body, and the wrists, throat, and bill resting on the ground. I examined a chick about three days old. It could not raise its head and its bill lay in the sand of the floor. It shook constantly as if shivering although the air was not cold. Twenty minutes after the adult left a chick that was about eight days old the youngster was shivering. Evidently temperature control is poor for the first week.

At one week of age a chick raised its head high toward the head of its parent. Another stood on its tarsi with the body almost erect for more than one minute when alarmed. Then it dropped onto its belly and the bill dropped to the floor. When strongly alarmed, a chick about 12 days old turned around easily, shuffling on its tarsi. For half an hour while a man was in the nest, this chick stood on its tarsi and its head did not droop to the floor. Probably the nervous mechanisms for some motor coordinations appear before the chick has the strength to accomplish them.

From the age of eight to 14 weeks, chick 1 lay on the floor continuously for periods as long as one hour. It lay on its belly, usually half on one side, its head lying on the sand. When the head was raised, the posterior half of the throat rested on the ground. The wings often sagged to the floor. One or both legs lay slanting posteriorly, the soles of the feet upward. The chick seldom lay for as much as 15 minutes without moving a wing or a leg. In laying its head on the floor the chick put its bill down and allowed the head to fall sideways. The sitting position, with the tarsi beneath the breast, usually preceded or followed the lying position, and the chick changed gradually from one position to the other. There was little improvement in the skill and strength of the chick between eight and 12 weeks of age, but considerable improvement between 12 and 14 weeks of age. Possibly this difference was due to variations, caused by disturbance, in the regularity of feeding.

When chick 1 was eight weeks old, I saw it remain

standing on its feet for as long as one-half hour at a time. However, while it was active, it usually stood on its tarsi. At 14 weeks of age this chick remained on its feet for at least 50 minutes while active. One chick 18 weeks old stood on its feet for at least seven of 10 hours of observation on one day.

Nest 1 was so small that when the chick moved about it was visible to the observer. By the time the bird was 12 weeks old, it was evident that it tended to be alternately active and inactive during most of the day, to be inactive commencing shortly after being fed, and to be active shortly after sunset.

The alternate periods of activity and inactivity were from one-half hour to one hour in maximum length when the chick was 8 weeks old. When it was 12 weeks old, the periods were slightly longer. In 4 hours of observation one afternoon when the chick was 12 weeks old, the minutes spent lying or sitting as against standing or walking alternated as follows: down 85, up 20, down 55, up 5, down 75. In 8 hours of observation on another day the total time down was 310 minutes and the total up was 170 minutes. At that stage the chick spent about half again as much time down as up. At 12 weeks of age chick 1 retired from view for 1½ or 2 hours once or twice each day. Chick 2, at about 18 weeks of age, once remained at the same spot without turning around for over 3 hours. In the middle and late nestling stages chick 1 was sometimes active as late as it could be seen (7:15 p.m.). At nest 2, on occasions, the chick was active as early as it could be seen (5:30 a.m.).

For one month after juvenile 1 left the nest it spent about half of the daylight hours in a sitting position. One day, when it was 24 weeks old, between the hours of 11 a.m. and 5 p.m. it spent the following periods sitting and standing:

Minutes sitting   55   1/10   7   22   38   Total 123
Minutes standing   113   45   48   31   Total 237

When this juvenile was older, it spent less time in sitting. Another juvenile, at 30 weeks of age, did not sit at all during 9 hours of observation.

Nestlings avoid prolonged exposure to sunshine. When chick 1 was 10 weeks old, it was first noted that in the late afternoon when the sun shone into the south chamber of the nest the chick usually remained hidden in the north chamber but that shortly after sunset the youngster appeared in full view near the entrance. To the dismay of the photographer, the visibility and activity of the chick was often the best of the day just after sunset.

In the late nestling stage sunshine struck nest 2 only for a short period at about 11 a.m. and again between 3:30 p.m. and sunset. The chick remained on the outer shelf of the nest nearly all day except during the sunny period in the late afternoon. When there was sunshine on half of the outer shelf, the chick remained on the shaded half, and it retired into the cave at about 4 p.m. Within a few minutes after sunset (6:30 p.m.) the nestling again came to the outer shelf and was rather active.

When juvenile 1 was out of the nest, it usually sunned when sunshine first struck it, and it sat to roost at about sunset. Otherwise, it did not tend to be active or to perform any particular activity at a certain time of day. Juvenile 2 frolicked, shifted perches, sunned, and stretched during periods of activity. One day I watched it from 6 a.m. to 6 p.m. It was active from 9 a.m. to 9:45 a.m., shortly after the breeze increased; from 1 p.m. to 1:45 p.m., shortly after sunshine commenced to strike it; from 4:25 p.m. to 4:30 p.m., shortly after an adult flew close over it; and later during and after a rainstorm. When an adult perched near a juvenile but departed without feeding it, the youngster was usually very active for several minutes.

Normally the nestling is active for many minutes after it is fed, then it becomes inactive and remains so for one hour or longer. Evidently the excitement associated with feeding persists for a short time after the departure of the adult. The excitement is greatest when the adult departs before the chick is satisfied. About 10 days before chick 1 left the nest an adult fed it and departed at 4:35 p.m. For 10 minutes the chick pecked the floor, jumped about, turned completely around with several jumps, stretched one wing out of the entrance, scratched its head on the lip of the nest, and performed other actions. Then it stood quietly for several minutes and retired to the north chamber of the cave. Except for one brief appearance, it remained there for at least three-quarters of an hour. At two other nests I found that the late nestling was comparatively inactive commencing immediately or several minutes after the adult fed it.

On some occasions after juvenile 1 left the nest it was active for a long period after it was fed. One day, a month after it left the nest, this juvenile was active for one hour and attained a higher perch which it had failed to reach on earlier attempts. On two occasions when this youngster was fed by both parents in the morning, it remained comparatively inactive the rest of the day. Feeding by both parents may insure that the youngster is completely satisfied.

Wind stimulates activity in the juvenile. Herrick (1924:522) noted the same effect in eaglets. A sudden gust of wind sometimes caused juvenile 1 to fan its wings. On windy days this juvenile occasionally stood facing the wind with its wings half-extended for several seconds. It moved about and attempted short flights most frequently during wind. However, this juvenile first departed from the immediate vicinity of the nest on a relatively calm day.

Juvenile 1, out of the nest, spent the night in the sitting position. The latest time that I saw it standing was 5:35 p.m. (one month after it left the nest). The previous day when the air was warmer but there was fog, the juvenile sat for the last time at 4:38 p.m. and tucked its head out of sight within 10 minutes. At times the juvenile dozed with its eyelids narrowed or closed, sometimes with its head hanging down low in front of its body.

When juvenile 1 was sitting, its wings often sagged downward and outward so that they lay on their upper surfaces on the perch branch. In this position the secondaries hung down loosely and the tips of the primaries projected above the plane of the back. Occasionally the bird sat quickly to steady itself. This action occurred when the adult, in taking off, shook the small tree in which the juvenile was perched. Sitting was prolonged after the juvenile had exerted itself in climbing or in changing perches.

Chick 1 could walk when only 3 weeks old. At 7 weeks of age it walked slowly, its tarsi flat on the floor, by moving one leg forward, then the other about 2 seconds later. At 8 weeks of age it could walk while standing on its feet but between steps it paused from one to 3 seconds with its bill at the level of its heels. Between 12 and 14 weeks of age the locomotion of chick 1 improved greatly. At times it ran a few steps.

When chick 1 was 8 weeks old, I saw it turn completely around three times within 3 minutes while it was exploring the floor of the nest. To turn about while standing the nestling slid one foot back, brought the other foot alongside the first, and then repeated the action. About three such steps were required to turn 90 degrees. After juvenile 1 left the nest, it often turned about on its perch by stepping around, its wings up and occasionally flapping. Once I saw it turn completely around three times within 5 minutes. Frequently it turned about while eyeing a higher perch or when an adult approached.

The forward and backward stability of the nestling is poor. At eight weeks of age chick 1 normally held its wings out while scratching its head, pecking the floor, or turning around. It flapped and teetered in rising on to its feet, and from the standing position it sometimes plumped down heavily on to its heels. Occasionally it lost balance while preening. When about 18 weeks old, chick 2 slipped while standing near the edge of the nest. It thrust its wings up quickly and jumped toward the nest cave. While standing, this nestling often shifted one foot back a few inches and then replaced it beside the other foot.

The balance of juvenile 1 was poor for at least three weeks after it left the nest. In rising it usually opened its wings and teetered back and forth unsteadily. On some occasions, in reaching out toward another branch with its bill, it started to fall forward but suddenly raised its wings and tail. At times it lost its footing in turning about on a branch. The wings often struck the perch hard when the juvenile flapped in balancing. Young condors might injure their wings in this manner.

At nest 2 the late nestling tried to climb a wall about two feet high which bordered the outer shelf of the nest. The chick placed its throat on top of the wall, then beat its wings, stretched its neck, and put one foot part way up on the wall. Perhaps it left the nest by climbing this barrier. Finley (1910:10) found that his pet juvenile liked to climb to the top of a stump about 10 feet high and fly off.

The feet of juveniles may be more supple, and better adapted for grasping branches, than the feet of adults. Adults prefer large steady branches for perching, and when among small branches they generally place one or both feet on a crotch or fork. Shortly after leaving the nest, juvenile 1 perched on a branch three-quarters of an inch in diameter for at least two days. In attempting to reach a higher perch, this youngster grasped a smaller sloping branch with its feet and held on for half a minute before dropping. Twice in one day, I saw the juvenile grasp a branch with its bill when trying to hold on. For at least four days after I found juvenile 2 out of the nest its steadiest perch was the crotch of a long flexible limb, where the forks were less than an inch in diameter. Later, when on branches of conifers, this juvenile perched far out from the trunk. Once I noted that the perch was no thicker than the tarsus of the juvenile and that, in grasping the branch, the anterior toes of the bird were curved at least 180 degrees.

When juvenile 1 clung insecurely to a sloping branch and again when it clung to a sloping rock surface, I saw it hold its wings extended and depressed against the perch. The friction of the wings helped to keep the bird from sliding backward, but in such a situation wing claws could be used to advantage. The wing claws of condors are too small to be of use but possibly ancestral condors had larger claws which could be used for clinging to perches.

Less than three weeks after juvenile 2 left the nest, it remained perched in a canyon oak during short thunderstorms on two successive days. Hail, wet snow, and rain fell. When the storm commenced, the juvenile faced the wind and occasionally fanned vigorously. A few times it moved one or two feet out on the perch and back. When there was steady rain but no wind, the bird stood with its wings folded. Within a few minutes after the rain stopped the juvenile shook, scratched its head, yawned, preened, and nibbled at wet leaves. Then the bird dried its wings by holding them out and by flapping them. In spite of these storms, and others at night, the juvenile did not seek shelter or leave its usual perch. The sparse foliage over the bird gave it some protection from the hail.

Fanning the wings and frolicking.—"Wing fanning is a matter of maturation of instinctive action; i.e., the organ is ready before the instinctive coordination" (Nice, 1943:63). When chick 1 was eight weeks of age I saw it fan its wings as many as 11 flaps in succession at a rate of about two flaps per second. At 12 weeks of age and later the chick often stood on a low rock, the highest point on the floor of the nest, and fanned.

Chick 1 sometimes held its wings out at the sides for a few seconds before or after fanning. If this wing extending action bears the same relation to soaring flight that fanning bears to flapping flight, the soaring and flap-gliding actions, as well as the flapping action, mature long before the "instinctive coordination" of flight.

Juvenile 1 fanned, on occasions, until at least 53 days after it left the nest. Later, short flights seemed to take the place of fanning. There was no significant increase in the number of successive flaps as the bird developed. The maximum observed number was 15 for juvenile 1 and 14 for another juvenile; the usual number was five.

When chick 1 was 8 weeks old I saw it jump up and down four times in rapid succession, turning completely around in this action, and then repeat the entire performance twice more. During the jumping the wings were partly extended and they jounced at the sides or were fanned. I consider this action to be analogous to what Nice (1943:51) calls "frolicking" and an evidence of "surplus of energy." The method of frolicking was similar throughout the nestling stage. On one occasion, the chick traveled from one end of the cave to the other and back in four quick jumps with the wings partly opened. The late nestling in nest 2 sometimes hopped in and out of the nest cave from the outer shelf two or three times within a few minutes.

During periods of activity after juveniles 1 and 2 left the nest they turned around, jumped up and down, moved in and out on the perch, and shifted to other perches. There may be less "surplus of energy" available to the young bird out of the nest than in it, for the juvenile out of the nest expends much energy in shifting between perches and in making short flights. Frolicking often ensued when the juvenile seemed to be frustrated by its inability to reach some higher perch.

Exploratory pecking.—The tendency to peck at various objects is pronounced in young condors. While I was examining a nestling about eight days old, it picked up a bit of eggshell in its bill and dropped it again. This action may have been a misdirected attack upon me. When chick 1 was eight weeks old, it often spent many minutes in wandering slowly about the nest, its head lowered as if searching for particular objects. From time to time it pecked at the floor, taking two or three bites at one spot. On occasions it seemed to eat pieces of feathers or other objects. Six times in succession it picked up a short stick and dropped it. Again, it extended its neck and drew the bill back along the floor 10 times in suc-

Plate 25. Chick 9 at about 8 days of age. Photograph taken on May 3, 1941.

Plate 26. Chick 9 at about 20 days of age. Photograph taken on May 15, 1941.

Plate 27. Chick 9 at about 29 days of age. There is more dark gray down than white down at this age. Photograph taken on May 24, 1941.

Plate 28. Chick 9 at about 42 days of age. The coat of second down is complete at this stage. The bird is in threat attitude. Photograph taken on June 6, 1941.

cession as if raking sand toward its body. It pecked at the wall, ceiling, or rim of the cave as if scraping its bill or biting at excrement.

From the time chick 1 was five weeks old, an adult secondary which lay in the nest was a favorite "toy." On some occasions the chick picked up the feather by the shaft, held it for about 15 seconds, then dropped it. At other times it dragged the feather several feet. At eight weeks of age the chick often put one foot, then the other, on the feather and held it down while pecking or pulling at the shaft or barbs. This action resembled the method of feeding from a carcass and was seen many times when the bird was older.

When juvenile 1 was perched outside the nest, it tugged at the branch underfoot, or it extended its neck far upward, downward, or forward in order to bite twigs. Once I saw it break off sections of twigs and drop them. The day that the juvenile first gained the top of the ledge near the nest, it commenced to pull at a green prickly phlox (*Leptodactylon*) about six inches tall. Within two days the plant had been torn apart or consumed by the youngster. Other vegetable matter, including manzanita leaves, was also eaten. Occasionally it picked up a pebble and dropped it again.

Another juvenile pecked at the leaves and twigs of a live oak in which it perched soon after leaving the nest. While in a big-cone spruce this youngster pecked at the bark and apparently at dry excrement. Once I saw it break off a few tufts of needles and watch them fall to the ground. Another time it clamped its mandibles onto a dead twig and twisted its head as if to break the wood. When juvenile 1 was 46 weeks old, I saw it biting at the wood and bark at the top of a big-cone spruce.

Finley (1910:8, 10) says of his captive juvenile: "He was especially attracted by any small white object, such as a light-colored rock, a bit of broken china, or a piece of paper. . . . Down he jumpt and pounced upon a stick or a leaf, shook it in his bill, dropt it, just to jump upon it with both feet and toss it up again. . . . He was extremely fond of pulling on a rope. . . . He had to be nibbling all the time and liked to tug at my shoe-strings. . . . He liked to nibble at my hand, run his nose up my sleeve, and bite the buttons on my coat. . . ." The nibbling habit caused the death of three captive condors which died from eating foreign objects.

I attempted to feed a late nestling and a juvenile by offering them a ball of ground beef on the end of a stick. They struck at the stick, then nibbled and swallowed some of the meat. Finley's photographs show a juvenile holding food down with one foot and biting at it. Evidently the young condor is capable of feeding itself before it leaves the nest. Doubtless exploratory pecking is, in part, concerned with learning what is edible.

Preening.—A downy chick five weeks old, the youngest that I watched for long, preened its back. At seven weeks of age chick 1 preened its back, both surfaces of its wings, and the base of its neck in a skillful manner. Preening was the most common activity of the chick at eight weeks of age when the first wing quills were emerging. Several times I saw it preen continuously for 10 or 15 minutes, and a few times I saw it preen for half an hour. The action was accomplished while the chick was standing, sitting, or lying down. Preening was performed in the manner of the adult. Often one or both wings drooped to the floor as the chick preened. Once I saw it put its bill to the floor, then back to its belly, three times in succession as if using sand or dust in preening. When the chick was standing on its tarsi, I saw it raise one foot an inch above the floor and nibble the under side of its toes.

At 12 weeks of age chick 1 spent about a fifth of the daylight hours in preening. In five hours one morning it preened almost constantly for 20-, 10-, and 20-minute periods at about 8 a.m., 10:30 a.m., and 11 a.m., and it preened for a minute or less many times. The preening of the bases of the remiges was performed with one wing half-extended forward, its tip on the floor. The nestling extended its neck behind the wing with the head inverted, and the bill opened and closed rapidly as it worked out the wing.

At 15 weeks of age, when a short tail became evident, chick 1 preened its tail dexterously in the manner of the adult. The day after this chick was handled and banded, it preened especially frequently, including a 15-minute period before 7 a.m. Sometimes the bird tugged at clots of excrement in its down.

Preening is perfected before the juvenile leaves the nest. When out of the nest, juvenile 1 often ran the shafts of the flight feathers lengthwise through its bill. On one occasion the tip of a single rectrix was run through the bill 10 times in succession. Once, while sitting, juvenile 1 preened with its head below its body and the bill pointing vertically upward. Another juvenile extended one wing down behind the perch and preened it by reaching under the branch. These preening methods are unusual in adults. On a foggy day juvenile 1 preened more than usual, probably because its feathers were damp.

Scratching, wiping, and shaking the head.—By the time chick 1 was eight weeks old it could scratch its head while standing on one foot. However, because of poor balance, the bird could take only one or two quick swipes at its throat before replacing its foot on the floor. The entire action was repeated as many as five times at intervals of about two seconds. Either foot was used for scratching. While standing on its tarsi, the chick was seen to scratch as many as seven strokes before replacing its foot on the floor.

The number of consecutive strokes taken by the chick in scratching its head while standing on one foot provided a quantitative index to the development of coordination. The maximum number of strokes at eight weeks of age was two, at 12 weeks four, and at 15 weeks ten. The juvenile out of the nest was not seen to scratch more than 10 successive strokes; adults seldom exceeded this number.

At eight weeks of age chick 1 wiped the side of its head on its back in the manner of the adult. Often it shook its head to remove some particle. At 12 weeks of age, and later, the nestling rubbed its head and neck on the rim of the nest as if scratching, or it wiped the side of its bill on the rocks.

Stretching.—At eight weeks of age, an upward stretching of one wing was the most common activity of chick 1 as it lay on the floor of the nest. The wing was extended out and forward, held out for 3 to 5 seconds, then moved posteriorly about 60 degrees before being folded. At times the wing lay on the floor for 10 seconds or longer before being folded. I saw one wing extended seven times in 5 minutes. While lying half on one side, the chick occasionally moved one foot forward, planted it on the floor, then pushed it backward slowly until the leg was extended to the rear with the toes flexed. Sometimes the toes were flexed two or three times while the leg was extended. The stretched foot lay with its toes extended for 20 or 30 seconds before the foot was moved forward again. Once I saw both legs stretched to the rear simultaneously. During a representative period of

one-half hour one leg was stretched five times.

When chick 1 was 12 weeks old, its most common movement while lying on the floor was a simultaneous backward stretch of one wing and the corresponding leg. The chick raised the upper wing, flung it back on the floor at full extension, and simultaneously stretched one leg back and extended the toes. The wing lay on the floor for several seconds before it was folded. This action seemed to be the side stretch of adults performed in a lying position. Another chick about 12 weeks old performed this stretch while standing, extending one wing down outside of the nest cave. On occasions the stretch was performed only halfway; that is, the heel was lifted but the leg was not extended backward, and the wing was but half extended. Sometimes the side stretch was performed three or four times at intervals of 3 to 5 minutes. In 4 hours of observation one wing was extended at least halfway 15 times. When out of the nest, juvenile 1 performed the side stretch in the manner of adults, the maximum observed frequency being three times in one hour.

Chick 1 was seen to perform the bow stretch at eight weeks of age, as soon as it began to stand on its feet. In rising from its tarsi on to its feet the chick often held the wings high over its back, the elbows close together, and kept its throat close to the floor until almost standing. This action resembled the bow stretch. After it left the nest, juvenile 1 performed the bow stretch in the manner of the adult.

Shrugging and resetting the wings.—Chick 1 reset its wings in place on its back, one wing about two seconds after the other, by flipping the tip of each wing up about 45 degrees and quickly folding the wing. Often the wing was reset without being opened or lifted from the back so that the action appeared to be a shrugging of the wings. The action was first noticed when the nestling commenced standing for long periods. The wings were commonly reset after preening. At 14 weeks of age, resetting occurred at intervals of one-half to 2 minutes as the chick stood. Occasionally one wing sagged down from its folded position and was quickly folded again.

At 15 weeks of age, chick 1 reset its wings every 2 to 5 minutes while standing. One week later the interval was as little as 15 seconds and the chick seldom remained standing for longer than 5 minutes without resetting the wings. At 19 weeks of age chick 1 reset its wings at intervals of from one to 15 seconds on some occasions. At other times resetting occurred at intervals of from 10 to 60 seconds. Presumably the frequent resetting of the wings was caused by the fact that the wing musculature of the nestling was poorly developed and the wings and quills were heavy with blood.

Sunning.—At an estimated age of 18 weeks one chick sunned its back for one minute or longer at times. The small size of nest 1 apparently prevented typical sunning, but when chick 1 was 19 weeks old, it occasionally extended one wing out of the cave as if sunning. Photographs by Finley and Bohlman show a young condor about 19 weeks of age holding its wings out to dry after taking a bath. A juvenile drying its wings after a rainstorm held them in a similar manner although there was no sunshine.

Less than two weeks after juvenile 1 left the nest, I saw it sun for one minute. The two juveniles which I observed extensively usually sunned just after sunshine first struck them each day or within one-half hour afterward, even when the sunshine did not strike them until afternoon. On occasions one sunned after having been in the sunshine for several hours. Sunning was performed in the manner of the adult. The maximum observed period of full and partial extension of the wings was six minutes.

Juvenile 1 made no apparent attempts to get into sunshine from the shade. One morning it flew from a sunny to a shady perch shortly after sunrise. It showed no reaction to the moment of sunset. At times it sat, settled for the night, as long as 15 minutes before sunset, and at other times it remained active for one hour after sunset.

Shaking.—Never did I see a nestling shake itself, but juvenile 2 shook less than three weeks after it left the nest and juvenile 1 shook one month after it left the nest. Evidently this activity does not appear in condors until about the time they leave the nest. In some passerines shaking appears at about this stage (Nice, 1943:34).

Raising the ruff.—The chick can draw the skin of the hind neck forward in the ruff-raising action when it is five weeks old. However, the down at the base of the neck does not form a well defined ruff until the chick is about 10 weeks of age. Nestlings raise the ruff when strongly alarmed.

Juveniles cannot raise the ruff as high on the neck and occiput as adults can. The dorsal cervical tract might not extend as far forward in the juvenile as in the adult. As the occiput and hind neck of the juvenile are protected by down, young condors do not have to raise the ruff high in order to protect these areas from cold. The ability, or inclination, to lower the ruff until the lanceolate feathers lie flat at the base of the neck is greater in the adult than in the juvenile.

Voice.—According to Finley (1906:140), a chick about one day old gave a "wheezing, hissing note." At about three days of age one chick hissed when a man entered the nest. The hisses were about one second in duration and occurred at intervals of two or three seconds. At one week of age, chick 1 hissed, *haaah,* when its disturbed parent walked a few steps away from it. The sound was audible 40 yards away. The hiss, or wheeze, was repeated as many as a dozen times at intervals of from one to 10 seconds. Young turkey vultures (Tyrrell, 1938:469) and black vultures (Bent, 1937:42) also hiss when men are near.

When a chick about eight days of age was approached, it gave the "hiss-grunt," *haaaaa-ungh ungh ungh,* in about the same manner as older nestlings. The grunts occurred at a rate of four or five a second in series of from three to six. The departure of the adult, as well as the approach of man, elicited the hiss-grunt. When the chick was 4 weeks old, the length of the hisses and grunts was greater than before. The change may have been due to the increased volume of the air sacs. I heard as many as 27 grunts in a series. At the beginning of each series the grunts were loud and guttural; then they rose in pitch and decreased in volume. Often the breast of the chick pulsated as if the bird were grunting but no sounds were audible, then when the alarm of the bird was increased the hisses and grunts became loud and hoarse. Occasionally, when suddenly alarmed, the chick gave a single hoarse growl.

At 10 weeks of age chick 1 gave the hiss-grunt when a man walked from a blind 40 yards away. At 13 weeks of age it wheezed when an adult landed on the nest cliff, again when the adult flew to a second perch one hour later, and several additional times before the adult entered the nest. At 14 weeks of age chick 1 gave grunts in series of five to 12 at a rate of three per second, with an interval between series of 10 to 60 seconds. Apparently the rate of grunting decreased with age. A chick 15 weeks old gave a hoarse growl when striking at the men who were banding it. This bird gave a series of grunts in response to an adult flying close to the nest. Except when disturbed by man or in reaction to an approaching or departing adult, nestlings were not heard to give the hiss-grunt.

When juvenile 1 was 21 weeks old, and out of the nest, the hiss of the hiss-grunt lasted from two to five seconds, sometimes increasing in volume as it progressed. The grunts were throaty and staccato, given at a rate of about two per second, and usually in series of about six. The tongue was protruded during the hiss-grunt and was farthest out in the hiss. At various times, a juvenile was heard to give a short grunt in the manner of older birds.

Threat attitude.—When strongly alarmed by a sudden loud sound or by the close approach of a man, a young condor holds its head low in front of the body, opens its bill and protrudes the tongue, erects the interscapulars and raises the ruff (when these feathers are present), and gives the hiss-grunt (plates 28, 30). If too closely approached, the bird attacks from this position. The youngest bird seen in the threat attitude was 8 days old. At 3 and 4 weeks of age a nestling remained in this attitude as long as a man was close. With decrease in alarm the bill is closed and the head is gradually raised; with increase in alarm, the head is lowered, the bill is opened, and the body becomes more erect.

At 8 weeks of age chick 1 showed no reaction to men moving in the open near a blind 40 yards away, but loud clapping from the same distance immediately induced the threat attitude. The chick stood at the entrance of the cave, head down and wings drooping to the floor. Two minutes after the alarm the chick folded its wings, but it did not raise its head until 3 minutes later. At 12 weeks of age chick 1 assumed a mild form of the threat attitude when a man entered or left the blind.

In strong alarm the nestling opens its wings a few inches and thus increases its apparent size and prepares to strike with its wings. In addition to the interscapulars, the humerals and the lesser coverts near the bend of the wing are erected (plate 30). Normally the bird remains standing on its tarsi. The head may be lowered to the floor and the tongue may be protruded beyond the lower mandible (plate 28). The head of the threatening youngster usually points from 45 to 90 degrees away from the threatened object, as if close vision is most acute at these angles. The tail is held stiffly and is raised above the line of the back at an angle of about 30 degrees (plate 31). In some observations I noted that the legs of the bird shook as if with fright. For several weeks after juvenile 1 left the nest it usually assumed the threat attitude when first approached to a distance of about 10 feet. When the bird was disturbed for long, it became increasingly difficult to induce this reaction. Harriet Boyce of the Forest Service told me that when a raven flew near a juvenile perched near her lookout station, the condor ruffled up and hissed.

Defensive striking and biting.—One chick was too weak to bite when it was about 3 days old, but 5 days later it struck out with its bill at the spot made by a flashlight. At 12 days of age it struck at a steel tape and weakly nibbled my fingers. Its wings remained folded and were not used in defense. At 3 weeks of age this chick struck out at my finger at a maximum distance of 10 inches. A week later it struck my hat 2 feet away and gave it a hard tug. With each strike the chick extended its wings out and down. At 6 weeks of age the same chick lunged toward me every few minutes shortly after I entered the nest, but later it struck out only when I approached within 3 feet. Finley (1908b:64, 65) states that a chick about 8 weeks old "lunged about and fought while he was in the cave; but when . . . out of his home, he seemed to change tactics and to become quite meek."

At 15 weeks of age, a nestling gripped my glove so strongly with its bill that I was able to draw the bird several inches along the floor before it released its hold. When I moved a rock near another late nestling it struck at the rock with its bill and held on for about one second. It struck when a pebble was tossed near it, then picked up the pebble and dropped it. Usually it bit two or three times after it secured a hold on an object. When held for banding, nestlings struggled little, but sometimes they bit their own wings or legs as well as their captor. One nestling climbed up to my thigh after striking my leg. Striking was usually performed in a sudden startling manner. The bill and wings lashed out and the bird gave a hiss or growl at the same time. Often the chick did not touch the object at which it struck so that the action served mainly for intimidation.

The distance to which a late nestling can be approached before it strikes is usually about three feet but occasionally as far as five feet. At times, by approaching carefully, a man can reach within one foot of the head of a chick before it strikes. The maximum distance of striking does not increase after the chick is two months old. Before and after striking the young condor usually remains in the threat attitude, but sometimes it moves its head toward any object which is brought near it. Striking with the wings does not always accompany striking with the bill. The flap of the wings may be primarily a balancing action. The feet are apparently not used as defensive weapons.

The threshold for the striking reaction increases greatly when the stimulus is repeated several times. On one occasion, a juvenile struck the first two times that I extended a branch toward its head, but then it allowed me to tickle its head and did not strike. However, it bit at the branch and cut cleanly through manzanita leaves. In banding a juvenile recently out of the nest, I found that the neck was very strong but that the wings were weak.

Avoiding actions.—When I reached behind a chick 3 weeks old, it turned quickly to face my hand. Up to 4 weeks of age this nestling did not retreat when I approached, but at 6 weeks of age it moved a few feet away to the end of the cave when I approached within 10 yards. Chick 1, at 8 weeks of age and later, often came to the entrance of the cave in response to sounds or movements by men outside. Nestlings beyond the downy stage usually retreat in their nests when a man approaches, but while in the threat attitude they stand their ground and may move a few steps toward a man in striking at him. A chick 15 weeks old, placed outside of the nest, struck at men who approached closely but it did not retreat.

For several weeks after juvenile 1 left the nest it allowed men to approach within five yards without retreating or showing strong alarm. Another young juvenile, which had not encountered men before I found it out of the nest, crouched as if to fly when I first reached a point 15 yards away, but it allowed me to approach to within five yards without assuming the threat attitude. At 31 weeks of age juvenile 1 stretched its neck high up when I approached to a distance of 30 yards, it turned and faced me when I reached a point 15 yards away, and it flew several feet away from me before I came within five yards.

Regurgitation and nasal discharge.—Young turkey

vultures and black vultures often regurgitate when strongly alarmed (Bent, 1937:17, 33), but young condors rarely do so. On days when one chick was about 3, 8, and 12 days old, I entered the nest and handled the bird but it did not regurgitate. At 3 weeks of age, this chick disgorged three chunks of meat with an up and down pumping of the lowered head as I approached. It had not been fed for at least one-half hour before regurgitating. A week later, the same chick threw up about 5 ounces of meat when I turned on a flashlight near it. Only a part of the contents of the crop was thrown up. Although Finley (1906, 1908b) handled a chick at one day, 3 weeks, and 5 weeks of age, he did not mention that the chick regurgitated. Several older nestlings have been handled by myself and others without causing regurgitation. One late nestling vomited one ounce of a mushy substance while I was in the nest. Late nestlings driveled when repeatedly disturbed. When juvenile 1 was 25 weeks old, I saw it cast up two pellets.

Many times when I was close to a young condor, I noted that there was a watery discharge from its nostrils. This discharge sometimes amounts to only a drop but at other times it runs almost to the tip of the bill. The liquid dries quickly and leaves a whitish deposit around the nares. This white area is conspicuous on most dark-headed immatures. The path of the light band usually leads to the gape posterior to the horny bill.

Probably nasal discharge is associated with digestion as well as with alarm. Spallanzani (1784:172) found that whenever a captive eagle ate, a watery secretion flowed from each nostril and generally passed into the mouth. He suspected that this secretion might act like saliva in moistening food and facilitating digestion. Some of the photographs by Finley and Bohlman show a discharge from the nostrils of a juvenile in the act of feeding.

Defecation.—In general, young condors do not raise the rump to defecate in the manner of adults until after they leave the nest. Yet, the only time that I saw an early nestling (about 12 days old) defecate, it did raise its rump. Before the chick is motile the excrement might be projected to some distance so that the floor near the chick is kept clean. At four weeks of age the same chick raised its rump in defecating. A chick about eight weeks old rose up on its feet, defecated, and then dropped its heels to the floor again. Juvenile 1 was first seen to raise its rump to defecate when it was 26 weeks old, more than five weeks after it left the nest.

Feeding is not immediately followed by defecation. I saw defecations occur from one to 31 hours after feedings. After one period of activity, an undisturbed juvenile voided twice within 10 minutes.

Both nestlings and juveniles may defecate when closely approached by man. While I was near, a nestling 14 weeks old defecated twice in 15 minutes, and an older nestling defecated six times in one hour. Juvenile 1 usually defecated when it was first approached to within a distance of 10 feet. The excrement of young and adults appears the same.

Distension of the crop.—The ventral cervical apterium in the region of the crop bulges for many hours after the chick is fed. When chick 1 was eight weeks old and had been fed recently, the outline of this apterium was oval in front view, the smaller end of the oval bisecting the collar of down. Several hours later the outline was pear-shaped, and 18 hours after the feeding the apterium appeared circular with a band of naked skin connecting it with the anterior naked throat. In nestlings, as well as in adults, a bulging crop does not denote that the bird has fed that day. When chick 1 had not been fed for 54 hours, the apterium was almost hidden by the adjacent down and, in lateral view, the region of the crop appeared concave.

When a young condor hisses, the inflation of the anterior air sacs adds to the distension of the region of the crop (plate 26). During each hiss the bulge of the lower neck is reduced. This use of the air sacs accounts for the statement by Finley (1908b:61) that a chick puffed out its neck and seemed to fill its crop with air.

Hiccupping.—The body of the nestling occasionally gives a jerk as if shaken by a great hiccup, and the action may be repeated at intervals of a few minutes. The wings are lifted above the body by each jerk and are then reset. Sometimes the body turns about 30 degrees with each hiccup. Hiccupping occurs as long as 24 hours after the chick is fed.

Movements of the head.—The late nestling turns its head as frequently as an adult. Even when the nestling is quiet and inactive, its head seldom remains in one position for more than half a minute. After leaving the nest, juvenile 1 frequently moved its head

about below the level of the branch upon which it sat as if searching the ground below. It stretched its neck upward to look toward a rolling boulder 200 yards away. It watched pebbles which were tossed near it and turned its head as if watching ravens, soaring condors, and even an airplane.

Heart rate.—When chick 1 was 19 weeks old its heart rate, shortly after a man entered the nest, was 156 beats per minute. One minute later the rate was 132 per minute. Five minutes later, when the chick appeared calm, the rate was 72 per minute. Sumner (1933:304) found, in studying captive raptores, that the heart rate was highly variable and depended much upon the "emotional state" of the subject. In one golden eagle the rate varied from "180 per minute when the bird was calm, to 244 when it was slightly alarmed." As condors are phlegmatic in comparison with golden eagles, one would expect the heart rate of the condor to be slower than that of the eagle.

Respiration rate.—When chick 1 was 12 weeks old, I noted that its rate of breathing was 40 inspirations per minute just after I entered my blind and probably disturbed the bird; later it was 15 to 18 per minute. At 15 weeks of age the rate was 40 per minute when the bird stood calmly five minutes after a period of vigorous activity.

Travels and flight of the juvenile after leaving the nest.—Judging from the activity of chick 1 while it was in the nest, it probably fell out of the small cave during a period of post-feeding frolicking or in trying to reach an adult which was approaching with food. Chick 2 probably succeeded in climbing over the low wall which separated the nest from an adjacent slope. These young may have been stimulated to leave by the hundreds of cimicids which infested the two nests. Both left during periods of high winds. Wind stimulates activity in juveniles.

One juvenile left a nest which had not been entered by man at about the same age that two other juveniles left nests which were entered by man a few days before the birds departed. Apparently entry of these nests by man did not cause early departure. Chick 5 left the nest at a greater age than chick 1 or 2. Nest 5 was many times as large as the other two nests so that the bird could move around freely inside of it and, in addition, there were few cimicids in nest 5. The juvenile leaving nest 5 evidently flew directly to a tree several yards out from the nest.

Juvenile 1 traveled one mile from the nest in 10 weeks. This journey was made in several trips of increasing length. After each trip the juvenile remained near one perch until making the next trip. The young bird moved about locally during the day but returned to the same perch after each such excursion. This constancy of location probably aids the adults in finding the young.

On September 28, less than five days after juvenile 1 left the nest, I found it perched 50 feet out from the nest and 30 feet below it on a shelf slightly below the level of the top of the chaparral. Five days later this juvenile was perched on the dead top of a manzanita bush, 2 feet above the shelf. After another 5 days the young bird was 20 feet from the bush and 8 feet above it on the lowest branch of a dead oak tree below the nest (see plate 16). For 8 days the juvenile remained on this branch most of the time, but occasionally it hopped down on to a boulder one foot below the branch. From there it walked into a wide cleft at the base of the cliff and remained for as long as 2 hours before returning to the branch. There was condor excrement 30 feet back in the cleft. This excursion to the boulder or cleft and back to the branch was repeated at least seven times within one period of 5 hours. On occasion the juvenile hopped to a branch one foot higher than its main perch and hopped down again within a few seconds.

Three weeks after I found juvenile 1 out of the nest it was 10 feet higher in the oak. Five days later it was back on the lowest branch. The next day it ascended to the higher branch again after making several unsuccessful attempts, and the next day it leaped six feet from the top of the oak to the ledge of the nest cliff. The juvenile remained there for at least two days. One week later, when the bird was 26 weeks old, I found it on top of the nest cliff near the point where the adults usually landed. It was at the same spot 12 days later. One day the youngster moved to another point on top of the same stratum of rock but 300 yards down the canyon. This movement apparently required flights of at least 50 feet across gaps in the cliff.

The juvenile remained at the new site for at least 10 days. On some days it did not move more than 25 feet from its main perch. At 201 days of age, the juvenile moved 50 yards back toward the nest in several short flights, then flew back to the starting point. Later that day it flew 200 feet down the canyon and landed; then it flew back to the base of the cliff below its main perch and ascended the slope in short flights. At this time the bird could fly 100 yards at a time but not without losing many feet of altitude.

Twelve days later I found the juvenile perched one mile from the nest at the tip of a high ledge overlooking a canyon. Frequently the adults had perched near that point when approaching the nest. For at least two days the young bird remained there, most of the time within 30 feet of one spot. One day it flew 100 feet parallel to the cliff, flapping, and later it flew about 100 feet out from the cliff and back. Several days later, on December 7, the juvenile spiraled down to this perch from a point 60 feet higher.

I did not recognize this juvenile again until March 21, when it was almost 47 weeks old. Then I saw it, with several other condors, at a popular watering and roosting place 2 miles from nest 1. The following morning it soared one mile to a group of trees where several condors were roosting. Later that day it circled and rose, and it landed on its perch of December 7. Two days later the juvenile roosted 2½ miles southwest of the nest. Apparently it could soar at least 2 miles and ascend at least 500 feet in altitude by the time it was 10½ months old.

The wandering of juvenile 1 after it left the nest and the slow development of its ability to soar were apparently normal, for juvenile 2 behaved in a similar manner. Less than three weeks after juvenile 2 left the nest it was perched on the lowest branch of a live oak which grew from the face of the cliff 50 yards from the nest and at the same level. For at least four days, the main perch of the young bird was a crotch near the tip of a limb where the branches were flexible. There the juvenile endured hail, rain, and wind. Several times a day it edged sideways out on one fork of the branch for about two feet, then returned to the crotch with quick clumsy steps. In half an hour this action was repeated six times.

Eight days after I last saw juvenile 2 in the oak it was perched 10 feet from the top of a big-cone spruce. Apparently it had reached this tree by a direct and descending flight of about 40 yards. Five days later it was 80 yards from the spruce on a perch 30 feet lower. It remained in the new tree at least five days but moved about from branch to branch. This tree was close to one which had been used by the parents in approaching the nest. Eighteen days later, 5½ weeks after I found it out of the nest, juvenile 2 was in a small oak 300 yards from the last tree and 200 yards from the nest. Every change of perching tree had involved a loss of altitude so that the juvenile was gradually moving down the canyon from the nest.

Finley (1910:10) found that his pet juvenile could fly "but a few yards" when it was about 25 weeks old. Several times in winter and spring I saw juveniles, evidently eight to 11 months old, flying with adults near old nest sites.

To summarize, most juveniles are not capable of flying more than about one-quarter of a mile at a time until more than two months after they leave the nest. They can do little more than move between trees or other perches in December when the weather is often severe. Not until spring can they fly well enough to search for their own food.

Relations of the juvenile with other condors.—In its relations with condors other than its parents, the juvenile acts like older immature condors. When juvenile 1 was 30 weeks old and was perched on a point which was used as a resting perch by many condors, two adults and an immature landed 10 yards away from it. The immature and the juvenile stood side by side for several minutes and seemed to nuzzle each other, while the adults paid no apparent attention to the young birds.

When juvenile 1 was 10½ months old, I saw it soaring with one or two other immatures. Once it perched beside an older immature for at least 10 minutes. Each nibbled the head and feathers of the other. The juvenile did most of the nibbling and seemed to tolerate nibbling the least. When this bird was perched on a cliff, an adult landed several yards away and walked toward the juvenile. The young bird flew 15 feet away from the adult. When the adult departed, the juvenile returned to its original perch. On two of the last three days that I saw juvenile 1 (10½ months of age) it went to roost within several feet of another immature. The last time that I saw juvenile 1 it was perched in a tree with two adults and two other immatures in the late afternoon.

Variation in the development of young.—Chronological age, feathering, and time of leaving the nest are indications of the stage of development of young birds. In four young condors whose chronological age

was known within one week, I found no significant difference in the rate of feather development. Bond (1942:81) found that the "physical and psychological schedule followed by normal and well-fed young hawks of the same species and sex is subject to very slight variation. . . ."

In one year (1940) I discovered at least eight weeks variation in the age of three young found within a distance of 12 miles (age estimated by feather development). The Finley chick hatched March 22 (1906) and the latest fairly certain date of collecting a fertile egg is May 25 (1902). These dates indicate a spread of at least nine weeks in the time of hatching of young; the extreme spread might be three months. A chick with a broken wing was about three weeks behind any other known to me in rate of feather development.

When chick 1 was 25 weeks old, I noted that the outer rectrices bore a crosswise streak about two inches from the tips, as if they had been creased. The juvenile photographed by Bohlman and Finley showed a similar condition. Chick 1 was removed from the nest and banded at 15 weeks of age and was not fed for at least two days at that time. Finley's bird was removed from the nest and taken to Oregon at the same age. The vanes of the rectrices are about three inches long at this age. These circumstances suggest that the streaks on the rectrices were "hunger streaks." Bond (1942:81) states that "young hawks deprived of food for unusual periods during the growth of rectrices and remiges show very distinct marks of weakness across the feathers, which falconers call 'hunger streaks' or 'hunger traces.'"

The degree of feather development of three individuals at the time of leaving the nest varied by five weeks of estimated age (20 to 25 weeks). For these birds the earliest date for leaving the nest was before September 17 (1939). If Finley's chick fledged at the same rate as my chick 1, his chick would have been out of the nest in mid-August. The latest date for leaving the nest was after November 11 (1940). Apparently young leave the nest over a period of about three months, most young leaving in September and October. Chick 1, the only condor for which I know the chronological age at leaving the nest, left between September 23 and 28, 1939, when between 142 and 147 days of age.

Two juveniles left the nest at about the time that

Plate 29. W. L. Finley's chick at 55 days of age. The feathers are beginning to grow on the head.
Photograph taken by H. T. Bohlman and W. L. Finley in 1906.

Plate 30. Chick 4 at about 16 weeks of age. The head feathering is similar to that of the adults. The back
feathers are raised in a threat attitude.
Photograph taken on October 9, 1940.

Plate 31.   Juvenile 1 at 175 days of age. The bird is slightly alarmed. Within a few days it had consumed the plant in the left foreground. The light gray tips of the upper secondary coverts are characteristic of the juvenal plumage. Photograph taken on October 25, 1939.

the dorsal surface of the wings became fully feathered. The last down to disappear from this region was at the proximal anterior border of the forearm. About two weeks before these birds left the nest their heads turned from pale flesh color to dark bluish gray and the juvenal down commenced to hide the skin of the occipital region.

The fledging period of five months is perhaps as long as that of any land bird. Including the incubation period, a nest cavity may be in daily use for seven months. Allowing for six weeks variation in time each way for differences among pairs and seasons, it is apparent that nests should be protected from molestation for at least ten months of the year. This period includes neither the important season of courtship and nest selection nor the two months or more that the juvenile is out of the nest but entirely dependent on its parents for food. The last phase is especially worthy of protection because the juvenile may wander far from the nest, the parent birds are especially cautious in approaching the young, and seven months of labor on the part of the parents (and the persons who protect them) already have been "invested" in the growing bird. Obviously, then, nesting areas must be kept free from disturbance the year around if a program for conserving the California condor is to be effective.

Associates at Nests and Roosts

Insects and ticks.— Kellogg (1910:34) reported two species of Mallophaga, probably *"Lipeurus" assessor* and *Menopon fasciatum,* as being taken from a condor by C. S. Thompson. According to Kellogg, these species were apparently the same as had been reported from the South American condor and the king vulture. He speculated that these parasites might have occurred on the common ancestor of the three large vultures and persisted, practically unchanged, on the descendants of the ancestral host. G. F. Ferris advises me that the identification of these insects is only tentative.

In three nests I collected specimens of the Mexican chicken bug, *Haematosiphon inodora.* This insect is of the order Hemiptera, family Cimicidae. In two nests there were hundreds of these cimicids at the time that the young bird left the nest. Three months after one chick left the nest there were at least 50 of these bugs still in the cave. In another nest, I found a few of these bugs before the egg hatched. In some nests the bugs were rare or absent. These insects have the characteristic smell of bedbugs, they move quickly, and they produce numerous bites on humans. According to Usinger (1947:140), this insect is a rather common pest of poultry in the southwestern United States and Mexico and it has also been found in the nests of owls. Possibly condors get the parasites by using perches or holes which have been frequented by owls.

Flies, probably Calliphoridae, were common near nests. I saw fly specks on one egg. At about the time that the egg hatched in nest 1 flies were especially numerous there. In another nest, I estimated that there were 50 flies when the chick was one month old. Twice I saw a flat-bodied fly, probably a hippoboscid, on the head of a nestling.

There was a swarm of honeybees in a crevice a few feet outside of the entrances of two nests. The bees were not seen to sting condors.

In one nest cave I found many ticks, *Argas reflexus,* of the family Argasidae. The ticks were not seen on condors but they were under a leaf of rock on the ceiling of the cave. According to Cooley and Kohls (1944:16), this tick is commonly associated with pigeons and chickens and is probably associated with swallows. Swallows may have introduced th[em] into the condor nest. The ticks were still pre[sent in] the cave several years after condors nested th[ere].

Mammals.—In one nest where a young cond[or was] found dead, in one nest where an egg was smashed, and in another nest where an egg wa[s] punctured, there were fresh droppings of [a] carnivore, perhaps a skunk, badger, raccoon[,] tailed cat, or gray fox. Most of the nests of [condors] could be entered by these carnivores but th[ere was] no evidence that they were responsible for the [break-] ing of the egg or the death of the chick. If dist[urbance] by men keeps an adult condor from the nest a[way,] the egg or young might be a tempting f[ood for] carnivores.

In several condor nests I found acorns, sticks[,] droppings, and other signs of wood rats (*N[eotoma] fuscipes*). Probably some caves are used conc[urrently] by condors and wood rats. I saw no indicati[on that] the rats harmed the condors. Coles (1944:222[) noted] that some nest sites of turkey vultures serve[d as] winter homes of wood rats.

Birds.—Many times I saw turkey vultures [within] 50 feet of nest 1 while an adult condor wa[s there.] On one occasion, five turkey vultures soared [near] the nest cliff and one passed within six fee[t of the] nest. The sitting condor merely held its neck s[tretched] out toward the vultures. When two vultures [soared] 10 feet directly above the nest, the sitting adu[lt stood] up. A condor which was perched above [a nest] showed no reaction to two turkey vultures [which] soared as close as five yards. Ten minutes [after an] adult disgorged some foul-smelling meat at [the en-] trance of a nest, seven turkey vultures circl[ed close] to it, approaching within 10 yards.

In the air condors usually circle with turk[ey vul-] tures in a peaceable manner. On rare occasion[s I saw] an adult or an immature condor pursue a turk[ey vul-] ture for several yards in air, but the chase [was not] vigorous. A few times I saw a condor and a [turkey] vulture perched only six or eight feet apart fo[r many] minutes. Once I saw four turkey vultures per[ched in] the same tree with six condors but there were n[o inte-] ractions between the two species. Yet, I saw a j[uvenile] walk several feet toward a turkey vulture and

from a branch. Again, an adult was perched above three turkey vultures in a tree. One of the vultures moved to a perch two feet from the condor and above it. The condor moved toward the vulture and the latter departed. Occasionally a condor, in landing, displaced a turkey vulture. A few times I saw one or two turkey vultures drink at one of the favorite pools of the condors.

Ravens (*Corvus corax*) may approach the nests of condors. About two weeks before the egg hatched at nest 1 a raven flew back and forth in front of the nest, cawing. The incubating condor stretched its neck and seemed to watch the raven closely. The next day a raven hovered within five feet of the nest. The sitting condor merely turned its head slowly. About noon on the day that the egg hatched, four squawking ravens remained near the nest for eight minutes. A dozen times one hovered at the mouth of the cave. Five times one alighted on the lip of the nest and cawed toward the sitting condor less than two feet away. Twice a raven walked into the nest and dragged a condor feather to the entrance. The sitting condor did not rise while the ravens were present. Later that day, a raven landed on the lip of the nest and several times it hovered at the entrance. The brooding adult merely turned its head as if watching. If the adult had been absent from the nest when the ravens arrived, the egg or chick might well have been attacked by these birds. I did not see ravens pay any attention to a condor nest after the brooding stage.

The attitude of the nesting adults toward ravens changes at about the time that the young bird leaves the nest. Near two nests I saw an adult chase from one to three ravens which flew or alighted within 100 yards of the juvenile. Either parent did the chasing. On one occasion near nest 1, *A* ceased feeding the juvenile as a raven landed 10 feet away and then it walked toward the raven. The raven flew and landed 10 feet farther from the juvenile. *A* ran toward the raven and flushed it. Soon *A* departed. *B* then fed the juvenile and took off, but just as it left a raven landed 10 feet from the young bird. *B* immediately landed and ran at the raven, flapping. The raven flew a short distance and landed. *B* gave chase and the raven left. *B* perched near the juvenile for 12 minutes and then departed.

Once I saw a raven attack two adult condors as they soared near its nest. Each time that the raven overtook them, the condors dove away. Two ravens also chased a golden eagle (*Aquila chrysaëtos*) from that vicinity. Another time, a condor landed in a pothole after a raven had chased it through two or three dives. Golden eagles occasionally reacted in the same way to pursuit by ravens. Ravens nested within 50 yards of a ledge which was used by condors in spring and equally close to several old nest sites of condors.

Normally there is no reaction when a raven perches within six feet of a condor. In one instance, an immature condor paid no apparent attention to a raven which perched on the same branch only two feet away. Occasionally ravens take off when a condor alights near them. Ravens may perch in potholes and drink in pools which are used by condors.

Golden eagles may circle peaceably with a group of condors so that it is difficult to distinguish between the two species. I saw eagles perched in the favorite trees of condors but I did not see the two birds perched in the same tree concurrently. In November, 1939, I saw a condor pursue an eagle. After passing above a soaring adult and immature condor, the eagle perched in a tree. The adult condor soared toward the eagle and the eagle took off. The condor followed and once dove at the eagle from behind. The adult condor may have been protecting its young one. Another time, immediately after being pursued by an eagle, a condor perched near a flightless juvenal condor.

Except near food, I did not see a golden eagle actually strike a condor, but in the vicinity of perches and roosts eagles may chase condors. Once I saw an adult condor leave its perch on a high tree when an eagle approached within 50 feet. The two flapped a quarter of a mile in file, then they dove down into a canyon. On another occasion, a pursuit continued about five minutes. Twice in succession the eagle dove at the adult condor. The condor dove away and soon had descended about 500 feet to the level of the tops of the roost trees. There the eagle pursued the adult and an immature condor. As the adult commenced to alight on a tree, the eagle dove at it. The condor dodged and then perched immediately. The eagle dove again. The condor flew a few yards but returned to the same perch. The eagle departed.

I saw three old nests of golden eagles within 100 yards of a formerly used condor nesting site.

A pair of peregrine falcons (*Falco peregrinus*) nested in a high cliff past which condors frequently

soared. Often one of the falcons chased a condor in air. The condor usually flapped, dove, and twisted from side to side as it descended. The pursuit seldom persisted for more than a quarter of a mile, but in one instance the falcon pursued the condor through four successive dives. I could never be sure that the falcon actually struck the condor. Near one peregrine nest I saw a falcon drive a condor from the same tree twice within 15 minutes. Each time the condor returned to the same perch. Finally the falcon perched 100 feet from the condor and there was no further interaction. Harold Hill found the nest of a peregrine falcon about 50 yards from the nest of a condor and 50 feet above it. There was a falcon nest within half a mile of three condor nests which I watched.

There are prairie falcons (*Falco mexicanus*) in some areas where condors roost or forage. Dawson (1924:1722) reports seeing a prairie falcon chase two adult condors in turn. Sharples (1897:21) noted that a prairie falcon "pestered" an adult condor which was flushed from a nest. Twice I saw a Cooper hawk pursue a condor for a short distance.

Between condors and red-tailed hawks (*Buteo jamaicensis*) I saw no indication of animosity. These hawks and condors often soar close together. Several times I saw a red-tailed hawk perched within six feet of a condor for many minutes. A condor perched close to its nest paid no apparent attention to a hawk which soared 10 feet above it. Seibert (1941:5) reports seeing a red-tailed hawk dive at a condor which passed close to the hawk nest.

On several occasions, I saw a Swainson hawk (*Buteo swainsoni*) dive at a condor. Sometimes the condor did not dive away from the hawk; at other times it dove, twisting, for a short distance. These encounters took place in treeless country far from any possible nest of the hawks. The difference in the relations toward condors of the two kinds of *Buteo* may be due to the fact that Swainson hawks are migratory and do not encounter condors during a large part of the year.

Violet-green swallows (*Tachycineta thalassina*) often visited nest 1 while an adult was incubating or brooding. In the incubation stage the greatest activity of swallows occurred the day before the egg hatched. At least six times that day, I saw one or two swallows alight at the edge of the nest. For a week after the egg hatched the activity of swallows was much greater

than before. On each of two days, I saw from one to four swallows land on the lip of the nest more than 20 times, and nearly all the activity occurred before 11:30 a.m. In about a third of the observations, a swallow walked into the nest and remained there for many seconds. One dragged an eight-inch condor feather out of the cave, then hovered near the feather as it fell.

The brooding condor seldom moved while the swallows were close to the nest. The maximum reaction was a slow turning or raising of the head. Once two perched swallows took off suddenly when the condor made a sudden movement in preening. As the increase in the activity of swallows corresponded with the hatching of the egg, it is probable that effluvia from the broken egg attracted insects upon which the swallows fed. The swallows may have secured some fragments of feathers for nesting material.

In the week following the hatching of the egg, I often saw one or two ash-throated flycatchers (*Myiarchus cinerascens*) close to nest 1. One perched momentarily on the lip of the nest and the sitting adult raised its head. Continuous calling by two flycatchers 20 feet from the nest did not seem to alarm the brooding condor.

Scrub jays (*Aphelocoma coerulescens*) often called near nest 1. Once, as a condor was about to sit on the egg, a jay called shrilly and the condor came to the entrance of the nest. At other times, the sitting adult turned its head quickly as a jay called. Possibly condors associate the shrill cry of the jay with danger. However, any sudden sound such as the *kvork* of a mountain quail (*Oreortyx picta*) or the *tsuckatsuck* of a red-shafted flicker (*Colaptes cafer*) may cause the sitting adult to raise or turn its head quickly. A perched adult raised its head at the sharp whistle terminating the dive of a hummingbird, but it showed no reaction to the roar of a flock of band-tailed pigeons (*Columba fasciata*) which passed 200 yards away.

Usually when any bird such as a flycatcher, jay, or white-throated swift (*Aëronautes saxatalis*) flew close past the entrance of nest 1, the sitting adult stretched its neck toward the entrance. Twice while chick 1 was in the nest, I saw a canyon wren (*Catherpes mexicanus*) perch on the rim or inside of the cave, but the chick did not seem to notice the wren.

Summary.—The only important known parasite of condors is the Mexican chicken bug which infests nests. Small carnivores may enter nests and they have opportunity to damage eggs. Ravens too, if given opportunity, might harm eggs or young nestlings. Golden eagles, peregrine falcons, and prairie falcons chase condors with vigor but are not known to harm them directly. Apparently no measures to control these animals need be taken for the benefit of the condor.

Conservation

Inasmuch as the condor has persisted in spite of apathy and predictions of its early extinction, let us be optimistic and assume that the species will persist indefinitely if we will give it aid. In the course of the past 60 years, the attitude of those who have written about condors has been mainly one of pessimism and of resignation to the approaching extinction of the species. An article written by Cooper in 1890 was entitled, "A Doomed Bird." Beebe (1906:258) stated: "Its doom is near; within a few years at most, the last individual will have perished." Loye Miller (1937: 160) wrote that the condor had developed a "strong candidacy for the pluperfect status" and asked (1942: 212), "Is it not a species with one foot and even one wing in the grave?" Sheldon (1939:22) wrote that the condor had "outlived its time" and that it was "on the trail of the dodo." Many of the older generation hold this pessimistic view.

Grinnell, in a letter written in 1937 to a prominent ornithologist, criticized this pessimistic viewpont and pointed out that of course the condor was doomed to extinction if human attitudes toward it did not change and if nothing were done, but that one could adduce evidence that the human race itself was also doomed. Pessimism leads to apathy and defeatism. The major obstacle to all attempts to aid the condor has been the disinterest of persons capable of effective action.

MAJOR MORTALITY AND WELFARE FACTORS

Wanton shooting.—A condor seems to be a tempting target for a man or boy with a gun. Cooper (1890:249) and Stephens (1919:14) gave shooting as one of the main reasons for the decrease in the numbers of condors. E. T. Mendenhall and J. B. Dixon, of San Diego County, told me that in the late 1800's it was the ambition of every boy to shoot a condor. W. Lee Chambers (1936:200) had a sporting goods store near Santa Monica from 1896 to 1905. At about that time the first high-powered sporting rifles came into use and there was much indiscriminate shooting. Two condors which had been shot were brought into Chambers' store about 1905. In December, 1908, an immature condor was shot near the Finley nest by a constable (Finley, 1928:169). About 1910, the Peyton brothers found a wounded condor which had been

shot (specimen). Boys shot two condors near Santa Paula in 1916 (specimens).

In 1925, the San Diego Natural History Museum was given a freshly mounted condor by an anonymous party with the stipulation that no questions be asked. In 1927, a hunter drove into Santa Barbara with a condor, which he had shot, tied to his car (specimen). In 1929, a young condor, shot through the wing, was found near Fillmore. This bird survived for 10 years at the Zoo in San Diego. About 1932, a condor which had been shot was found near Lebec by Harold Bowhay of Bakersfield. The bird died in captivity. In 1940, a hunter told me of the location of a condor which he said had been shot. I found the carcass, but it was too decomposed to allow verification of the cause of death.

In 1944, a rancher flushed a large group of condors near Porterville. One struck a wire fence and was injured. The rancher shot it and the specimen was mounted. Another rancher admitted to me that a few years ago he shot several times at a large bird in the belief that it was a golden eagle before he saw that it was a condor. A sheep rancher, who killed two golden eagles in San Luis Obispo County about 1946, said that he would shoot any condors which he saw near his sheep. He refused to be convinced that condors were not predatory. This was the only rancher that I found to bear malice toward condors.

It is not improbable that, on the average, at least one condor is shot each year. There are several thousand hunters on some ranger districts on the Los Padres National Forest in the first week of the deer hunting season. Many of these hunters are from distant areas and they have not heard of condors. Those sportsmen who are acquainted with condors generally state that they would not shoot one but that they believe that many other hunters would shoot anything. On a few occasions I saw men shooting with rifles at turkey vultures in areas within the range of condors.

Collecting.—I know the present location of 130 skins or mounted specimens of the condor. Those institutions having five or more such specimens are: American Museum of Natural History (18), U. S. National Museum (16), Los Angeles County Museum (14), Museum of Comparative Zoology (14), California Academy of Sciences (11), Chicago Museum of Natural History (7), Museum of Vertebrate Zoology (7), British Museum (5). Most of these specimens were collected for "scientific purposes." One collector, Frank Arundell, assisted in the shooting of 10 condors for museum specimens about 30 years ago. E. B. Towne acquired about 13 condors from various hunters. In 1884 and 1885, H. W. Henshaw gathered about nine specimens, all apparently from hired hunters (Harris, 1941:45).

Perhaps the highest price ever paid for the skin of a condor was the £45 received by W. C. Blake (1895: 96) from Rothschild. About 1917 a well known museum in California refused to pay a collector more than $200 for collecting three condors. The last legally taken specimens were procured about 1920. In all, approximately 200 condors or their eggs have been taken as specimens. Undoubtedly collecting activity has contributed significantly to the decline of the condor in some areas.

Poison.—For nearly 100 years, most of the published accounts of condors have included the statement that many condors were killed by feeding on carcasses which had been poisoned for the purpose of killing carnivores. Alexander Taylor (1859c:20) related that condors were often killed by feeding on meat which had been poisoned with strychnine. Beebe (1906:258) stated that "hundreds" of condors had perished from poison. Henshaw (1920:8) wrote that "hundreds fell victims of the poisoned meat which the sheep herders put out for the purpose of killing the bears, cougars, and coyotes which preyed upon the sheep." As late as March 14, 1949, the Los Angeles Times stated that many condors had died from eating poisoned meat which had been set out for coyotes. Cooper (1890:249), Stephens (1919:14), and others have considered poisoning to be one of the main causes for a decrease in the numbers of condors in the late 1800's.

The only reported "observation" which indicates that a condor may have died from eating poisoned bait is given in a mimeographed pamphlet by Fry (1926:2). He claims that in 1890 he saw two dead condors which a sheepherder had found near a poisoned carcass. Bleitz (1946:39) states that arsenic was found in the remains of a chick which died in the nest. As the body of this bird lay for a week in a cabinet which was normally used for specimens pre-

served with arsenic, and as arsenic is rarely used as a poison for squirrels or carnivores, the poison found in the specimen was probably acquired after death.

An intensive program of control of ground squirrels by means of grain poisoned with thallium sulphate was commenced in the foraging range of the condor about 1926. Many birds and mammals which fed on the poisoned squirrels were killed by the poison. Among the carnivorous birds reported to be killed were ravens, red-tailed hawks, golden eagles, and turkey vultures (Linsdale, 1931:102). Many persons became alarmed about the possible effect of the poison on condors. One letter (November 20, 1935) from a government official to an inquiring citizen stated that, on the basis of experiments on "raptorial birds," a condor would have to eat 20 squirrels at a feeding to be seriously affected and it would have to eat five squirrels a day for two or three months to accumulate a lethal dose. If this information is correct for condors, it is probable that some condors have acquired a lethal or near lethal dose of thallium.

The fact that the bodies of condors killed by poison have not been found in poisoned areas is not evidence that such poisoning does not occur, for it is unlikely that the birds would die at the site of feeding. Grinnell (letter June 1, 1935) pointed out that although thallium might not kill a condor, the poison might weaken the bird so that it would succumb during periods of food scarcity or severe weather, and that the poison might affect the endocrine system.

Commencing in 1945 a new poison replaced thallium in much of the feeding range of the condor. This poison is Compound 1080 (sodium flouroacetate). Joseph Keyes and others of the Fish and Wildlife Service watched for the effects of this poison on condors and other birds during trial applications in Kern County. So far, neither condors nor turkey vultures have been found to be killed by eating squirrels poisoned with 1080. Experiments on the toxicity of 1080 have been carried out (National Research Council, 1948). For a ground squirrel, the minimum lethal dose of 1080 is about .5 milligrams per kilogram of body weight as against 25 milligrams for thallium.

The results of experiments on the feeding of Compound 1080 to eagles and vultures were as follows (*ibid.*:3):

Bird	Number	Dosage	Per Cent Killed
Golden eagle	8	5.0 mg./kg.	50
Turkey vulture	7	20.0 mg./kg.	71
Black vulture	10	15.0 mg./kg.	50

Judged by these results, a turkey vulture would have to eat as much as 40 times its own weight in poisoned squirrels before it would probably be killed. The amount would be less if the contents of the cheek pouches and stomach were eaten or if the squirrel had ingested more than the minimum lethal dose. At least in rats, "the ingestion of sub-lethal doses of 1080 has shown no significant cumulative effect" (National Research Council, 1948:4). Perhaps, then, the use of Compound 1080 is less dangerous to condors than the use of thallium. Again, however, the physiological effect of the ingestion of sublethal doses of this poison over a long period might well be harmful to condors.

In southern California, ranchers poison coyotes and other carnivores by putting out chunks of pork containing capsules of strychnine. It is conceivable that occasionally a condor eats one of these baits. To a limited degree, strychnine poisoned grain is used to poison squirrels. This poison acts very fast so that a high proportion of the squirrels die outside of their burrows where they are accessible to carnivorous birds. So far as I know, its effect on vultures has not been tested. We can only discover the true dangers of poison by experimentation on living condors, and none can be spared for this purpose.

Trapping.—A condor was caught in a coyote trap set by a state trapper on Tejon Ranch in February, 1939. One toe of the bird was nearly pulled off. The toe was amputated and the bird was released (P. S. Sprague, letter March 2, 1939). Early in 1941, a trapper for Kern County found a condor in one of his traps and released it (B. L. Fox, letter March 13, 1941). In November, 1947, an immature condor was found in a coyote trap by Lester Arnold, game warden of Kern County. The trap had been set by the carcass of a cow. The leg of the bird was broken and the bird was so badly injured that it could not be saved. It died and was sent to the Los Angeles County Museum (L. Arnold, letter February 13, 1949). Eben McMillan told me that two condors were caught in traps near Avenales Ranch about 1935. One bird died and the other was released.

Doubtless there have been several other instances of the trapping of condors in recent years, for the trapping campaign is intensive in many areas which condors frequent. Most trappers would not advertise the fact that they had caught a condor. Normally trappers employ a double set and use liquid scent rather than bait. After a coyote is caught, it usually springs the second trap, so that condors which feed on trapped coyotes are not usually in danger. Traps set near carcasses are dangerous to condors, but the normal practice is to set the trap in a trail which leads to a carcass, not at the carcass itself.

Accidents.—Inasmuch as condors alight in a rather clumsy fashion, it is probable that they often injure their wings. About 1934, some boys found an emaciated young condor with a broken wing. The bird died in captivity and it is now mounted in the courthouse at Ventura. Early in 1941, I found a dead juvenile on a high grassy ridge near Fillmore. The humerus of the bird was broken but there was no other apparent injury. When found, the bird lay a few yards from a slender vertical pipe which had been used as a surveying marker. I believe that the condor had collided with the pipe in soaring low over the ridge.

At one nest, I found a nestling in an apparently retarded state of development. It left the nest in late fall and its remains were found several hundred feet from a point below the nest. One wing of the bird had been broken apparently before the bird left the nest, and had healed in an irregular manner. Daggett (1898: 134) tells of an immature condor with a broken wing which was captured. While confined in a cage at the National Zoological Park, a young condor (U.S.N.M. 804) suffered four fractures of wing and leg bones, without apparent cause, during one summer and autumn.

In early June one parent arrived at nest 1 with a severe leg injury. The bird could scarcely walk and it generally stood with the injured leg off the ground. It spent long periods in sitting on the nest cliff. Four months after the injury was noticed, this bird still walked with a limp. In June, 1941, an adult condor was found dead in a water tank on the Still Ranch near Annette. Presumably the bird had entered the tank to drink and had been unable to get out. Oil workers near Maricopa told Robinson (1939:17) that about 1927 several condors were killed by wading into pools of oil "in the belief that it was water."

Starvation.—Condors which are unable to fly well because of injury or sickness probably die of starvation or thirst. On the other hand, condors weakened by starvation may be killed by other agencies. For these reasons, there is no record of a condor which has died solely of starvation. The majority of the condors observed by me seemed to be able to find food on every day when the weather was suitable. I encountered no emaciated condors, but a nesting adult observed by H. M. Hill (MS) in June seemed to be thin and light in weight.

From the standpoint of food, winter is the most critical period for condors. The hours of the day which are suitable for soaring are few. Storms preclude foraging on some days. Juveniles are entirely dependent and must be fed. Many condors gather in the principal nesting region so that adults with young must compete with other condors. Livestock is withdrawn to the lower parts of its range. There are no carcasses of poisoned squirrels. Cold probably increases the need for food.

Fire.—The roosting and nesting areas of condors have often been swept by fire. About 1917, a fire burned from the Piru River to the Sespe River and included some nesting and roosting sites. Another fire swept the lower Sespe region about 1928. In 1933, a fire in central Ventura County burned off the area about a nesting site known to Sidney Peyton. I found burned sticks in one nest. In 1939, fire swept the area of the condor roosts at McChesney Mountain. In 1941 there were two brush fires within half a mile of nest sites in the Sespe region. On the Los Padres National Forest, where many condors roost and nest, about 90 per cent of the fires are caused by man (F. P. Cronemiller, verbal).

Some effects of fire are of benefit to condors. Animals suitable for food may be killed. Areas of thick brush where condors could not find food or reach it are opened up by fire. Many of the favorite perches and roosts of condors are fire-killed conifers. Fire apparently has not caused condors to abandon any roosting area permanently.

As most fires occur in summer when young condors are still in the nest, young could be suffocated by smoke. After they leave the nest, flightless juveniles could be burned by fire. The thick chaparral which protects some nesting areas from disturbance by man is removed by fire.

The main purpose of the Los Padres National Forest is the protection of the watershed from fire. Adequate protection requires the construction of roads, trails, and firebreaks. In some areas, this construction has made the roosts and nests of condors easily accessible to man and construction work has disturbed the birds. Thus, there is a conflict between those who would protect the condors from man and those who would protect the forest from fire. The increased use of aerial patrol for fire detection on the national forests has decreased the amount of travel on roads and trails by forest personnel and has increased the efficiency of fire protection. It is hoped that new methods will decrease the necessity for expansion of the system of roads and trails on the national forests.

Roads and trails.—In many roosting and nesting areas, the natural closure by brush and ruggedness has been eliminated by the development of roads and trails. Dynamiting and the noise of heavy machinery and trucks can seriously disturb condors at a long distance. The construction of an aqueduct along the upper San Luis Rey River in the early 1900's probably contributed to the cessation of nesting there. On Breckenridge Mountain a public road passes within a few hundred yards of trees in which condors roost, and there are many summer homes nearby. Condors have been seen over each of the four United States highways which pass out of the southern San Joaquin Valley, and I have seen condors on the ground within a few hundred feet of some State highways. Several years ago it was planned to place a dam in lower Sespe Canyon and to build a resort at Sespe Hot Springs. Fortunately for the condors, these plans did not materialize.

Some of the changes in roads and trails during the past 30 years have decreased the accessibility of areas inhabited by condors. At one time there was a road for several miles up lower Sespe Canyon and there was a resort in the lower part of the canyon. Floods demolished the road so that the area became accessible only by a makeshift foot trail. A recently constructed truck trail has partly reopened this area to travel. Many trails and firebreaks which were made in the 1930's have disappeared because of the growth of chaparral. If the present trends in government economy continue, it is doubtful that these trails will ever be restored.

During the period of active field work, little logging

was being done in the range of the condor. This activity has increased with the rise in the price of lumber and logging has occurred near at least one nest (Tulare County). Extensive operations have been carried out on Bear Mountain, Kern County, where condors roost. As these operations are of the selective type which results in minimal disturbance of the forest, and as roosting trees are generally poor for lumber, the main harm of logging has been in the increased development of roads and the consequent influx of people.

Oil development.—Exploration and drilling for oil and gas have had an adverse effect upon condors in several important areas. Many oil workers are from out of the state and they have little knowledge of, or respect for, California game laws. Men working far from towns are none too apt to observe bird protective regulations. Roads to the drilling sites make condors accessible to persons who shoot from automobiles and to well-meaning but not harmless photographers and sightseers. In the vicinity of Bakersfield, Maricopa, and McKittrick, oil fields occupy large areas which would otherwise be used for grazing.

The discovery of oil in the Cuyama Valley has encouraged the mineral leasing of a great deal of land in the Los Padres National Forest. In Sespe Canyon there are several oil wells in operation. One long-abandoned derrick is located within half a mile of a current nesting site. A few years ago a well was drilled at the foot of a small canyon in which at least three formerly-used nesting sites are located. The region where most of my nesting observations were made was accessible because of a road which had been built for the purpose of hauling oil drilling equipment but which was little used.

During World War II an oil exploration company built a road into the center of a principal winter roosting and nesting canyon. This road passes within a few hundred yards of four nest sites known to me. For three years before the installation of a locked Forest Service gate, this road gave easy access to the area to photographers and others who disturbed the nesting birds. In the last few years this road has been seldom used and much of it has been destroyed by erosion. Although a large proportion of the important condor nesting area in Ventura County has been leased from time to time, most of the interest has been in buying and selling leases rather than in drilling and production.

Photographers.—Condors have been photographed a great deal. In 1906, Bohlman and Finley took about 250 photographs of two adult condors and their young one. Although the photographs were taken on slow glass plates, they surpass any series of still pictures of the condor which have been taken with modern high-speed equipment. J. R. Pemberton took several thousand feet of colored 16-millimeter motion pictures of condors between 1936 and 1941. Ed N. Harrison and Telford Work have each taken hundreds of feet of motion pictures as well as many colored still photographs of condors. John H. Storer photographed condors in slow motion in order to study their flight. Don Bleitz has taken a good series of colored still pictures and I have taken a few hundred pictures in black and white. Several other persons have many photographs of condors. Just about every activity except the mating display and copulation has been adequately photographed.

The activities of photographers have been far from harmless to condors. The failure of some nests known to me was probably due, at least in part, to the activity of these men. Even with great care, a party which I assisted kept the nesting adult from the egg or chick on some occasions. Other photographers were much less solicitous of the welfare of the birds and some of their activities were literally cruel. Even when photographing a large bird with a telephoto lens, one must be comparatively close to the subject. The use of a blind does not preclude disturbance. Few men are qualified to judge whether a condor is acting in a normal undisturbed fashion. There is little to be gained by attempting to obtain more photographs of these birds.

MINOR MORTALITY AND WELFARE FACTORS

Sickness and disease.—Cooper (1890:248) encountered a torpid adult condor perched on a hillside in May, 1872. He approached close to the bird but it did not move except to open its bill. There was no external evidence of disease, injury, or recent feeding. Wilson (1928:159) captured an adult condor which could not fly. The bird disgorged some food and did not fly after it was released, but it was gone by the next day. On January 1, 1937, on Tejon Ranch, Perry Sprague captured an adult condor which could not fly. The bird was put in a pen. It disgorged everything shortly after eating. About 10 days later it died in an emaciated condition.

A condor in the New York Zoological Park died in 1913 of indigestion. According to Lee Crandall, the bird was sick for a long time but it showed improvement for a short time after it was given bicarbonate of soda in its drinking water. Rett (1946:182) examined the remains of an adult condor which had been found dead near a water trough. The processes of the femur and tibia of one leg were eaten away almost entirely by a disease similar to osteomyelitis.

Eating foreign objects.—As condors peck and nibble at various indigestible objects, it is not surprising that they sometimes swallow harmful materials. A condor at the New York Zoological Park died in 1906 from eating an elastic band. Dissection of a condor which died at the National Zoological Park in 1905 revealed a small stick protruding through the wall of its stomach. A condor died after 10 years in the zoo at San Diego from eating a strip of rubber which it had pulled from a hose. According to the keeper, Karl Koch, this bird had been very ill on a previous occasion but it had been cured by pushing a hose down its throat and thus apparently freeing some obstruction.

Storm.—Rett (1938:225) examined two condors which were found dead near the carcass of a horse after a hailstorm. The condition of the bodies suggested that the birds had been killed by hailstones. It is conceivable that if a period of severe cold should immediately follow a period of wet fog or rain, condors roosting in the open could be rendered flightless by the formation of ice in their feathers. Storms may prevent foraging and thus facilitate starvation. Stormy winds might increase the possibility of flight accidents.

Killing for quills.—In accounts of the condor, it has often been stated that many condors were shot so that their quills could be made into containers for carrying gold dust. The main support for the idea that this practice was common is the account of condors in Lower California by Anthony (1893:233). He wrote: "Every Indian and Mexican gold miner is provided with from one to six of the primary quills of this species for carrying gold dust. . . . All [only two recorded] of the dead birds that I saw in Lower California had been killed for their quills alone." J. D. Reyes, resident of Cuyama Valley since 1887, told me that the quills of condors and other large birds were formerly used for carrying gold dust and that they were sold for a dollar each.

Two persons told me that a certain man, who collected condors in Ventura County about 1900, shot condors to get feathers to use for bee brushes. Sidney Peyton, an experienced bee keeper, assures me that a condor feather would make a very poor bee brush.

Indians.—Among some tribes of Indians in southern California there was an annual mourning ceremony or feast at which a condor or other large bird was killed. According to Kroeber (1925:676), among the Luisenos the nests of eagles and condors were personal and hereditary property, and the young were sometimes taken from the nest and reared. An account of an annual feast at which a condor was killed and skinned is given in Boscana's "Chinigchinich" (Harris, 1941:33). Scott gives a similar account from his own inquiries (*in* Bent, 1937:10). At the Rincon Indian Reservation, Scott (MS) saw two dancing skirts made of the large feathers of condors. Edward Davis of Mesa Grande has a similar skirt which the Indians made for him. In parts of the present area of San Diego County the taking of young condors for ceremonial purposes was once common.

Lassoing.—Some published accounts of the condor include the report that vaqueros used to lasso the birds for sport. I heard similar stories from ranchers and old-timers. Stephens (1899:88) gives an account of the lassoing of an adult condor at a carcass. The bird appeared stupid. It could run but apparently it could not fly. A vaquero rode up and lassoed it. The bird died, presumably from being choked by the rope. Bryant (1917:176) tells of another condor which was lassoed near a carcass. This bird died in Golden Gate Park six months later. I did not encounter any condors on the ground which could be approached close enough to lasso. Not improbably the birds which were caught in this manner were unable to fly because of sickness or injury.

"Penning".—Shields (1895:148) tells of hearing from an old-timer that condors were caught in former days by placing a carcass within a small pen so that a condor which alighted at the carcass would not have room to take off. I do not know of a first-hand account of this practice. Probably the story was borrowed from the account by Darwin (1909:198) of a similar method employed to capture South American condors in Chile.

False information.—False and harmful information about condors has often been printed, especially in newspapers. In the Los Angeles Times for July 6, 1934, there was a large drawing showing how a condor is "capable of carrying a fawn in its talons." The accompanying article was based on information from E. I. Dyer (1935:5) and others who wished to avoid erroneous and sensational publicity. The Newhall Sentinel for September 2, 1937, stated that a condor could easily pick up a sheep. These falsehoods encourage certain persons to shoot at condors.

The misinformation about the high value of eggs has often been repeated. Overemphasis of rarity leads egg collectors, photographers, and curious persons to seek condors and consequently to disturb them. The publication of false information cannot be stopped merely by making accurate information available. A few years ago an inquiring reporter for a national weekly magazine was furnished with accurate information on the status of the condor. The printed version featured, as fact, the oft published but unsubstantiated conjecture that condors had become rare because of eating poisoned baits.

IMPRACTICAL PROPOSALS

"Artificial" feeding.—Feeding of condors by providing carcasses near their roosts is not practical except as an experiment. To provide a constant supply of food would entail much labor, expense, and waste. It would be difficult to insure that condors would get the meat and that other animals would not. Constant feeding at one locality would attract carnivores which might harm the feeding condors. A constant supply of food at one locality might keep condors from utilizing "natural" sources of food and perhaps would cause numbers to concentrate in one area where they could be wiped out by some disaster. By association with humans the birds might lose some of the cautiousness which is necessary to their survival.

Transplanting.—The trapping of condors for release in areas which they formerly inhabited is not practical in such a mobile species. For any promise of success, one would have to trap a mated pair. Not only would this be difficult, because the sexes look alike, but there is no season when such a pair might be taken without danger of causing the death of their young. Probably a transplanted pair would try to return to the site of their nest or young. This plan does not seem feasible.

Actually condors transplant themselves through wandering, and when vagrants find suitable condi-

tions at some extra-limital location, they might remain and breed. The nesting in 1950 in Tulare County, more than 100 miles from the nearest previously known nest site, may be an example of this kind of extension in range. The amount of extralimital wandering and the tendency to repopulate formerly inhabited areas should increase if the total population increases in size.

Breeding in captivity.—Breeding condors in captivity should be attempted only after all efforts to maintain the natural population have failed. South American condors have been bred in a large cage at the Zoo in San Diego and have even been induced to produce one young every year instead of in alternate years. In some years the egg has been taken soon after laying and hatched in an incubator, and the parent birds raised a second chick in the same year. Possibly the same avicultural feat could be accomplished with California condors although courting activities in captives of this species are unknown. It is extremely doubtful that a condor raised by hand and lacking the experience gained by being raised in the wild could survive for long if released. Release of captive condors might well introduce zoo diseases into the wild population.

The beauty of a California condor is in the magnificence of its soaring flight. A condor in a cage is uninspiring, pitiful, and ugly to one who has seen them soaring over the mountains. Condors are so few that their recreational value is one of quality rather than of quantity. As Leopold (1936:394) points out, the recreational value of wildlife is in inverse proportion to its artificiality. The thrill of seeing a condor is greatly diminished when the birds are being raised in captivity. Our objective should be to maintain and perhaps to increase the natural population of condors.

RECOMMENDATIONS

Protection by law.—About eighty years ago Cronise (1868:455) wrote that the condor should be protected by law from "reckless slaughter." Cooper (1890:249) stated that there was a law protecting the condor but that few persons knew of it. The present California law protects the condor as a nongame bird. Although the condor is excepted from scientific collectors' permits, permission was given in 1950 to the San Diego Zoo to take two young condors for the purpose of attempting to breed them in captivity. The Zoo personnel were unable to find a nest outside of the condor sanctuaries. In 1952 the California Fish and Game Commission granted the Zoo a permit to "trap and cage one pair."

The section of the Fish and Game Code (1963) under which the condor is protected is 3511. "Fully protected birds are: California condors (*Gymnogyps californianus*). . . . Fully protected birds may not be taken at any time and no provision of this code or any other law shall be construed to authorize the issuance of permits or licenses to take any fully protected bird and no such permit or license heretofore issued shall have any force or effect for any such purpose." (Added by Stats. 1957, Ch. 1972.) The penalty for violation is a fine of not over $500 or imprisonment for not over six months, or both. Apparently only one person has ever been punished for killing a condor. He shot a condor near Pasadena in 1908 and tried to sell it, but he was apprehended and fined $50 (Finley, 1928:169).

I discovered by inquiry among hunters, ranchers and others in the field that federal laws are respected far more than are state laws. As a striking and unique species, threatened with extinction, the condor is of national interest and is deserving of strict federal protection.

A start toward federal protection was made in 1942 when the "Convention on Nature Protection and Wild Life Preservation in the Western Hemisphere," sometimes known as the "Natural Resources Treaty," became effective. In the Annex to this convention, the California condor was listed among those species whose protection (Article VIII) "is declared to be of special urgency and importance," and the United States agreed to protect it "as completely as possible." Perhaps because of the intervention of World War II, however, no federal laws were passed to implement the good intentions of the treaty. However, the Convention has already had a beneficial effect in that persons who live in the range of the condor are proud of the fact that condors have received official national recognition.

More recently the California condor has received official international recognition as a threatened species. In 1949, the International Technical Conference on the Protection of Nature at Lake Success included the condor in a list of 13 birds of the world which are "in need of emergency action if they are to be saved from extinction" (UNESCO, 1950:133-137).

Of course mere recognition does not help the birds directly, but it focuses attention on the need for action, and it may lead to the passing of effective laws prohibiting the disturbance of condors or their nests.

Protection by closures.—The nesting and roosting areas of condors must be protected from disturbance by man. All the recently used nest sites known to me are within national forests, or, in one case, an Indian reservation. Three important roosting areas are outside of the national forests but these are not easily accessible by road and they are closed to the public by the surrounding landowners.

In 1937, an area of about 1200 acres surrounding Sisquoc Falls, Santa Barbara County, was closed to all travel and use by the United States Forest Service. This closure was in large measure due to the efforts of Robert E. Easton and the National Audubon Society. In order to make this closure effective, regulation T-9 of the rules and regulations governing the National Forests was modified so as to prohibit persons from going on areas closed for the protection of rare species. The amendment consisted of adding the following paragraph:

(I) The unauthorized going or being upon any area which has been closed by the Chief, Forest Service, for the perpetuation and protection of (a) rare or vanishing species of plants or animals, (b) special biological communities, or (c) historical or archeological places or objects of interest; also the unauthorized going or being upon any area so closed for scientific experiments and investigations, or for other purposes where controlled use is necessary in order to insure proper treatment and protection. The boundaries of each area shall be defined by the Regional Forester and indicated in so far as practicable by posting notices along such boundaries and on roads and trails leading into such areas.

Previous to 1941 there were many deer hunters in the Sisquoc River region in late summer, but the permits required of hunters stipulated that they were not to enter the closed area and apparently there was no trespassing. The protection of this area has not been altogether effective in preventing the disturbance of condors there, for a well-used trail passes along the edge of the sanctuary and through a stand of large pines where condors often roost. This trail is much used by fishermen in spring. The disturbance of condors in this area has been greatly lessened by the recent practice of closing a large part of the forest to travel during the summer, including the deer hunting season, in order to reduce the danger of fire. The fire closure and the relative inaccessibility of the area seem, so far, to have afforded condors adequate protection in that region.

Partly as a result of the findings of this study, the Forest Service, in 1947, closed to public travel and use a large area around the lower Sespe River. Access corridors were provided for fishermen, ranchers, and oil well operators. The Forest Service provides a special condor patrolman for eight months of the year, the National Audubon Society contributing the cost of the first four months, and the Forest Service that of the last four months. This area, the Sespe Wildlife Preserve, includes most of the condor nesting sites and the principal winter roosts. As all the area was normally closed in summer because of the danger of fire, the closure did not result in any appreciable loss of recreational area to the public. Inasmuch as the laying of eggs commences in February and as most juvenal condors cannot fly well by the following January, a year around patrol by a permanent warden is recommended.

The creation of the Sespe Wildlife Preserve was not entirely effective in protecting nesting condors from disturbance, for the Forest Service had no power to prevent issuance of oil and gas leases within the preserve by the Department of the Interior. New oil discoveries in the general region stimulated oil and gas prospecting. The Forest Service recommended disapproval of applications for leases of land within the preserve. The applicants objected strongly. As a result, a public hearing was held by the Department of the Interior so that both conservationists and oil interests could present their views. The final outcome was the issuance, by the Secretary of the Interior, Oscar L. Chapman, of Public Land Order 695. This order states that 55 square miles of land in the Los Padres National Forest are "withdrawn from all forms of appropriation under the public-land laws, including the mining laws, and" with certain exceptions "the mineral-leasing laws, and reserved as a condor sanctuary, under the jurisdiction of the Forest Service."

Within the 16 square miles where the concentration of nests is especially great no entry to the surface of the ground is permitted, but oil and gas may be tapped by directional drilling from outside the area. Within the remaining 39 square miles oil and gas deposits may be developed and extracted "subject to the condition that no lessee shall use or invade, for any purpose, the surface of any such lands within one-half mile of a condor nest active within three years." Valid mineral leases in effect as of the date of the Withdrawal Order were not affected thereby, but all such, covering approximately half of the "closed" area, will have matured by late 1955; no extensions thereof, let alone new leases, will be granted without inclusion of the restrictive regulations called for by the Order. Many geologists believe that actual drilling operations will not prove feasible.

Many persons oppose every closure of public land. Sheldon (1939:61) takes the extreme view that by setting up a condor sanctuary, the public sacrifices the recreational value of a large area "in exchange for the extremely doubtful preservation of a bird of no value, esthetically or otherwise." To a lesser degree, this view is held by some hunters and hikers. Stockmen who graze cattle on parts of the national forests resent further restriction of grazing land. Oil prospectors and speculators in mineral leases oppose the withdrawal of land from mineral entry.

The "natural" closure of certain areas by their inaccessibility should be maintained as far as possible or even augmented by the rerouting or cessation of maintenance of certain roads and trails. In 1936, the construction of a fire road to the vicinity of Sisquoc Falls was halted far short of that site through the efforts of the National Audubon Society and a few interested persons. The welfare of condors and other wildlife should be considered in the planning of roads and trails.

Education.—Condors cannot be made to stay on the national forests or within any area which might be closed for their protection. Most of the feeding areas are on private lands. Therefore, the only way of completely protecting condors from molestation is through the cooperation of people throughout the range of condors. Sensational publicity is harmful in that it causes persons who otherwise would have no direct influence upon condors to seek the birds and to disturb them. Educational efforts should be concentrated primarily upon those persons who may encounter condors. The interest and cooperation of these people can best be gained by helping them to understand something of the relation of the condor to its environment rather than by giving them a list of "don'ts." The principal groups of persons, within or near the range of condors, who should be informed and who have the opportunity to pass on this information to others, are as follows:

United States Forest Service supervisors, rangers, patrolmen, lookouts, and guards.

State and county forestry and fire department officials and lookouts.

County agricultural commissioners and their assistants.

Game wardens and trappers.

Ranchers upon whose property condors feed.

Sportsmen's organizations.

Teachers of conservation and biology.

Where school is held for forest guards, there is an excellent opportunity for enlisting their interest in condors. Some other important groups can be informed at local meetings of cattlemen's and wool growers' associations.

The most effective means of education is through personal contact with individuals. Many persons have little respect for signs and they do not bother to read printed matter which is given to them. On parts of the national forests where there are checking stations or where hunting or camping permits are required, there is an opportunity for forest officials to inform persons individually before they enter areas inhabited by condors. One man, truly interested in condors, can do a great deal toward educating others. If eventually it is possible to employ permanently a man to guard the interests of condors in the field, this man should spend much more time in visiting persons throughout the condor range and securing their cooperation than in patrolling nesting areas against intruders. With education and cooperation, little, if any, patrolling probably would be necessary.

Food.—Maintaining or augmenting the supply of food can best be accomplished through the education and cooperation of stockmen. At present there are a few ranchers who, because of their interest in condors, leave carcasses which are in suitable locations for the birds. If, through the cooperation of county health authorities, there were a system of special inspection of carcasses for disease, many more carcasses could be left on the range instead of being destroyed. Trappers have a constant supply of carcasses and means for transporting them. They should be encouraged to leave carcasses at sites suitable for feeding by condors. To secure the help of ranchers and trappers and to guide them in their efforts in behalf of the condor, the constant service of a man well acquainted with the birds is needed.

Carcasses of poisoned animals must be regarded as dangerous to condors until they are proven otherwise. The agricultural commissioners in the principal counties where condors feed on poisoned squirrels must be kept alert to this danger. Additional research on the physiological effects of eating poisoned mammals could be carried out on turkey vultures. If the poison proves harmful, gassing or other means of killing squirrels in their burrows should be encouraged where condors forage and the use of quick-acting poisons which cause squirrels to die outside of their burrows should be discouraged. Here again the need for a permanently employed field man who is interested in condors and well versed in their ways is needed.

Appendix

RECORDS OF OCCURRENCE

In the following pages are tabulated the most significant records of the occurrence of condors since 1835. For discussion of these records see section on distribution and numbers, pages 10 to 19. Many records have been omitted where they added nothing but bulk to the general picture of the distribution of condors. The abbreviations used to designate the present location of specimens are: A.M.N.H., American Museum of Natural History; C.A.S., California Academy of Sciences; C.M.N.H., Chicago Museum of Natural History; L.A.M., Los Angeles County Museum; M.C.Z., Museum of Comparative Zoology; M.V.Z., Museum of Vertebrate Zoology; S.D.N.H.M., San Diego Natural History Museum; S.N.H.M., Stanford Natural History Museum; U.C.L.A., University of California at Los Angeles.

Areas from which condors have disappeared since 1850.—

CALIFORNIA

HUMBOLDT COUNTY

1889 or 1890, Kneeland prairie, 18 miles from Eureka: specimen (Smith, 1916:205) [Kneeland is 6 miles southeast of Eureka].

1892, Yager Creek, about 60 miles east of Eureka: fall, specimen (Smith, *loc. cit.*) [Yager Creek is about 20 miles southeast of Eureka].

NAPA COUNTY

1845, Napa Valley: August 16, "the royal vulture in greate abundance"; September 8, shot one (Clyman, 1928:182, 183.).

1857 and 1860, lower Napa Valley: "frequently saw them" (Leach, 1929:23).

MARIN COUNTY

1847, mountains [near Fairfax]: July, "at least a dozen" (A. J. Grayson, *fide* Bryant, 1891:52).

1905 (prior to), "mountains north of San Francisco" [this county?]: one (C.M.N.H. 39613).

"San Rafael," mentioned by some compilers, refers to a locality in Monterey County.

SAN MATEO COUNTY

1865, "parts" of county: common (C. Littlejohn, *fide* Grinnell and Wythe, 1927:78).

1904, near Stanford University: January, one (Prof. Heath *fide* Fisher, 1904:50).

SANTA CLARA COUNTY

? , "vicinity of San Jose" [this county?]: two (Woodhouse, 1853:58).

1889, Pacheco Pass: February 3, 3 (Taylor, 1895a: 78).

1885-1889, near Los Gatos: 2 (Van Denburgh, 1899:159).

The locality "Berryessa" mentioned by some compilers is the home of F. H. Holmes who collected condors in Monterey County in the 1890's and who kept a pet condor.

SANTA CRUZ COUNTY

1849-1854 (between), Santa Cruz: February to October, 3 or 4 pairs, "constantly" (Heermann, 1859:29).

1866, county: "W. O. Emerson, on the verbal authority of Cooper, records them as common. . . ." (McGregor, 1901:5).

1879, county: 2 eggs (C.M.N.H.).

1884 (about), Santa Cruz: 3 (A. M. Ingersoll, verbal, 1940).

1884, Santa Cruz: "common" (Skirm, 1884:149).

1885, county: September, 2, last seen (E. H. Fiske, *fide* McGregor, *loc. cit.*).

1890, "around Santa Cruz": "tolerably common" (J. Skirm, *fide* Belding, 1890:24).

1903, mountains north side Pájaro Valley: summer and autumn, "seen several times" (Hunter, 1904: 24).

TUOLUMNE COUNTY

1850, Tuolumne River near Hawkin's Bar: March 29, 3 or 4 "couples"; April 5, one (J. W. Audubon, *fide* Harris, 1941:34).

SAN BERNARDINO COUNTY

1886, Bear Valley: June 7, one; June 8, 4; June 15, 2 (F. Stephens, *fide* Morcom, 1887:40).

1888, Bear Valley: summer, 14 (Gilman, 1907:107).

1890, San Bernardino: "very rare" (F. Stephens, *fide* Belding, 1890:24).

1896 (about), near Bear Valley: 4 (Arnold, 1909: 101).

1905-1907, mountains: summer, found none (Grinnell, 1908:50).

RIVERSIDE COUNTY

1886, Banning: April 22, immature (F. Stephens, MS; Morcom, 1887:40) [doubtful, judging from description].

1886, 15 miles south of San Bernardino: August 2, immature (M.C.Z.).

1893, "Cottonwood forest on San Jacinto River": June 18, one (S.N.H.M.).

?   , El Casco: immature (M.C.Z.).

1904, near Mt. San Jacinto: 13 (Joseph Dixon, verbal, 1941).

?   , Snow Creek Falls: for "several years," pair and nest; none, 1907 (Gilman, 1907:107) [nest doubtful].

1913, San Jacinto area: during expedition, not seen (Grinnell and Swarth, 1913:235).

ORANGE COUNTY

1872, near coast near southern boundary: May, one (Cooper, 1890:248).

1897, near Santa Ana: adult (A.M.N.H.).

1901, Santiago Canyon: none seen for 12 years or more (Bryan, 1901:81).

1908, Trabuco Canyon: September 18, remains found (H. S. Swarth, MS).

1937, near Santiago Peak: October 8, one (Pequegnat, 1945:28).

1938, near Santiago Peak: February 14, one (Pequegnat, loc. cit.).

SAN DIEGO COUNTY

1849, Mission San Luis Rey: November 7 or 8, one (J. W. Audubon, fide Harris, 1941:34).

1875, near San Diego: June 14 (S.N.H.M.).

1884, Poway Valley: April, one (Emerson, 1887: 426).

1884, Volcano Mts.: January - March, none (Emerson, loc. cit.).

1886, near De Luz (near Fallbrook): egg (S.D.N.H.M.).

1888, Julian: March 12, immature (M.C.Z. 214367); May 11, one (M.C.Z. 80166); June 25, adult (Hoffman, 1895:18).

1890, Santa Ysabel: August 13, adult (S.D.N.H.M.).

1891, Santa Margarita Ranch: December, 2 (A. W. Anthony, fide Taylor, 1895a:76).

1892, near Rincon: about August 13, one shot (Lawrence, 1893:300).

1897 [near Palomar Mtn.]: March 11, egg (Sharples, 1897:21).

1897, Palomar Mtn.: June 18, 4 (J. M. Hatch, fide McGregor, 1899:67).

1898, mountains, northern part of county: 7 (Dixon, 1924:192).

1899, Santa Ysabel Rancho: May 24, one caught (Stephens, 1899:88).

1900, near Eagle Peak, near Julian: March [4], egg (Gedney, 1900:124).

1901, Volcan Mtn.: spring, one shot (Gilman, 1907: 106).

1903, Santa Margarita Ranch: one (S.D.N.H.M.).

1908, Santa Margarita Ranch: 2 (J. B. Dixon, verbal, 1940).

1908, Julian: July 16, one (F. Stephens, MS).

1908, mouth Tiajuana River: November 11, one (F. Stephens, MS).

1919-1924, mountains, northern part of county: search revealed none (Dixon, 1924:192).

ARIZONA

1865, Fort Yuma: September, "individuals observed" (Coues, 1866:42).

MEXICO
LOWER CALIFORNIA

1887, Guadaloupe Valley, 40 miles south of Ensenada, near coast: dead bird (Anthony, 1893:233; Taylor, 1895a:75).

1887, east of El Rosario, about 30° north: carcass (Anthony, 1893:233; 1895:137).

"At one time," near Real del Castillo, San Rafael Valley: "W. W. Anthony, reported seeing" (Anthony, 1893:233).

1893, Sierra San Pedro Mártir: May, "rather common," "seen daily about the meadows at altitudes of 8000 and 9000 feet" [actually at least 1000 feet lower] (Anthony, loc. cit.); "as many as three at once" (Anthony, fide Taylor, 1895a:75).

1905, Santa Rosa Valley, southern Sierra San Pedro Mártir: July, "during our stay" a carcass "attracted about a dozen" [at once?] (Nelson, 1921:22).

1923, Sierra San Pedro Mártir: June 12, one (Huey, 1926:352).

1924, Sierra Juárez: July 21, one (Huey, loc. cit.).

1924, Sierra San Pedro Mártir: summer, 4 (S. Melling, fide Grinnell, MS).

1925, La Grulla, Sierra San Pedro Mártir: May 18, 2 (C. Lamb and A. E. Borell, MSS).

1925, Vallecitos, Sierra San Pedro Mártir: June 6 and 7, 2 (C. Lamb and A. E. Borell, MSS).

1932, La Encantada, Sierra San Pedro Mártir: about June, 2 (G. Bancroft and M. Bancroft, verbal, 1946; S. Melling, verbal, 1949 [no doubt].

1935, La Encantada: November 5, one (S. Melling, *fide* Scott, 1936:42).

1937, La Encantada: July, 2 (W. M. Longhurst, verbal, 1941).

Areas in which condors are still present.—

CALIFORNIA
SAN BENITO COUNTY

1884, summer, 14 (W. R. Flint, *fide* Bendire, 1892: 158).

1889, Sargents: June 22, 3; July 16, 6; August 7, 16; August 8, one killed (W. A. Burres, *fide* Taylor, 1895*a*:78).

1890, "M. Sargents": adult (Univ. Arizona).

1894, Sargents: 2 (Taylor, *loc. cit.*).

1898, Pinnacles: April 6, egg (Willett, 1931:31).

1900, Pinnacles: last seen, plentiful "early eighties" (B. F. Bacon, *fide* Willett, *loc. cit.*).

1940 (about), Pinnacles: 2 (D. M. Selleck and O. R. Shaw, verbal, 1947).

1951, Bitterwater: 1 at least verified September 2; 5 reported by others in days just preceding (A. S. Leopold, MS).

FRESNO COUNTY

1890, Huron, about 16 miles east of Coalinga: January, 2 dead (Fry, 1926:2).

1895-1914, near Coalinga: one seen twice (W. W. Terrill, letter, January 30, 1940).

1900, near Wheatville, about 25 miles southwest of Fresno: July 1, one (Tyler, 1913:37).

1946, Castle Mtn., south corner of county: June 30, 7 (C. B. Koford, MS).

MONTEREY COUNTY

1855, Monterey: July, 2 shot (Taylor, 1859*c*:17, 18) [several specimens from Taylor sent to Norwich Museum and the British Museum].

1859, Monterey: March 13, 20 (Taylor, 1859*b*:543).

1859, "vicinity of Tularcitos, near a place called Conejos": April, egg and young taken (Taylor, 1859*a*:537).

1861, Monterey: August 9-September 26, one of the "most characteristic land birds" (Cooper, 1871: 757).

1860's [est.], San Rafael, 30 miles from Monterey: egg (U.S.N.M. 9983).

1865 [near Monterey?]: young taken (Sclater, 1866: 366).

1884, Jolon: October 10, adult (M.C.Z. 80168).

1884, San Antonio Mission: September 27, 4 (Henshaw, 1920:8).

1885, Jolon: March, immature (U.S.N.M. 103375).

1894, upper Salinas Valley: seen (Willett, 1908:137).

1895, Santa Lucia Range: April 22 and 23, eggs (U.S.N.M. 29256 and 28052).

1898, Big Sur River [probably Island Mtn.]: March, one (M.C.Z. 80167).

1898, near Mt. Santa Lucia: June 16, immature (M.C.Z. 80170).

1900 (prior to), Big Sur and south: seen (R. H. Beck, verbal, 1947).

1902, head Nacimiento River: egg (S.D.N.H.M.).

1902, 2 miles east of Jolon: August 26, 5, perhaps 9 (C. H. Merriam, MS).

1905, Villa Canyon, near coast and south boundary: July 18, 8 or 10 (Jenkins, 1906:126).

1909, Big Creek, central Santa Lucia Range: May 27, one (Pemberton and Carriger, 1915:192).

1910 (and before), San Miguelito Ranch: many, none since about 1915 (G. Thompson, verbal, 1940).

1910 (about), Big Sur: last, none since (S. Yaeger, verbal, 1940).

1915 (about), Big Sur: last condors (W. Post, verbal, 1940).

1917 [Mill Creek, San Miguelito Ranch]: June, one captured (C. A. S. 19010).

1922, Cholame Ranch: August, 4, none since (H. Jack, *fide* C. S. Robinson, MS).

1944, Cholame Ranch, just south county line: June 14, 20 (Johnson, 1945:38) (see San Luis Obispo County).

1945, 6 miles east of Parkfield: August 3, 16 (D. and A. McMillan, verbal, 1946).

1946, 5 miles north of Cholame: June 29, 11 (C. B. Koford, MS).

1947, 5 miles north of Cholame: June 18, 22 (C. B. Koford, MS).

1947, Castle Mountain: August 6, 3 (I. L. Wiggins, letter, March 3, 1948).

1948, 4½ miles north of Parkfield: October 5, 7 (H. C. Ludeke, Jr., letter, February 8, 1949).

1948, near Parkfield: December 20, one (D. Shaffer,

letter, February 22, 1949).

1950, near Parkfield: October 15, 21 (H. C. Ludeke, Jr., letter, October 18, 1950).

SAN LUIS OBISPO COUNTY

1889, Santa Lucia Range: early May, egg (Taylor, 1895b:88).

1891, coast near San Simeon: common (Nelson, *fide* Fisher, 1893:34).

1893 (about), head Little Pico Creek: about 50 (H. DeTracey, verbal, 1946).

1900, near Burnett Peak: March 5, egg (H. DeTracey, letter, March 5, 1946).

1902, Santa Lucia Range: December 3, adult (A.M.N.H. 90572).

1905 (about), near Simmler: 2 (F. Truesdale, verbal, 1947).

1908 [McChesney Mtn.]: February 27, egg (A. E. Price, letter, November 15, 1915).

1911 [McChesney Mtn.]: April 3, nest (Dawson, 1924:1724).

1913 (about), near Rocky Butte: skeleton (H. DeTracey, specimen).

1920 [McChesney Mtn.]: March 12, egg (G. G. Stuart, letter, April 29, 1940).

1940, McChesney Mtn.: July 29, 2 or 3 (C. B. Koford, MS).

1944, about 5 miles northwest of Cholame: June 14, 20 (Johnson, 1945:38).

1945, McChesney Mtn.: May 27, 5 (H. Hjersman, MS).

1945, near Cholame: June 1, 13 (E. Z. Rett, verbal, 1946).

1946, Bitterwater Valley: March 13, 3 (E. McMillan, verbal, 1946).

1946, McChesney Mtn.: May 15, 2 (E. McMillan, verbal, 1946); July 7, 6, probably 8 (C. B. Koford, MS).

1946, near Cholame: June 29, 11 (C. B. Koford, MS).

1947, near Cholame: June 18, 22 (C. B. Koford, MS).

1947, McChesney Mtn.: September 8, 14 (A. H. Miller, MS).

1948, Pinole Ranch, about 8 miles north of Simmler: March 5, 2; August 1, 12; September 26, 6 (E. McMillan, letters, March 5 and September 27, 1948).

1948, Bitterwater Valley: July 7, 12; June 11 and September 3, 3 (E. McMillan, letters, June 11, July 6, and September 27, 1948).

1948, San Juan Ranch: December 11, 3; December 22, 2 (I. McMillan, verbal, 1948).

1949, Bitterwater Valley: May 31, 9; October 12, 3; October 27, 4; November 2, 3 (D. and J. McMillan, letter, May 31, 1949; E. McMillan, letter, November 9, 1949).

1949, Pinole Ranch: July 10, 4; October 4, 19 (E. McMillan, letters, August 11 and October 5, 1949).

1950, Bitterwater Valley: October 20, 15 (E. McMillan, letter, October 20, 1950).

SANTA BARBARA COUNTY

1886, Santa Barbara: "nearly extinct," "occasionally seen" in Santa Ynez Mts. (Streator, 1886:67).

1889, Santa Ynez Mts.: July, one (A.M.N.H. 469948).

1891, Santa Ynez Mts.: common (Nelson, *fide* Fisher, 1893:34).

1895, Santa Ynez: February 20, adult (M.V.Z. 23334).

1895, Sisquoc Canyon: April 25, egg (Willett, 1912: 45).

1895 (about), Falls Canyon: about 75 (G. Willett, verbal, 1940).

1896, Santa Ynez Mts.: April 21, egg (M.C.Z.).

1896, Falls Canyon: April, about 15 (O. J. Zahn, letter, February 17, 1949; specimen).

1897, San Roque Canyon: April 29, egg (Willett, 1912:45).

1898, near Lompoc: February 20, one (S.N.H.M.).

1899, San Marcos Pass: one (A. P. Redington, *fide* Barlow, 1899:19).

1901, 2 miles from Santa Barbara: February 26, egg (W. Gallaher, letter, March 27, 1905).

1902, Big Pine Mtn.: March 20, egg (A.M.N.H. 6937).

1905, near Los Olivos: June 3, one (Ray, 1906:409).

1910, Divide Peak: 3 (Pemberton, 1910:19).

1921 (about), junction Mono and Indian creeks: 16 (R. M. Bond, verbal, 1940).

1930, San Rafael Mtn.: about September, 10 (Hoffmann, 1930:6).

1931, Montgomery Potrero: 5 (S. Easton, letter, March 15, 1932).

1934 [Montgomery Potrero: July 1], 7 (Dyer, 1935:6).

1935, Montgomery Potrero: July, 10 (E. I. Dyer, letter, July 31, 1935).

1935, La Cumbre Peak: June 22, 5 (A. J. Nolder,

U.S.F.S. files).

1936, Falls Canyon: March 28, 18; June 24, 32; August 9, 6 (Pemberton, MS).

1936, Branch Canyon, Cuyama Valley: September 24, 34; October 10 and 11, 24 (Pemberton, MS).

1936, Peachtree Canyon: October 17, 2 dead (Rett, 1938:225).

1937, Falls Canyon: May 12 and 21, 29 (W. H. Maples, MS); July 8, 17 (Pemberton, MS).

1937, Big Pine Mtn.: September, 15 (C. Swartz and W. E. Caldwell, U.S.F.S. files).

1937, Figueroa Mtn.: December 2 and 3, 3 (E. M. Lyda, U.S.F.S. files).

1938, Branch Canyon: October 8, 30 (Pemberton, MS).

1938, Big Pine Mtn.: December 2, 10 (E. E. Horn, verbal, 1939).

1939, Falls Canyon: July 14, 9; November 2, 2 (C. B. Koford, MS).

1939, near Loma Pelona: about December 7, 3 (H. Twining, verbal, 1940).

1939, Alamar Saddle: about December 11, 6 (H. Twining, verbal, 1940).

1940, Madulce Peak Lookout: June 27, 12 (B. Choice, U.S.F.S. files).

1940, San Rafael Peak: July 14 and 15, 20 (C. B. Koford, MS).

1940, Falls Canyon: November 14, 5 (C. B. Koford, MS).

1945, Salisbury Potrero: mid-November, 22 (W. F. Douglas, verbal, 1946).

1946, West Big Pine Lookout: April 23, 5 (C. B. Koford, MS); August 23, 11 (H. Boyce, U.S.F.S. files).

VENTURA COUNTY

1881, Wheeler Canyon near Ventura: April 2, one (Evermann, 1886:608).

1898 (about), Simi Mts.: 7 (Grinnell, 1898:20).

1900, Piru Canyon: young taken (U.S.N.M. 201427).

1902, Santa Paula Canyon: May, egg (specimen, R. W. Tufts).

1904, Conejo Ranch: one (Univ. Michigan).

1904, Mt. Pinos, summit: June 26 and July 11, one (Grinnell, MS).

1905, foothills northwest of Santa Paula: 16 (T. Arundell, letter, September 15, 1907).

1905, Sespe Valley, Piedra Blanca: egg (M.C.Z.; Gallaher, 1906:57).

1907, Hopper Mtn.: September 13, 5 (T. Arundell, letter, September 15, 1907).

1909, Piru Canyon: young taken (New York Zool. Park files).

1910, Sulfur Peak: 3 (Pemberton, 1910:19).

1915, Pine Canyon near Fillmore: April 4, egg (C.M.N.H. 6164).

1916, Santa Paula Canyon: April 2, 2 (A.M.N.H. 352005, G. Willett 2685).

1916, Simi Hills: March, 6 (Grinnell, letter, March 25, 1916).

1917, Coldwater Canyon: May 5, 11, and 17, 3 collected (C.A.S.); May 4 and 5, 20 seen (J. P. Herring, MS).

1917, Hopper Canyon: May 19, 9 (J. P. Herring, MS).

1922 (about), 5 miles north of Ventura: 10 (E. Percy, verbal, 1941).

1923, Coldwater Canyon: October 23, young taken (L.A.M. 15885).

1925 (about), near Santa Susana: 3 (W. L. Chambers, verbal, 1939).

1929, Sespe Canyon: March 23, 5 (Peyton, 1932:24).

1929, Pole Canyon, near Fillmore: August, one captured (S.D.N.H.M. 18117).

1929, about 8 miles from Ventura: March 24, 6 (Ashworth, 1929:66).

1930, Hopper Ranch: 36 (E. Percy, verbal, 1939).

1933, Sespe Canyon: December 4, 7 (Bolander, 1934:2).

1935, Reyes Peak: September, 2 (R. L. Kloppenburg, verbal, 1939).

1936, Hopper Ranch: January 13, 30 (E. Percy, fide C. D. Scott, MS); January 17, 15 (C. D. Scott, letter, January 25, 1936).

1936, Hopper Canyon: May 24, 8 (J. Johns, U.S.F.S. files).

1937, Thorn Point Lookout, Pine Mtn.: November 4, 5 (L. L. Pinkerton, U.S.F.S. files).

1937, Sespe Canyon: May 3, 8 (Webb, 1937:2).

1938 and 1940, South Mtn. Lookout: summer, occasional 1 to 3 (C. Lepper, verbal, 1941).

1939, Frazier Mtn.: December, 4 (M. C. Badger, verbal, 1940).

1939, Cobblestone Mtn.: June, one almost daily (J. F. Ashley, verbal, 1939).

1939, Pine Mtn.: remains found (C. B. Koford, MS).

1939, Topatopa Peak: October 12, 2 (C. B. Koford, MS).

1939, Pine Canyon near Fillmore: December 14, 3 (C. B. Koford, MS).

1939, Big Sespe Canyon: October 15, 5 (C. B. Koford, MS).

1939, Santa Paula Canyon: October 16, 12; December 13, 5 (C. B. Koford, MS).

1939, Hopper Canyon: February 17, 16 (Pemberton, MS); March 16, 32; April 1, 17; June 28, 13; August 9, 10; December 2, 14; December 16, 16 (C. B. Koford, MS).

1940, Mt. Pinos, summit: about June 16, one (S. B. Peyton, verbal, 1940).

1940, Thorn Point: July 24, 3, perhaps 5 (C. B. Koford, MS).

1940, Piru Creek near Agua Blanca Creek: June 4, 3 (C. B. Koford, MS).

1940, Big Sespe Canyon: May 28, 4; August 21, 5 (C. B. Koford, MS).

1940, Hopper Canyon: January 4, 27; March 22, 21; July 6, 14; December 15, 28 (C. B. Koford, MS).

1940 or 1941, head Tapo Canyon, south Piru: up to 26 (H. Shebley, verbal, 1941).

1941, head Tapo Canyon: May 5, 2 (C. B. Koford, MS).

1941, near Lake Sherwood: spring, 6 (D. Bleitz, verbal, 1941; photographs show two immatures).

1941, Hopper Canyon: January 1, 24; March 10, 25; April 19, 22; June 6, 10 (C. B. Koford, MS); January 16, 33 (E. Percy, verbal, 1941).

1945, Pole Canyon: January 21, 42 (E. Percy, letter, January 26, 1945) [no doubt].

1946, Hopper Canyon: February 11, 30; March 3, 24; April 13, 28; June 13, 25 (C. B. Koford, MS).

1946, Big Sespe Canyon: April 21, 5 (C. B. Koford, MS).

1946, Santa Paula Canyon: March 26, 3 (C. B. Koford, MS).

1947, Hopper Canyon: January, 26 (T. Work, verbal, 1947); December 28, 11 (C. B. Koford, MS).

1947, Thorn Point Lookout: June-November, one to 3 seen almost daily (H. L. Lemmer, MS).

1948, Thorn Point Lookout: July 19 and August 1, 5 (H. L. Lemmer, MS).

1948, Hopper Canyon: February 18, 8 (C. B. Koford, MS); March 24, 16 (A. J. Wool, verbal, 1948).

1949, Hopper Canyon: April 3, 8 (S. B. Peyton, letter, May 8, 1949).

LOS ANGELES COUNTY

1889 (in or about), near Puente: one captured (Lawrence, 1893:301).

1892, 27 miles north of Santa Monica [near Saugus]: about June, one captured (*ibid.*:300).

1893, San Gabriel Range: September 25, one (Lawrence, 1894:76).

1895, about 7 miles northeast of Santa Monica [near Calabasas]: April 21, one shot (Hoffman, 1895: 18).

1896, Mt. Wilson: February 1, one; May 9, 4; October 31, one; December 12, one (Grinnell, MS).

1897, Mt. Brown: June 25, 4 (Grinnell, MS).

1898, near San Gabriel River Canyon: March 5, immature (L.A.M., F. S. Daggett 3225).

1898 [Escondido Canyon], Santa Monica Mts.: August 25, adult shot, young captured (Rising, 1899:25).

1890's, Puente Hills near Whittier: frequently seen (G. Willett, verbal, 1940).

1900, Santa Monica Mts. [probably Encinal Canyon according to W. L. Chambers]: April 11, egg (Willett, 1912:45).

1901, Sierra Madre Range north of Pomona: January 16, immature (Daggett, 1901:48; L.A.M. 5859).

1905, near Calabasas: June 1, one (Ray, 1906:408).

1906, Eaton Canyon: March 10, nest (Finley, 1906: 138); July 6, 4 (Finley, 1908b:65).

1908, Eaton Canyon: May 9, nest (Grinnell, MS); December 31, immature shot (M.V.Z. 7857).

1910, Pasadena: one, about last seen (A. J. van Rossem, verbal, 1940).

1911, near Calabasas: April 8, one (Dickey Coll. 11036).

1911, Fish Creek near Redrock Mtn.: April 11, one (L. Miller, MS); 8 (L. Peyton, *fide* L. Miller, MS).

1911, near Chatsworth: June, immature (L.A.M., G. Willett 1325).

1913, Eagle Rock: February 14, one (Edwards, 1913: 74).

1930, Gorman: May 31, 2 (L. Miller, MS).

1934, near Neenach, Antelope Valley: August 9, 7 (Anderson, 1935:170).

1934, Liebre Ranch headquarters: December 14, 3 (Anderson, *loc. cit.*).

1934, Sandberg: December 15, 3 (Anderson, *loc. cit.*).

1935, Sandberg: January 12, 3 (Anderson, *loc. cit.*).

1937, Topanga: one (H. Anderson, verbal, 1941).

1940, Liebre Mtn., weather station: fall, up to 31 (H. Root, verbal, 1941; photograph shows 15 in air).

1940, north slope Liebre Mtn.: September 11, 6 (H. J. Bauer, letter, September 23, 1940).

1942, 4 miles northwest of Neenach: January 22, 85 at once (D. D. McLean, letter, October 3, 1949) [This is more than my estimate of the total population].

1944, Tapia Ranch, Santa Monica Mts.: about April 1, 2 (W. L. Chambers, verbal, 1946).

1947, Gorman: December 27, 2 (C. B. Koford, MS).

1949, Liebre Gulch: October 15, 2 (L. Sumner, letter, October 26, 1949).

KERN COUNTY

1849-1854, Tejon Valley: seen (Heermann, 1859: 29).

1875, Fort Tejon and Walker Basin: summer, 2 or 3 individuals at most (Henshaw, 1876:265).

1872-1879, southern San Joaquin Valley: usually not more than 2 seen (Stewart, 1908:130).

1891, near Tejon Ranch: July 11, 3 (Fisher, 1893: 33).

1891, 3 miles from Walker Basin: July 16, one (Fisher, *loc. cit.*).

1891, San Emigdio: October, common (Fisher, *op. cit.*:34).

1894, Walker Basin: October 10, 26 (Stephens, 1895:81).

1894, near Tehachapi: summer, 9 (J. G. Tyler, letter, March 19, 1905).

1898, Breckenridge Mtn.: one shot, one or 2 often seen (H. Allen, verbal, 1940).

1900 (about), Breckenridge Mtn.: often some perched (P. Sprague, verbal, 1940).

1904, Fort Tejon: July 23, 2 (Grinnell, MS).

1905, Bear Mtn.: 20 or 30 roosting (P. Brite, verbal, 1940).

1908 (about), San Emigdio Ranch: 18 (L. Tevis, Sr., verbal, 1946).

1908 (about), Chico Martínez Canyon near McKittrick: 5 (W. W. Terrill, letters, January 23 and 30, 1940).

1908, 3 miles southwest of McKittrick: October 1, 18 (Arnold, 1909:101).

1918, Tejon Ranch: January 3 (about), 6 (G. Willett, letter, January 5, 1918).

1926, Tejon Ranch near Grapevine: September, one captured (Wilson, 1928:159).

1926, Mt. Pinos, north side: May 28-30, 3 (L. Miller, MS).

1930 (about), Monolith, near Tehachapi: at least 15 (R. C. Welch, verbal, 1946); 37 (D. D. McLean, letter, October 3, 1949).

1932 (about), 3 miles east of Lebec: one captured (H. Bowhay, verbal, 1940).

1934, near Woody: summer, 3 (M. Gross, verbal, 1940).

1935, about 9 miles east of Delano: April 25, 9 (B. L. Fox, verbal, 1940); daily for 2 weeks, maximum about 18 (E. E. Horn, verbal, 1940); before July 31, 13 or 14 several times, up to 23 (F. Bradshaw, verbal, 1940).

1935, Cummings Valley: late summer, about 35 (L. Arnold, verbal, 1940).

1936, mid-way between Bakersfield and Kern Canyon: April 25, 20 (Lofberg, 1936:177).

1937, Tejon Ranch: January 1, adult captured (M.V.Z.).

1939, Tejon Ranch: February 10, one trapped (P. S. Sprague, letter, March 2, 1939).

1940, Cottonwood Ranch near Breckenridge Mtn.: spring, 8 (H. Castro, verbal, 1941).

1940, Mt. Abel: July, 2 (H. Bowhay, verbal, 1940).

1940, western Cummings Valley: early September, 5; September 16, 5 (F. Bradshaw, verbal, 1940); September 17, 2 (C. B. Koford, MS); fall, about 20 (E. Cummings, verbal, 1940).

1940, 6 miles east of Arvin: September 16, 30 (C. B. Koford, MS).

1940, White Wolf, near Bear Mtn.: about October, 6 (P. S. Sprague, verbal, 1940).

1941, White Wolf: mid-January, 7 (P. S. Sprague, verbal, 1940).

1941, near Antimony Peak: February, 2 to 5 (R. Richardson, U.S.F.S. files).

1941, Tejon Ranch, near headquarters: March 26, 22; March 29, 24 (J. A. Reynolds, letters, March 26 and 29, 1941).

1941, Cummings Valley: May, 5 (J. A. Reynolds, verbal, 1941).

1941, Cottonwood Ranch: May 29, at least 6, probably 10; June 3, 11 (C. B. Koford, MS).

1941, near Edison: September 14, 14 (B. L. Fox, letter, September 15, 1941).

1941, Temblor Ranch: spring, 3 (C. Twisselman, verbal and photograph, 1946).

1941, Antelope Valley near Annette: June, one dead (Fresno State College).

1942, Antelope Valley near Annette: July, 4 (F. T. Ross, verbal, 1948).

1942, Temblor Ranch: spring, 14 (C. Twisselman, verbal and photograph, 1946).

1944, 6 miles southwest of White River: about August 24, 35 (M. J. Vincent, letter, February 11, 1946; specimen).

1945, about 10 miles east of Famoso: May 25, 16 (J. Keyes, MS).

1945, Edison: 17 (B. L. Fox, verbal, 1946).

1945, Temblor Ranch: May 23, one dead (Rett, 1946:182; specimen); June, 7 (C. Twisselman, verbal, 1946).

1946, Bear Mtn., west side: February 3, 9 (C. B. Koford, MS).

1946, 8 miles east of Famoso: May 4, 14 (C. B. Koford, MS).

1946, Breckenridge Mtn.: July 20, 3 (C. B. Koford, MS).

1946, Carneros Canyon: April 13, 3 (I. McMillan, letter, April 24, 1946).

1946, Shale Hills: June 26 and 28, 10 (C. B. Koford, MS).

1947, Pleito Canyon near Wheeler Ridge: March 12, 4 (A. J. Harris, letter, March 18, 1947).

1947, near Poso Creek: June, 7 (B. L. Fox, letter, October 30, 1947).

1947, Tejon Ranch: November, 43 at once (P. and T. Sprague, letter, August 11, 1948) [These people know condors].

1947, near Bear Mtn.: November 23, one trapped (L. Arnold, letter, February 13, 1949; specimen L.A.M.).

1948, Cedar Canyon, Temblor Range: June 14, 2 (E. McMillan, letter, June 19, 1948).

1948, Tejon Ranch: early August, 5 (P. S. Sprague, verbal, 1948); August 22, 2 (C. B. Koford, MS).

TULARE COUNTY

1849, Tulare Valley [this county?]: late fall, many (J. W. Audubon, fide Harris, 1941:34).

1866-1868, Tulare Valley [this county?]: 6 to 15, "moderately abundant" (Bendire, 1892:157).

1879, between Tule River and Deer Creek: summer, 3 (Stewart, 1908:130).

1899, near Castle Rocks, Sequoia National Park: September 15, 2 (Fry, 1926:1).

1908 (several years before), Yokohl Valley: 8 or 10 in one day, not over 4 together, none for 4 or 5 years (W. F. Dean, fide Stewart, 1908:130).

1919, Wet Meadows, Sequoia National Park: September 27, one (Fry, loc. cit.).

1920, Deer Creek east of Hot Springs: May 11, one (Redington, 1920:133).

1920 (about), near White River: up to 17 (M. J. Vincent, verbal, 1946).

1936, near Pine Flat: July 3, one (W. B. Richardson, letter, May 6, 1941).

1944, near White River (just outside county): August, 35 (M. J. Vincent, see Kern County).

1946, Fountain Springs: July 14, 12 (C. B. Koford, MS).

1946, 5 miles east of Porterville: August 31, 3 (C. B. Koford, MS).

1946, Yokohl Valley: August, 6 (J. Birchfield, verbal, 1946).

1949, about 14 miles east of Porterville: about September 10, 12 (R. C. Welch, letter, December 10, 1949).

1950, about 10 miles east of Porterville: August 19, 10 (R. C. Welch, letter, September 8, 1950).

1950, Tule River Indian Reservation: August 19, young in nest (C. B. Koford, MS). [Nest discovered in June by Claude Rouch, Jr., logger, of Springville.]

As the entire southern San Joaquin Valley was called "Tulare Valley" by early travelers, the localities of the earliest records are in doubt.

TABLES

Table 1

SIZE OF SPECIMENS OF THE CALIFORNIA CONDOR

Adults

Sex	Wingspread (ft. in.)	Length (in.)	Wt. (lbs.)	Reference
male	9 7	50		M.V.Z.* 23334 (E.B. Towne)
male	9 6.5		20	C.A.S. (J.P. Herring)
male	9 6	52	31	C.A.S. 19001 (E.B. Towne)
female	9 6	51		M.C.Z. 180862
male	9 6	54		C.M.N.H. 130025 (R.H. Beck)
male	9 5	50	29	C.A.S. 19002 (E.B. Towne)
male	9 4.3	45.7	19 (evis.)	M.C.Z. (F. Stephens)
female	9 4	44		F. Stephens (letter, 1907)
male	9 4	45		F. Stephens (letter, 1907)
male	9 3	48.5		M.V.Z. 23336 (E.B. Towne)
female	9 3	44	20.25	L.A.M. 4896 (J.P. Herring)
male	9 3	46.5	21.5	S.D.N.H.M. (F. Stephens)

female	9	2.7	43.1	21	F. Stephens (letter, 1907)
male	9	2.5	47		M.V.Z. 23335 (E.B. Towne)
male	9	2	44.3	20	F. Stephens (letter, 1907)
male	9	2	46	17 (evis.)	A.M.N.H. 352005 (M.C. Badger)
male	9	2	46		A.M.N.H. 469945 (E.B. Towne)
female	9	1		19	C.A.S. (J.P. Herring)
female	8	10	47		A.M.N.H. 469949 (E.B. Towne)
female	8	10	48.5		C.A.S. 44495 (E.B. Towne)
female	8	9	45		A.M.N.H. 469946 (E.B Towne)
female	8	7.5	40.5		Fresno State College (W.T. Shaw)
male	8	4	46		Dickey Coll. 11036
female	8	2.5		18.75	Rett (1938:225)
?	8	2 (alive)			H. M. Hill (MS)

Dark-headed Immatures

?	8	11‡		17.75+	C.B. Koford (MS)
?	8	10.5	41		U.C.L.A. 386 (L. Miller)
?	8	7.5		18	C.A.S. (J.P. Herring)
female	8	6.4	44.1	18	M.C.Z. 214367
female	8	6.5	46.5	17	L.A.M. 5859 (F.S. Daggett)
?	8	2.5	44.25		U.S.N.M. 10365
male	8	2.5		22.5	Rett (1938:225)

* For meanings of abbreviations see p. 139
‡ broken wing

Table 2
OBSERVED PERIODS OF INCUBATING AND BROODING AT NEST 1

		Period adult in nest			Period no adult in nest
		A	Parent B	?	
Stage	Date	hrs. min.	hrs. min.	hrs. min.	hrs. min.
	March 23 (—42)			? F	35
				3 25 F	17 00+ N
	March 29 (—36)	1 50+			?
	April 1 (—33)			? F	2 18
			1 20	F	1 40+
	April 3 (—31)	21 33+ N			00
	April 4 (—30)	-----			1 25
			5 07		
		22 56 N			1 20
	April 5 (—29)	-----			
		16 41 N			
a	April 6 (—28)	-----			1 39
o		2 16	F?		1 05
			21 45+ N		?
i	April 15 (—19)			? F	35
t				50 F	45
a				42 F	27
				2 41 F	14 08 N
b	April 16 (—18)	2 22	F		40
u		3 50	F		?
c	April 18 (—16)	26 35+ N			
n	April 19 (—15)				45
I		19 16	N		
	April 20 (—14)	-----			00
			26 19	N	
	April 21 (—13)				1 01
		24 29+ N			
	April 29 (— 5)	-----			56+
			2 39	F	42
					?
		24 43+ N			
	May 1 (— 3)		4 13+ F		1 43
			17 19 N		
	May 2 (— 2)		-----		43
			23		18
		1 15			
		46 05 NN			
	May 3 (— 1)	-----			00
	May 4 (0)	-----			00
			6 28		

		Period adult in nest			Period no adult in nest
Stage	Date	A	Parent B	?	
Continuous brooding	May 5 (+ 1)	21 08 N			00

	May 6 (+ 2)		25 39 N		16

	May 8 (+ 4)	15 39+ N	18		?
		1 33+			00
	May 9 (+ 5)		40 00+ NN		?
	May 11 (+ 7)	4 20+ F	-----		45
			16 40+ N		53
	May 13 (+ 9)			? F	21
			22 F		?
			05+		
Night brooding only	May 27 (+23)				3 58+
			55 F		1 29
	May 28 (+24)		17 51 N		5 18
			----- F		?
			14 27+ N		

TOTALS:

	A	B	?
Incubation stage			
Hours and minutes	209 51	85 33	7 38
Per cent	70	28	2
Nights on	9	3	0
Brooding stage			
Hours and minutes	42 40	116 17	
Per cent	27	73	
Nights on	2	6	
Incubation and brooding stages			
Hours and minutes	252 31	201 50	7 38
Per cent	55	44	1
Nights on	11	9	0

Explanation of symbols:
(42) Number of days before (—) or after (+) hatching
F Flushed from nest at end of period
+ Plus unknown period; observation commenced or ceased while adult was in nest
N Period includes all night; adult in nest at night assumed to remain until at least 7 a.m.
NN Period represents 2 nights in nest
----- Part of period above occurred on this date

Table 3
TIME DATA RELATING TO CHANGING GUARD AT NEST 1

			Period together in nest (min.)		Preceding period no adult in nest (min.)	
Date	Time entered nest		A	B	A	B
	Relieving Adult					
	A	B				
April 4		9:32		1		0
	4:04		0		85	
April 6		2:00		0		65F?
April 20		9:15	1		0	
April 21	12:35		0		61	
April 29	2:17		0		42F	
May 2	10:27		0		43	
May 4		9:56	10		0	
	4:22		2		0	
May 5		1:26		4		0
May 6	3:22		0		16	
May 8		3:01	2		0	
May 11		2:20	0			45F
Instances	6	7				
Range	10:27-4:22	9:15-3:01	0 to 10		0 to 85	
Ave., all	2:11	12:09	3.3		51	
Ave., not F	2:10	11:21			51	

Note: "F" means adult was flushed before relieving adult entered nest; zero is not included in averages.

GROWTH AND FEATHER DEVELOPMENT OF YOUNG

I did not attempt to make a detailed study of growth and feather development. Much of my information on this subject was obtained by examination of the classic series of photographs taken by H. T. Bohlman and W. L. Finley in 1906. The glass negatives of these photographs are on file at the Museum of Vertebrate Zoology. The ages of Finley's bird and of my chick 1 are known within one day and the age of my chick 9 within 3 days. I have scattered data for these three birds up to the ages of 6 months, 10½ months and 1½ months. Harold Hill (MS) provided brief notes on the development of another nestling. Six other young in various stages of development were examined by me.

The sequence of downs in the condor apparently follows the same course as described by Sumner (1933:299) for the golden eagle: "Down (a). Present at hatching . . . comparatively sparse, and succeeded by the true feathers upon whose tips it is later borne, until lost by abrasion." White in *Gymnogyps.* "Down (b). Composed of very short tufts, growing sparsely here and there among down (a). . . ." I did not distinguish this from down (a). "Down (c). . . . long, coarse, and woolly. . . . It completely conceals down (a) for a time, until the true feathers emerge from it later; and it bears on its tips the short down (b). This coarse woolly coat is later shed when the first true feathers are nearly grown and its place is then taken by the adult down, which is of a different structure . . . from any of the above." Down (c) is dark gray in *Gymnogyps.*

One day of age.—A chick of this age was photographed by Bohlman and described by Finley (1906: 140). The chick was still damp and one end of the egg was beside it. Its head was "flesh-pink" in color. The down was "pure white." The belly and under surface of the wings were naked. The eyes bulged greatly and the orbit was elliptical.

Three days.—Chick 9 was estimated to be of this age when I first examined it. The egg membrane and crushed shell lay six inches from the bird. The down was fluffy and dry. The eyes bulged greatly and the orbit was elliptical. The naked head, neck, ventral cervical apterium, and abdominal apterium were yellowish-orange in color. The umbilical scar was crater-like. The bill anterior to the nares was dark gray except for a yellowish area just proximal to the

white egg tooth. The upper surface of the feet was dark gray but the sides of the toes and most of the tarsi were light yellow. The claws were dark in color and well formed.

Eight days.—Fragments of egg shell remained near chick 9. The orbit was circular. The ventral cervical apterium reached the naked throat anteriorly and the abdominal apterium posteriorly. The latter apterium was about 75 mm. long and included the umbilical scar and the vent. The ventral surface of the wings was still naked. As the chick normally sat (plate 25), the length of its body from the base of the naked neck to the tip of the uropygium was 140 mm., and the total length of the bird was estimated to be 230 mm. The wing, measuring from the side of the body, was 100 mm. in length. Hill's chick had claws on digits 1 and 2 at about this age. A color photograph of a chick of about this age has been published by Don Bleitz (1946:38).

Twelve days.—The head of chick 9 was more elongated and more yellowish than before. The area around and between the eyes was grayish, apparently because of dark structures beneath the thin skin. The tongue was about the same color as the head. Chick 9 had a dark claw, 2 mm. in length, at the tip of each pollex. The body length was now 155 mm. The wing measured 75 mm. from tip to elbow, and the head measured 70 mm. from the tip of the bill to the occiput.

Twenty days.—Harold Hill found that one chick of about this age weighed 1400 grams. The body of chick 9 was 205 mm. long and the head was 83 mm. long. The tail was a brush of down. The most conspicuous change from the previous week was the appearance of dark gray down, especially in the lateral crural and femoral tracts (plate 26). Nine days later this chick had more dark gray down than white down (plate 27).

The time of appearance of the second down is not greatly different in the condor and the golden eagle. In the eagle, Sumner (1933:299) found that the first traces of the second down appeared at 18 days of age, and at 30 days of age this down formed a dense wool over the body. On the other hand, the age at which the primaries appear in the condor is twice the age at which they appear in the eagle.

Thirty-five days.—Finley (1908b:61) found that his chick was "as large as a good sized chicken" and that "his whole body was covered with dark gray down with the outer edgings of lighter gray." These "outer edgings" were apparently down *b,* borne on the tips of the dark gray down *c.*

Forty-two days.—Chick 9 was 28 cm. high from the heels to the top of the interscapular hump when it was in the threat attitude (plate 28). The head, neck, and ventral cervical apterium were still pale yellow flesh color, and the tarsi were yellowish posteriorly and proximally. The down was uniformly dark gray tipped with light gray filaments. The egg tooth was nearly imperceptible.

Eight weeks.—Photographs by Bohlman and Finley of a chick 55 days old show the sheaths of four large feathers, probably the greater primary coverts, protruding two or three centimeters (plate 29). This chick had a sparse covering of small black fuzzy feathers in the frontal and loral regions and a sparse covering of short gray down in the occipital region. Chick 1, at 59 days of age, had similar sooty areas at the sides of the occipital and dorsal cervical regions. Its head was pale grayish flesh color. The ventral cervical apterium was gray centrally but flesh color at the margins. The anterior half of the ventral surface of the wings bore white down, and there was a separate triangular area of white down at the axilla.

Twelve weeks.—At 82 days of age, the wings of the chick photographed by Bohlman and Finley had two rows of feathers, the remiges and their upper greater coverts, and a half dozen smaller coverts near the wrist. The tips of the wing feathers of chick 1 bore long scraggly filaments of down. The sheaths of the remiges formed a prominent row on the ventral surface of the wing, and anterior to this row a band of white down tapered to a point near the wrist. The black frontal, loral, and cheek feathers were developed in approximately the adult pattern, the main difference being that, in the young bird, the frontal feathering was poorly developed medially near the posterior margin. Anterior to the ear opening and curving posteriorly above and below it was a crescent of sparse dark down. The crown and ventral cervical region were naked but the occipital and dorsal cervical regions were sparsely covered with short down. This down was most dense in the lateral anterior dorsal cervical region but it nowhere obscured the color of the skin.

Fifteen weeks.—Finley's chick was photographed at 109 days of age. It weighed 15 pounds (Finley, 1908*a*:5). Chick 1 was banded and photographed at the same age. The development of the feathers of the two birds was apparently the same. The head of chick 1 was pale grayish flesh color, almost without hue, and the tongue was ochraceous. In relation to the stage of feathering of the wings, the color of the head turned gray about two weeks earlier in chick 1 than in two other nestlings.

The vanes of the secondaries were about twice as long as the vanes of the greater secondary coverts, judged by the appearance of the upper surface of the wing. Near the wrist there were about one dozen lesser or marginal coverts. The vanes of the rectrices were about three inches long and formed a stubby tail. The tip of each rectrix came to an obtuse point which bore a long tassel of down. About three dozen juvenal interscapulars formed a conspicuous erectile group, and at least a dozen humerals were present on each side. The dorsal and pelvic regions, the ruff, and the entire ventral tract were downy.

Finley's chick was removed from the nest and taken to Oregon. This bird was photographed several times between the ages of 110 and 191 days but the photographs are not dated. For beyond the age of 15 weeks I have no definite information on the chronological age of any photographed or described nestling or juvenile except chick 1. In the following accounts, I have used the degree of feather development of the upper wing coverts as an index of the relative age of young condors. However, ages estimated by wing feathering and head feathering differ by as much as three weeks.

Sixteen weeks.—At approximately this age chick 4 had about fifty lesser and marginal coverts near the bend of the wing (plate 30). Groups of erectile feathers of the anterior humeral tracts protruded from the down of the back. There were several rows of pin feathers anterior to the juvenal interscapulars.

Eighteen weeks.—The head of chick 2 was mainly dark bluish-gray but was still a pale flesh color in the occipital region. One week earlier its head appeared grayish orange. Apparently the head color changes from pale flesh color to dark gray at about this age, but the change is gradual. The development of a solid area of juvenal down in the anterior dorsal cervical and occipital regions occurs at about the same time that the skin of the head becomes dark gray. A band of down remained at the anterior margin of the dorsal surface of the wing of chick 2. This band was widest at the elbow and extended to the wrist.

Nineteen weeks.—The head and neck of chick 1 were mainly bluish-gray but the anterior auricular region was still grayish flesh color. The ventral cervical apterium was bluish-gray but had a tan tinge when seen in strong light. The covering of short gray woolly down on the back of the head and neck was not yet solid. The distal secondaries of chick 2 protruded half the width of the wing beyond the tips of their greater coverts. Some vaned upper tail coverts were present. The posterior humerals were long and they covered the downy rump when the wings were folded.

Twenty weeks.—At about this age Finley's chick had an opaque covering of juvenal down in the occipital and dorsal cervical regions, but the down was sparse in the anterior ventral cervical region and the throat was naked at the site of the red throat patch of adults. The crown was naked. There was a row of about eight pin feathers in the posterior subaxillar row, the distal feather having a short expanded white vane. Hill's chick weighed 18.6 pounds at this age.

Twenty-one weeks.—At 153 days of age about three square inches of down were visible at the proximal margin of the forearm of juvenile 1 when the wing was folded. Juvenal down covered most of the neck, including the submalar region, but it stopped abruptly at the crown. Some flesh-colored skin was still visible through the down at the occiput of another juvenile and, when the ruff was down, a flesh-colored ring around the neck was visible just anterior to the ruff.

I examined the remains of a nestling which died at about this age. The skull and ulna were shorter than those of an adult specimen by 5 per cent and 2.6 per cent. Apparently the juvenile does not increase greatly in skeletal size after leaving the nest. The longest primaries of the nestling were numbers 4 and 5. The erupted portion of the vane of primary 5 was 460 mm., 80 mm. shorter than the vane of the corresponding feather of an adult. Primary 10 was shortest, only 300 mm. having burst from the sheath. The greater secondary coverts were tipped with as many as 20 filaments of down up to 5 mm. in length. The barbless shaft extended 25 mm. beyond the tips of the vanes of some rectrices. There was no down on the leading edge of the wing. The back, rump, and crissum were downy. The upper tail coverts were about 150 mm. in length.

Twenty-five weeks.—The lanceolate feathers of the ruff and sternal region of juvenile 1 were well developed (plate 31). At 175 days of age the rump, flanks, belly, and legs were still downy. Another juvenile had a superciliary band of down connecting the occipital and frontal regions and a sparse covering of down on the crown. Finley's bird showed a similar condition when it was not over 26 weeks old. At about this age the pet juvenile kept by Finley (1910: 11) measured over 8 feet in wingspread, weighed 20½ pounds, and was 46 inches in length.

Twenty-seven weeks.—When Finley's juvenile was not over this age, the extent of the white area under the wings was about the same as in the adult except that many of the feathers had poorly defined irregular brown markings. The region of the emerging dark-colored under greater secondary coverts was mostly covered with dark gray down, although a few vaned feathers were evident. These coverts were well developed in juvenile 1 at 31 weeks of age.

Ten and one-half months.—The juvenal plumage of juvenile 1 was apparently fully developed in March.

Summary.—Following are data for estimating age of nestling and juvenal condors:

Age (weeks)	Characters
1	Orbit circular
	Wing chord, without feathers, 100 mm.
2	Length of head and culmen 70 mm.
3	Mottling of dark gray down
	Length of head and culmen 83 mm.
4	More dark gray than white down
5	Solid dark gray down
	Egg tooth still visible in profile view
8	Quills appear on hand
	Sparse fuzz in frontal and occipital regions
12	Row of vaned upper greater secondary coverts
	Head feathering like adult
15	Vaned rectrices and interscapulars obvious
	About 12 lesser coverts near wrist
18	Head and neck mainly dark gray
20	Solid covering of down in occipital region
	Some vaned subaxillars
22	No down visible at anterior dorsal margin of wing
30	Under wing coverts complete
	Sparse down on crown

Literature Cited

ANONYMOUS [=Barlow, C.]
1899. [Editorial note]. Bull. Cooper Ornith. Club, 1:19.

ANONYMOUS [=Bryant, H. C.]
1917. California condor on exhibition in Golden Gate Park, San Francisco. Calif. Fish and Game, 3:176.

ALLEE, W. C., EMERSON, A. E., PARK, O., PARK, I., AND SCHMIDT, K. P.
1949. Principles of animal ecology (Philadelphia, W. B. Saunders Co.).

AMERICAN ORNITHOLOGISTS' UNION COMMITTEE
1931. Check-list of North American birds. Fourth edition (Lancaster, Pa., Amer. Ornith. Union).

ANDERSON, H. T.
1935. Condors in northern Los Angeles County, California. Condor, 27:170.

ANTHONY, A. W.
1893. Birds of San Pedro Martir, Lower California. Zoe, 4:228-247.
1895. Birds of San Fernando, Lower California. Auk, 12:134-143.

ARNOLD, R.
1909. Condors in a flock. Condor, 11:101.

ASHWORTH, C. W.
1929. California condor. Oologist, 46:65-66.

AUDUBON, J. J.
1834. Ornithological biography. Vol. 2 (Edinburgh, Adam and Charles Black).
1839. Ornithological biography. Vol. 5 (Edinburgh, Adam and Charles Black).

BAIRD, S. F., BREWER, T. M., AND RIDGWAY, R.
1874. A history of North American birds. Land birds. Vol. 3 (Boston, Little, Brown and Co.).

BANCROFT, H. H.
1890. History of California. Vol. 7 (San Francisco, The History Co.).

BARLOW, C. SEE ANONYMOUS.

B[EEBE]., C. W.
1906. The California condor. Bull. Zool. Soc. New York, No. 20:258-259.

BELDING, L.
1879. A partial list of the birds of central California. Proc. U. S. Nat. Mus., 1:388-449.
1890. Land birds of the Pacific district. Occas. papers Calif. Acad. Sci., II: 1-274.

BENDIRE, C.
1892. Life histories of North American birds. Smithsonian Inst., Special Bull. No. 1:viii+446 pp.

BENT, A. C.
1937. Life histories of North American birds of prey. Order Falconiformes. Part 1. Bull. U. S. Nat. Mus. 167:viii+409 pp.

BLAKE, W. C.
1895. Big price for a bird skin. Nidiologist, 2:96.

BLEITZ, D.
1946. Climbing for condors. Pacific Pathways, 1(10): 37-41.

BOLANDER, G.
1934. A rhapsody of raptors. Gull, 16 (August):1-2.

BOND, R. M.
1942. Development of young goshawks. Wilson Bull., 54:81-88.

BRYAN, M.
1901. A study of the birds of Santiago Canyon. Condor, 3:81-82.

BRYANT, H. C. SEE ANONYMOUS.

BRYANT, W. E.
1891. Andrew Jackson Grayson. Zoe, 2:34-68.

CHAMBERS, W. L.
1936. The hunter versus wild life. Condor, 38:199-202.

CLYMAN, J.
1928. James Clyman American frontiersman 1792-1881. Ed., C. L. Camp. Calif. Hist. Soc., Special Publ. No. 3:1-251.

COLES, V.
1944. Nesting of the turkey vulture in Ohio caves. Auk, 61:219-228.

COOLEY, R. A., AND KOHLS, G. M.
1944. The Argasidae of North America, Central America and Cuba. Amer. Midland Nat. Monograph No. 1:1-152.

COOPER, J. G.
1870. Geological survey of California. Ornithology. Vol. 1. Ed., S. F. Baird. Land birds (Cambridge, University Press, Welch, Bigelow, and Co.).
1871. Monterey in the dry season. Amer. Nat., 4:757.
1890. A doomed bird. Zoe, 1:248-249.

COOPER, J. G., AND SUCKLEY, G.
1859. The natural history of Washington Territory (New York, Bailliére Bros.).

COUES, E.
1866. List of the birds of Fort Whipple, Arizona. . . . Proc. Acad. Nat. Sci. Philadelphia, 18:39-100.
1903. Key to North American birds. Vol. 2 (Boston, Dana Estes and Co.).

CRONISE, T. F.
1868. The natural wealth of California (San Francisco, H. H. Bancroft and Co.).

DAGGETT, F. S.
1898. Capture of a California condor. Osprey, 2:134.
1901. Capture of a California condor near Pomona, Cal. Condor, 3:48.

DARWIN, C.
1909. The voyage of the Beagle. Ed., C. W. Eliot (New York, P. F. Collier and Son).

DAWSON, W. L.
1924. The birds of California. Vol. 4 (San Diego, South Moulton Co.).

DIXON, J.
1924. California condors breed in captivity. Condor, 26:192.

DOUGLAS, D.
1914. Journal kept by David Douglas during his travels in North America 1823-1827 (London, William Wesley and Son).

DYER, E. I.
1935. Meeting the condor on its own ground. Condor, 37:5-11.

EDWARDS, H. A.
1913. California condor. Oologist, 30:74.

EMERSON, W. O.
1887. Ornithological observations in San Diego County. Bull. Calif. Acad. Sci., 2:419-431.

EVERMANN, B. W.
1886. The yellow-billed magpie. Amer. Nat., 20:607-611.

FARNER, D. S.
1945. Age groups and longevity in the American robin. Wilson Bull., 57:56-74.

FINLEY, W. L.
1906. Life history of the California condor. Part I. Condor, 8:135-142.
1908a. Life history of the California condor. Part II. Condor, 10:5-10.
1908b. Life history of the California condor. Part III. Condor, 10:59-65.

1910. Life history of the California condor. Part IV. Condor, 12:5-11.

FINLEY, W. L., AND FINLEY, I.
1928. Wild animal pets (New York, Charles Scribner's Sons).

FISHER, A. K.
1893. The Death Valley expedition. North Amer. Fauna No. 7:1-402.
1920. In memoriam: Lyman Belding. Auk, 37:33-45.

FISHER, H. I.
1944. The skulls of the cathartid vultures. Condor, 46:272-296.
1945. Locomotion in the fossil vulture Teratornis. Amer. Midland Nat., 33:725-742.
1946. Adaptations and comparative anatomy of the locomotor apparatus of New World vultures. Amer. Midland Nat., 35:545-727.
1947. The skeletons of recent and fossil Gymnogyps. Pacific Sci., 1:227-236.

FISHER, W. K.
1904. California vulture in San Mateo Co., California. Condor, 6:50.

FRY, W.
1926. The California condor . . . . Sequoia Nat. Park, Nature Guide Service, Bull. No. 23. Mimeographed, 2 pp.

GABRIELSON, I. N., AND JEWETT, S. G.
1940. Birds of Oregon (Corvallis, Oregon State College).

GALLAHER, W.
1906. A novel find. Condor, 8:57.

GASS, P.
1904. Gass's journal of the Lewis and Clark expedition. Reprint of edition of 1811 (Chicago, A. C. McClurg and Co.).

GEDNEY, P. L.
1900. Nesting of the condor on the slope of the Cuyamacas, San Diego Co., Cal. Condor, 2:124-126.

GILMAN, M. F.
1907. Measuring a condor. Condor, 9:106-108.

GRAHAM, R. R.
1930. Safety devices in wings of birds. Brit. Birds, 24:2-21, 34-47, 58-65.

GRINNELL, J.
1898. Birds of the Pacific slope of Los Angeles County. Pasadena Acad. Sci. Publ. No. 2:1-52.
1905. Old Fort Tejon. Condor, 7:9-13.
1908. The biota of the San Bernardino Mountains. Univ. Calif. Publ. Zool., 5:1-170.
1932. Type localities of birds described from California. Univ. Calif. Publ. Zool., 38:243-324.

GRINNELL, J., DIXON, J. S., AND LINSDALE, J. M.
1937. Fur-bearing mammals of California. Vol. 2 (Berkeley, Univ. Calif. Press).

GRINNELL, J., AND SWARTH, H. S.
1913. An account of the birds and mammals of the San Jacinto area of southern California. Univ. Calif. Publ. Zool., 10:197-406.

GRINNELL, J., AND WYTHE, M. W.
1927. Directory to the bird-life of the San Francisco Bay region. Pac. Coast Avifauna No. 18:1-160.

HANKIN, E. H.
1913. Animal flight (London, Iliffe and Sons).

HARRIS, H.
1941. The annals of Gymnogyps to 1900. Condor, 43:3-55.

HEERMANN, A. L.
1859. Reports of explorations and surveys . . . Railroad Route . . . to the Pacific Ocean. 1853-6. Vol. 10, part 4. Report upon the birds collected on the survey (Washington, Beverly Tucker).

HENSHAW, H. W.
1876. Report on the ornithology of the portions of California visited during . . . 1875. Pp. 224-278, in Annual report upon the geographical surveys . . . . by G. M. Wheeler (Washington, Govt. Print. Off.).
1920. Autobiographical notes. Condor, 22:3-10.

HERRICK, F. H.
1924. The daily life of the American eagle; late phase. Auk, 41:517-541.
1934. The American eagle (New York, D. Appleton-Century Co.).

HILL, N. P.
1944. Sexual dimorphism in the Falconiformes. Auk, 61:228-234.

HOFFMAN, W. H.
1895. Notes on California condors. Avifauna, 1:17-19.

HOFFMANN, R.
1930. California condor. Gull, 12 (October): 6.

HOLMES, F. H.
1897. A pet condor. Nidologist, 4:58.

HORNADAY, W. T.
1913. Our vanishing wild life (New York, Charles Scribner's Sons).

HOWARD, H.
1929. The avifauna of Emeryville shellmound. Univ. Calif. Publ. Zool., 32:301-394.
1930a. A census of the Pleistocene birds of Rancho La Brea from the collections of the Los Angeles Museum. Condor, 32:81-88.
1930b. Science news. Items. Science, 71 (No. 1840): xiv.

HOWARD, H., AND MILLER, A. H.
1933. Bird remains from cave deposits in New Mexico. Condor, 35:15-18.

HUDSON, G. E.
1948. Studies on the muscles of the pelvic appendage in birds II, the heterogeneous order Falconiformes. Amer. Midland Nat., 39:102-127.

HUEY, L. M.
1926. Notes from northwestern Lower California. Auk, 43:347-362.

HUNTER, J. S.
1904. Records from the vicinity of Watsonville, California. Condor, 6:24-25.

JENKINS, H. O.
1906. A list of birds collected between Monterey and San Simeon in the coast range of California. Condor, 8:122-130.

JOHNSON, H. T.
1945. California condors in San Luis Obispo County, California. Condor, 47:38.

JOLLIE, M.
1947. Plumage changes in the golden eagle. Auk, 64:549-576.

KELLOGG, V. L.
1910. Mallophagan parasites from the California condor. Science, 31:33-34.

KNIGHT, A. M.
1942. Modern seamanship (New York, D. Van Nostrand Co., Inc.).

KROEBER, A. L.
1925. Handbook of the Indians of California. Smithsonian Inst., Bureau Amer. Ethnology, Bull. No. 78: xviii+995 pp.

LACK, D.
1940. Pair-formation in birds. Condor, 42:269-286.

LAWRENCE, R. H.
1893. Pseudogryphus californianus. Auk, 10:300-301.
1894. The California vulture in the San Gabriel Range, California. Auk, 11:76-77.

LEACH, F. A.
1929. A turkey buzzard roost. Condor, 31:21-23.

LEOPOLD, A.
1936. Game management (New York, Charles Scribner's Sons).

LEWIS, M., AND CLARK, W.
1905. Original journals of the Lewis and Clark expedition 1804-1806. Ed., Reuben Gold Thwaites. Vol. 3, part 2; vol. 4, parts 1 and 2 (New York, Dodd, Mead and Co.).

LINSDALE, J. M.
1931. Facts concerning the use of thallium in California to poison rodents . . . . Condor, 33:96-106.

LOFBERG, L. M.
1936. Twenty condors dine together. Condor, 38:177.

LORENZ, K. Z.
1937. The companion in the bird's world. Auk, 54:245-273.

McALLISTER, M. H.
1923. California's large game animals. Calif. Fish and Game, 9:49-50.

McGREGOR, R. C.
1899. Some summer birds of Palamar mountains, from the notes of J. Maurice Hatch. Bull. Cooper Ornith. Club, 1:67-68.
1901. A list of the land birds of Santa Cruz County, California. Pac. Coast Avifauna No. 2:1-22.

MILLER, A. H.
1941. The significance of molt centers among the secondary remiges in the Falconiformes. Condor, 43:113-115.
1942. A California condor bone from the coast of southern Oregon. Murrelet, 23:77.

MILLER, A. H., AND FISHER, H. I.
1938. The pterylosis of the California condor. Condor, 40:248-256.

MILLER, L.
1910. The condor-like vultures of Rancho La Brea. Univ. Calif. Publ., Bull. Dept. Geol., 6:1-19.
1911. Avifauna of the Pleistocene cave deposits of California. Univ. Calif. Publ., Bull. Dept. Geol., 6:385-400.
1927. Pleistocene fauna and flora. Bird remains. Science, 66:156.
1931a. The California condor in Nevada. Condor, 33:32.
1931b. Bird remains from the Kern River Pliocene of California. Condor, 33:70-72.
1937. Feather studies on the California condor. Condor, 39:160-162.
1942. Succession in the cathartine dynasty. Condor, 44:212-213.
1943. The Pleistocene birds of San Josecito Cavern, Mexico. Univ. Calif. Publ. Zool., 47:143-168.

MILLER, R. F.
1942. Sheep production in California. Calif. Agric. Ext. Serv., Circular 49, 79 pp.

MORCOM, G. F.
1887. Notes on the birds of southern California and south-western Arizona. Ridgway Ornith. Club, Bull. No. 2:36-57.

MURPHY, R. C.
1925. Bird islands of Peru (New York, G. P. Putnam's Sons).

NATIONAL RESEARCH COUNCIL, SUBCOMMITTEE ON MAMMALOGY
1948. Instructions for using sodium fluoroacetate (compound 1080) as a rodent poison. Mimeographed, 11 pp.

NELSON, E. W.
1921. Lower California resources. Mem. Nat. Acad. Sci., 16:1-194.

NEWBERRY, J. S.
1857. Reports of explorations and surveys . . . Railroad Route . . . to the Pacific Ocean. 1854-5. Vol. 6, part 4. Report upon the zoology of the route (Washington, Beverly Tucker).

NICE, M. M.
1937. Studies in the life history of the song sparrow I. Trans. Linnaean Soc. New York, 4:vi + 247 pp.
1943. Studies in the life history of the song sparrow II. Trans. Linnaean Soc. New York, 6:viii + 329 pp.

NOBLE, G. K., WURM, M., AND SCHMIDT, A.
1938. Social behavior of the black-crowned night heron. Auk, 55:7-40.

PAN AMERICAN UNION
1942. Convention and documentary material on nature protection and wild life preservation in the Western Hemisphere (Washington, D. C., Pan American Union, Division of Agricultural Cooperation).

PEMBERTON, J. R.
1910. Some bird notes from Ventura County. Condor, 12:18-19.

PEMBERTON, J. R., AND CARRIGER, H. W.
1915. A partial list of the summer resident land birds of Monterey County, California. Condor, 17:189-201.

PEQUEGNAT, W. E.
1945. A report upon the biota of the Santa Ana Mountains. Jour. Entom. Zool. Pomona College, 37:25-41.

PEYTON, S. B.
1932. Visiting the condor country. Oologist, 49:23-24.

RAY, M. S.
1906. A-birding in an auto. Auk, 23:400-418.

REDINGTON, A. P.
1899. Taking of a condor's egg. Bull. Cooper Ornith. Club, 1:75.

REDINGTON, P. G.
1920. A California condor seen near head of Deer Creek. Calif. Fish and Game, 6:133.

RETT, E. Z.
1938. Hailstorm fatal to California condors. Condor, 40:225.
1946. Record of another condor death. Condor, 48:182.

RICHMOND, C. W.
1901. On the generic name of the California condor. Condor, 3:49.

RISING, H. G.
1899. Capture of a California condor. Bull. Cooper Ornith. Club, 1:25-26.

ROBINSON, C. S.
1939. Notes on the California condor collected on Los Padres National Forest, California. Mimeographed, 21 pp.

SCLATER, P. L.
1866. Living California vulture received in London. Proc. Zool. Soc. London, 1866:xiii, 366.

SCOTT, C. D.
1936. Are condors extinct in Lower California? Condor, 38:41-42.

SCOULER, J.
1905. Dr. John Scouler's journal of a voyage to N. W. Amer. III. Quart. Oregon Hist. Soc., 6:276-287.

SEIBERT, M.
1941. A week with the California condor. Field Ornith. (Mt. Lookout, W. Va.) (January): 3-6.

SHARPLES, R. P.
1897. The taking of a California condor's egg. Osprey, 2:21.

SHAW, G., AND NODDER, F. P.
1797. Vivarium naturae or naturalist's miscellany. Vol. 9 (London, printed for Nodder and Co.).

SHELDON, H. H.
1939. What price condor? Field and Stream (September):22-23, 61-62.

SHIELDS, A. M.
1895. Nesting of the California vulture. Nidiologist, 2:148-150.

SHUFELDT, R. W.
1883. Osteology of the Cathartidae. Ann. Rept. U. S. Geol. and Geog. Surv., 12:727-786.

SKIRM, J.
1884. List of birds of Santa Cruz, Cal. Ornith. and Ool., 9:149-150.

SMITH, F. J.
1916. Occurrence of the condor in Humboldt County. Condor, 18:205.

SPALLANZANI, L.
1784. Dissertations relative to the natural history of animals and vegetables. Translated from Italian. Vol. 1 (London, printed for J. Murray).

STEPHENS, F.
1895. Notes on the California vulture. Auk, 12:81-82.
1899. Lassoing a California vulture. Bull. Cooper Ornith. Club, 1:88.
1919. An annotated list of the birds of San Diego County, California. Trans. San Diego Soc. Nat. Hist., 3(2):(sep.)1-40.

STEWART, G. W.
1908. The condor in the San Joaquin Valley. Condor, 10:130.

STOCK, C.
1929. A census of the Pleistocene mammals of Rancho La Brea . . . . Jour. Mamm., 10:281-289.

STREATOR, C. P.
1886. List of birds observed in the vicinity of Santa Barbara, Cal., during the year 1885. Ornith. and Ool., 11:66-67.

SUMNER, E. L., JR.
1933. The growth of some young raptorial birds. Univ. Calif. Publ. Zool., 40:277-308.
1950. Condors observed from airplane. Condor, 52:133.

SWANN, H. K.
1924. A monograph of the birds of prey. Vol. 1, part 1 (London, Wheldon and Wesley, Ltd.).

SWARTH, H. S.
1914. A distributional list of the birds of Arizona. Pac. Coast Avifauna No. 10:1-133.

TAYLOR, A. S.
1859a. The egg and young of the California condor. Hutchings' California Mag., 3:537-541.
1859b. The great condor of California. Hutchings' California Mag., 3:540-543.
1859c. The great condor of California. Hutchings' California Mag., 4:17-22.

TAYLOR, H. R.
1895a. Habits of the California condor. Nidiologist, 2:73-79.
1859b. Collecting a condor's egg. Nidiologist, 2:88.
1895c. [Open letter.] Nidiologist, 2:100.

TYLER, J. G.
1913. Some birds of the Fresno district, California. Pac. Coast Avifauna No. 9:1-114.

TYRRELL, W. B.
1938. Nesting of the turkey vulture. Auk, 55:468-470.

U.N.E.S.C.O.
1950. Proceedings and papers, International Technical Conference on the Protection of Nature (Lake Success, N. Y.). (U.N.E.S.C.O., Paris-Bruxelles.)

U. S. DEPT. COMMERCE, BUREAU CENSUS
1937. U. S. Census of Agriculture: 1935. General Report. Vol. 3 (Washington, U. S. Govt. Print. Off.).
1942. Sixteenth census of the United States: 1940. Agriculture. Vol. 1, part 6 (Washington, U. S. Govt. Print. Off.).

U. S. DEPT. INTERIOR, CENSUS OFFICE
1883. Report on the productions of agriculture as returned at the tenth census (June 1, 1880). (Washington, Govt. Print. Off.)

USINGER, R. L.
1947. Native hosts of the Mexican chicken bug, *Haematosiphon inodora* (Dugés). Pan-Pac. Ent., 23:140.

VAN DENBURGH, J.
1899. Notes on some birds of Santa Clara County, California. Proc. Amer. Philos. Soc., 38:157-180.

WEBB, J. J.
1937. California condors and other birds of Sespe Canyon. Gull, 19 (August):1-3.

WETMORE, A.
1931a. The California condor in New Mexico. Condor, 33:76-77.
1931b. The avifauna of the Pleistocene in Florida. Smithsonian Misc. Coll., 85:1-41.

WETMORE, A., AND FRIEDMANN, H.
1933. The California condor in Texas. Condor, 35:37-38.

WILLETT, G.
1908. Summer birds of the upper Salinas Valley and adjacent foothills. Condor, 10:137-139.
1912. Birds of the Pacific slope of southern California. Pac. Coast Avifauna No. 7:1-122.
1931. The condor in San Benito County, California. Condor, 33:31.

WILSON, A. V.
1928. Condor caught in San Joaquin Valley. Condor, 30:159-160.

WOODHOUSE, S. W.
1853. Birds. Pp. 58-105, *in* Report of an expedition down the Zuni and Colorado rivers, by Captain L. Sitgreaves (Washington, Beverly Tucker).